Volume

Readings in **Technology and Civilization**

Edited by

Lindy Biggs
Auburn University

James Hansen

William Trimble

With contributions from

Karen H. Gardiner
University of Alabama

PEARSON

Custom
Publishing

Cover photographs:

"Inventor of the Polio Vaccine, Jonas Salk," courtesy of Bettmann/Corbis Images.
"Young Dressmakers Sewing," courtesy of Minnesota Historical Society/Corbis Images.
"Transistor Radio," courtesy of Corbis Images.
"Rice Farmer in Paddy Fields in Malaysia," courtesy of ImageState-Pictor/PictureQuest.
"Incandescent Lamps from the First to Present Time," courtesy of the National Archives and Records Administration.

Printed in the United States of America

10 9 8

ISBN 0-536-85840-3

2004300074

JC/JM

Please visit our web site at *www.pearsoncustom.com*

PEARSON CUSTOM PUBLISHING
75 Arlington Street, Suite 300, Boston, MA 02116
A Pearson Education Company

ACKNOWLEDGMENTS

Grateful acknowledgment is made to the following sources for permission to reprint material copyrighted or controlled by them:

"The Enlightenment," by Alan Bullock, reprinted from *Humanist Tradition in the West*, (1985), by permission of W.W. Norton & Company. Copyright © 1985 by Alan Bullock.

"Science and the American Experiment," by John Patrick Diggins, reprinted by permission from *Sciences*, November–December 1987.

"The Invention of the Balloon and the Birth of Modern Chemistry," by Arthur F. Scott, reprinted by permission from *Scientific American*, January 1984. Copyright © 1984 by Scientific American, Inc.

"The Origins of the Steam Engine," by Eugene S. Ferguson, reprinted by permission from *Scientific American*, January 1964. Copyright © 1964 by Scientific American, Inc.

"The Development of Machine Tools," by L.T.C. Rolt, reprinted by permission from *History Today*, (May 1971).

"The Uncommon Mill Girls of Lowell," by Helena Wright, reprinted by permission from *History Today*, (January 1973).

"The *Nemesis* in China," by Daniel Headrick, reprinted from *The Tools of Empire: Technology and European Imperialism in the Nineteenth Century*, (1981), by permission of Oxford University Press, Inc. Copyright © 1981 by Oxford University Press, Inc.

"The Neuroses of the Railway," by Ralph Harrington, reprinted by permission from *History Today*, 47, no. 7 (July 1994).

"The Work of the World," by Curt Wohleber, reprinted from *American Heritage of Invention and Technology* 7, no. 3 (winter 1992), by permission of American Heritage Inc.

"Does Improved Technology Mean Progress?" by Leo Marx, reprinted by permission from *Technology Review*, (January 1987), by permission of MIT Technology Review. Copyright © 1987 by MIT Technology Review.

"The Message Was Electric," by Pamela W. Lurito, reprinted from *IEEE Spectrum* 21, September 1984, by permission of the Institute of Electrical and Electronics Engineering. Copyright © 1984 by IEEE.

CONTENTS

SECTION ONE

THE ENLIGHTENMENT

In the 18th century, new ideas led to the period we call the Enlightenment, or Age of Reason. Enlightenment thinkers wanted to use the principles of science and the scientific method (reason) to improve society. They used their ideas and methods to develop new areas of inquiry such as the social sciences, and to improve education. They also used these principles to criticize traditional institutions (especially the Church), old customs, and traditional morals.

The first reading in this section provides a general background to Enlightenment ideas. They should seem familiar because they form the foundation of most modern Western societies; the American Constitution and the Declaration of Independence are products of the Enlightenment, so are the modern studies of economics, sociology, and political science.

The second selection discusses the way the writers of the American Constitution depended on the principles of the new science—Newtonian physics—as they designed the new system of government. Principles of the new physics lie at the foundation of the American version of democracy: balance of power, cause and effect, for every action a reaction.

The third reading in the section discusses the development of the science of chemistry and its importance to the invention of the hot-air balloon. This piece shows a science in transition from old to new, in this case, from alchemy to modern chemistry.

1

THE HUMANIST TRADITION IN THE WEST

Alan Bullock

THE ENLIGHTENMENT

After the Renaissance, the next step I want to look at in the development of the humanist tradition is the eighteenth-century Enlightenment, with a particular interest in the *philosophes*—not professional philosophers, but described by their historian Peter Gay as 'a loose, informal, wholly unorganized coalition of cultural critics, religious skeptics, and political reformers from Edinburgh to Naples, Paris to Berlin, Boston to Philadelphia.' Paris was its centre as Florence had been for the humanists three centuries before, and French its natural language as Latin had been in the fifteenth century.

These eighteenth-century *philosophes*—to name only the best known, Voltaire, Montesquieu, Diderot, Rousseau, Gibbon and Bentham, Hume and Adam Smith, Franklin and Jefferson, Lessing and Kant—these *philosophes,* like their Renaissance predecessors, carried on an unending debate with each other, were touchy, quarrelsome, and recriminatory. But, like the members of a family, to which they compared themselves, they were ready to unite in support of what they had in common, a program of humanity, secularism, cosmopolitanism and freedom, the right to question and criticize, free from the threat of arbitrary interference by either Church or state.

Never had the educated classes in Europe formed a more cosmopolitan society, with French as the *lingua franca* and frequent travel—the age of the Grand Tour—especially in the first half of the century when wars were less frequent. The publication of newspapers and journals, which first appeared at the end of the seventeenth century, supplemented the circulation of books, and anything of importance published in Paris, London or Amsterdam was immediately translated into the other principal European languages. To take one example, Montesquieu's *De l'Esprit des lois,* published in 1748, appeared in twenty-two French editions by 1751; in Latin in Hungary by the same year; in ten separate English translations by 1773; in Dutch, Polish and Italian in the 1770s, in German in 1789 and Russian in 1801. Voltaire's *Candide* went through eight editions in 1759 alone. There was of course no question of mass circulation—the famous *Encyclopédie* had no more than 4,000 subscribers. It was still a tiny if cosmopolitan elite which the *philosophes* were addressing, but it was a very receptive one, including many of the nobility (not to mention

Frederick the Great who would only speak French, and Catherine the Great of Russia) as well as a surprising number of clergy. The Archbishop of Salzburg had busts of Voltaire and Rousseau in his study, and there were *abbés* to be found in all the *salons*. Clerics and lawyers, doctors, officials of the royal administration, as well as the local nobility and richer merchants, made up the membership of such provincial academies as those of Bordeaux and Dijon and of the literary and reading societies. The society at Mainz in the 1770s had 300 members and subscribed to 47 newspapers and 41 French and German periodicals. It was through these, the masonic lodges, the clubs and coffee houses, that the new ideas percolated down to the provinces.

In one case at least, that of Scotland, once a kingdom, now reduced to the province of North Britain, with Edinburgh no longer a capital city but proudly known as the Athens of the North, the flow of ideas was reversed. With David Hume and Adam Smith, two of the most original and acute thinkers of the age; such substantial talents as those of Francis Hutcheson, Thomas Reid, Lord Kames, Lord Monboddo, John Miller, William Robertson and Dugald Stewart; with students, many from America, attracted to the reformed universities of Edinburgh and Glasgow, and with such debating clubs as the Select Society, all sharing a deep commitment to the discussion of moral, social, and economic issues, the Scottish Enlightenment could claim to put into circulation as many ideas as it received.

The century and a half which preceded the Enlightenment had seen the opening up of the tight, closed world of medieval and Renaissance Europe. The Copernican revolution in astronomy, developed by Galileo, left the earth and its inhabitants no longer as the centre of the universe, but merely one planet orbiting a local star. If the universe expanded, so did the known limits of the earth itself, with the voyages of exploration and the discovery not only of the American Indian peoples of the New World but also of other historic non-Christian civilizations in China, India and the Islamic world.

The Renaissance had been followed by a powerful revival of dogmatic religion, in a Catholic as well as a Protestant version. The seventeenth century did not lack great individual talents which have their place in the humanist tradition—Cervantes, Rembrandt, Molière—but more important is the fact that it was one of the great religious periods in European history—'total, imperious and profound,' as the French historian Paul Hazard described it. As the century wore on, however, the undercurrents of doubt grew. The outcome of the religious wars was a divided and unreconciled Christendom, and a tendency to carry further the separation of philosophical from theological thought. Descartes (1596–1650) and Spinoza (1632–77) might personally be devout men, but the impact of their reliance upon reason alone in the search for truth was unsettling. Thomas Hobbes (1588–1679), the Machiavelli of philosophy, whose search for security ('Fear and I were born twins,' he wrote) reflected the anxieties aroused by the English Civil War, eliminated religion altogether as a source of human values and based morality, as well as society solely, upon the purely human urge to self-preservation. Traditional beliefs, both religious and secular, were left disturbed by the experience of the seventeenth century. Men were shocked by the skepticism of a Hobbes or a Pierre Bayle, the French Protestant refugee who declared that reason destroyed accepted beliefs and even rendered the grounds for doubt itself doubtful; but they did not know how to answer them.

This tide of unease was reversed and replaced by a new mood of optimism in the first half of the eighteenth century. The grounds for such a change of mood had been predicted well before then, in the early years of the seventeenth century, by Francis Bacon (1561–1626) who rejected tradition in all branches of learning and staked everything on an experimental science which would free man from the burden of original sin and restore to him that control over nature which had been lost with the Fall. 'Men have been kept back,' he wrote, 'as by a kind of enchantment from progress in the sciences by reverence for antiquity, by the authority of men accounted great in philosophy and thereby general consent.'

There remained but one course, Bacon argued, that 'the entire work of the understanding be commenced afresh' on the basis neither of authority nor (the Cartesian prescription) of reasoning by deduction, but of observation and experiment.

Bacon died in 1626, a propagandist for the possibilities of science in advance of its achievements. But these were not long in coming. The impact of Isaac Newton's genius (he was born sixteen years after Bacon's death, in 1642, and died in 1727) was not far short of Pope's famous epitaph:

Nature and Nature's laws lay hid in night.
God said 'Let Newton be!' and all was light.

Not 'all' certainly; but Newton's formulation of the three laws of motion and the universal principle of gravitation not only laid the foundations of classical physics but offered the promise that the same methods would in time uncover what was still unknown. God, it appeared, was a mathematician whose calculations were accessible to human reason, and Nature, instead of being an arbitrary collection of mysterious powers of which man had to live in continual fear, was revealed as a system of intelligible forces.

If any man played the same role in relation to the Enlightenment as Petrarch to Renaissance humanism, it was Newton's friend, the Oxford philosopher, John Locke (1632–1704). Locke's *Second Treatise on Civil Government* provided the intellectual justification of the English Revolution of 1688, setting out a contractual view of government as a trust which can be revoked if it fails to provide for the security and liberty of the subject's person and property. Other works of Locke's dealt with education and human irrationality, and provided the classic statement of toleration for freedom of thought. But none attracted so much attention as his *Essay Concerning Human Understanding,* published in 1690. Rejecting Descartes' assertion that human ideas were innate, Locke argued that they were derived from our sense impressions, either directly, or else by the reflection of the mind on the evidence provided by them. Locke went on to elaborate the view that moral values, the meaning of good and evil, arose from the sensations of pleasure and pain with which human experience was associated. To the *philosophes* of the Enlightenment, he appeared to have discovered the scientific laws of the human mind as Newton had of the natural world, and thereby opened the way to reconstructing human society on more rational and therefore happier lines. Thanks to the enthusiastic advocacy of Voltaire (1694–1778), Newton's and Locke's ideas—which Voltaire believed were the fruit of the freedom that the English enjoyed—exercised a unique influence in the first phase of the Enlightenment.

Like the Renaissance humanists, the eighteenth-century *philosophes* admired classical antiquity. They no longer felt the excitement of rediscovering a lost continent; having shared a common classical education, they took it for granted, but they identified themselves with pre-Christian Republican Rome. Cicero, with his ideal of *humanitas,* was as much a hero to them as to the Florentines of the Quattrocento. Like the humanists again, they had no patience with abstract philosophical systems, attacking not only Catholic scholasticism but Cartesian rationalism. It was the critical, subversive use of the intellect, not its capacity to build logical systems, which they had in mind when they spoke of Reason; they were empiricists, the philosophers of experience and common sense, not rationalists in the seventeenth-century Cartesian sense of that term. Like the civic humanists of the early Renaissance, they exalted the active over the contemplative life, had no use for metaphysics, and were preoccupied with the practical problems—moral, psychological, social—of life here and now. Finally, they shared with the humanists a belief in the harmony of man and nature for which Newton and Locke had now provided an intellectual underpinning. In his *Song for St. Cecilia's Day* (1687) Dryden expressed that belief in terms an Alberti, Nicholas of Cusa or Pico della Mirandola would have immediately recognized:

From harmony, from heavenly harmony
This universal frame began;
From harmony to harmony,
Through all the compass of the notes it ran,
The diapason closing full in Man.

These similarities are enough to establish the continuity of a humanist tradition between the Renaissance and the Enlightenment, and the *philosophes* were well aware of this. But they were also aware of the differences—continuity, but not identity. Peter Gay puts it well when he says; 'The dialectic of the Renaissance was ancestor and pre-condition to the dialectic of the Enlightenment; but while the tensions were similar, the resolution was not.'

The humanists and artists of the Renaissance had found it possible, in a variety of ways, to combine, or at least to accommodate, classical themes and philosophies with Christian convictions, trust in man and trust in God. 'A wholly secular, wholly disenchanted world view was a relative rarity among Renaissance men of letters . . . the sacred remained a central theme for Renaissance sculptors, architects, and painters.'

The tone, the context, and the assumptions of the Enlightenment were very different. Accommodation was not enough for the *philosophes*. By the beginning of the eighteenth century, the seventeenth-century revival of religion had lost its impetus, but outside England, especially in the Catholic states, the structures of power which it had created were still in place: in addition to the wealth of the Church, the identification of Church and state, censorship, the persecution of dissent (the Huguenots driven out of France, for example, in 1685), the denial of freedom of thought, the monopoly of education. To the *philosophes* this was the enemy to be destroyed. Voltaire, taking his cue from Cato, the hero of Republican Rome, who ended every speech he made in the Senate with the words, *Delenda est Carthago*—'Carthage must be destroyed'—ended his letters with the phrase—*Ecrasez l'infâme*—'Wipe out this infamy.'

The time, they believed, was propitious for an assault on the citadel of orthodoxy. Anticlerical criticism of the Church for its wealth, its corruption and worldliness could now be supported by a naturalistic view of the cosmos, a triumphant scientific method and the critical, skeptical, empiricist habits of thought which these engendered.

What stood in the way of extending the new ways of thought to the reform of the human condition and human society—a science of man and society—were the fears and inhibitions produced by the mysteries, magic, and paradoxes of Revealed Religion which the Church had manipulated to sustain clerical power over men's minds. What was needed was to sweep these away in a program of demystification. For such a program, the pagan philosophers of the pre-Christian classical world could be enlisted (for example, Lucretius), as well as the empirical methods of natural science, and the criteria of historical investigation. (Gibbon, 1737–94, summed up his masterpiece, *The Decline and Fall of the Roman Empire,* in the famous phrase, 'I have described the triumph of barbarism and religion.')

This was a common theme, *the* common theme of the *philosophes*. None outstripped Voltaire with his mastery of every form of argument, from wit and irony to denunciation, in the fifty-year campaign which he waged against the pretensions of Christianity. 'Every sensible man,' he wrote, 'every honourable man, must hold the Christian sect in horror.' And in a letter of 1762 Diderot, acknowledging Voltaire's pre-eminence in the battle against error, affectionately saluted him as 'Sublime, honourable and dear "Anti-Christ."' His attack was sharper in the last sixteen years of his life than in his earlier years. 'May the great God who is listening to me,' he declared in a volume published in 1762, 'this God who surely cannot have been born of a virgin or have died on the gallows or be eaten in a piece of dough or have inspired these books [the Old Testament] filled with contradictions, madness and horror—may this God, creator of all the worlds, have pity on this sect of Christians who blaspheme him.'

When Voltaire published in 1744 his *Dictionnaire Philosophique* (more than half of which was devoted to religious questions), the governments of Geneva and the Netherlands (both Protestant), as well as of Catholic France and the Holy See, all burnt it and (as Voltaire remarked) would have liked to burn the author as well.

Voltaire's and the other *philosophes'* arguments, however, were directed not in favour of persecuting Christians but of stopping Christians from persecuting others. The most famous episode in Voltaire's career was his one-man campaign to rehabilitate the Huguenot Jean Calas, who was tortured, broken on the wheel and put to death by strangling in 1762 on the false charge of murdering his son to prevent his converting to Catholicism. Voltaire's most passionate plea was for toleration, toleration by Christians of other religions. While there were certainly atheists among the *philosophes*—for example, the Baron d'Holbach—or skeptical agnostics like David Hume, Voltaire himself retained a lifelong belief in a Supreme Being, the Creator of all things. Such a belief, he held, was not discredited but made necessary by Newton's discoveries—a belief with which Newton himself, obsessed with the search for religious even more than scientific truth, would have fervently agreed.

Deism represented Natural as opposed to Revealed Religion, a religion without miracles, priestly hierarchies, ritual, the Fall of Man, original sin, divine saviours, providential history, or religious persecution. This was a compromise originating in England, where the fevers of the seventeenth century had burned out the extremes of religious enthusiasm and left a Church of England willing to come to terms with a 'reasonable' version of the Divine Order. Deism was based on tolerance of all religions. Voltaire's Zadig (in the philosophical tale of that name) ended the theological disputes of the Egyptian, the Hindu, the Confucian, the Aristotelian Greek and the druidical Celt by convincing them that their particular observances were all related to a common divine creator. This was the central theme of another Enlightenment tract, the play by Lessing (1729–81), *Nathan the Wise:* since natural religion was universal it bound the whole of humanity in a moral law common to all. Providence was seen as the agent of a Divine Benevolence in which man shared. No longer regarded as a fallen creature, forced to labour under a burden of sin and guilt, man was held to be endowed with a natural moral instinct of benevolence, while Providence—the hidden hand—ensured that society was maintained by an identity between enlightened self-interest and the common good. To quote Pope once again, this time his *Essay on Man* (1733–34):

> *Thus God and Nature linked the general frame*
> *And bade Self-Love and Social be the same.*

Deism was never a popular religion. Even in England where it proved attractive to many of the educated, its failure to satisfy religious feelings is shown by the wide appeal of John Wesley (1703–91) and the Methodists. In Protestant Germany Pietism shows the same concern with 'a religion of the heart.' Outside a few cities, such as London, Paris and Amsterdam, the mass of the population remained attached to traditional religious teaching and practices.

And yet the penetrating power of Enlightenment ideas was such that the majority of Christian apologists adopted a defensive attitude and felt menaced by them, while others—Jesuits as well as latitudinarian English bishops—showed their anxiety to demonstrate that there was no conflict between the truths of Revelation and the new faith in human reason. The expulsion of the Jesuits from France and Spain in the 1760s and their suppression by the Pope in 1773 was primarily due to the Catholic governments' dislike of papal authority and clerical intervention in politics; but a secular view of the state and its separation from the Church was good Enlightenment doctrine and it can hardly have been a coincidence that the Jesuits had been the principal target of the *philosophes'* anti-clerical campaign.

The great discovery of the Enlightenment was the effectiveness of critical reason when applied to authority, tradition, and convention, whether in religion, law, government, or social custom. To ask questions, to put claims to empirical tests, not to accept what has always been done or said or thought, has become so commonplace a methodology—and we are so conscious of the damage it can do when pursued indiscriminately—that it is hard for us to recognize the novelty and shock of applying such critical methods to archaic institutions and attitudes in the eighteenth century.

For Diderot, for example (1713–84), to challenge the received orthodoxy on any subject was the first step, not to replacing it with a new one, but to opening the mind to fresh possibilities and encouraging speculation. This applied not only to philosophical and religious doctrine or petty conventions of sexual morality but to science as well. In his *Thoughts on the Interpretation of Nature* (1753) he wrote: 'If all beings are in state of perpetual change, if nature is still at work, . . . all of our natural science becomes as ephemeral as the words in use. What we take for the history of nature is only the very incomplete history of one moment.'

Although he was fascinated by the play of ideas and the elaboration of such hypotheses, Diderot had an equally strong respect for the particularity of facts. 'Facts, of whatever kind,' he wrote in the same essay, constitute the philosopher's true wealth. He proved that he meant what he said in the famous *Encyclopédie,* to the editing of which he devoted the best part of twenty years. If it was the *Encyclopédie*'s philosophical and religious articles which attracted the most attention—and led the *Parlement* of Paris to ban it in 1759—its most original feature was the amount of space Diderot devoted to technology and the care he took to get the details right, as can be seen by the twelve volumes of plates which accompanied the seventeen folio volumes of text.

The intellectual fireworks of a Diderot or a Voltaire should not lead us to underestimate the practical benefits which their efforts produced in the Europe of the *ancien régime.* Greater freedom of speech was only one of these. One can add Montesquieu listing the rights of accused persons; Lessing advocating toleration of Jews; Beccaria and Bentham labouring to humanize a brutal criminal code; Rousseau defending the claims of the child; Voltaire's efforts to rehabilitate the victims of judicial miscarriage; Montesquieu's and Diderot's, Voltaire's and Rousseau's denunciation of slavery, supported by the Scots economists Miller's and Adam Smith's demonstration that economically slave labour was the most expensive and wasteful of any. These are the beginnings of that series of rational, humanitarian reforms which—despite the pessimism over the results—are among the great achievements of the nineteenth and twentieth centuries.

What made the *philosophes'* use of critical reason so effective was their coupling of it with an equally new-found self-confidence that if men were emancipated from their fears and superstitions (including the false idols of Revealed Religion) they would discover powers in themselves to remold the conditions of human life. 'Man,' Bacon had declared, 'is the architect of his Fortune'—another Renaissance theme revived. Freedom of thought and freedom of expression were the conditions of progress; human invention and intelligence the keys, scientific empiricism the most powerful agent. These hopes were qualified by reservations, particularly about the price of progress; but progress, they believed, was possible, if not certain, and the possibility of it rested, not in an inscrutable Divine Grace, or the capricious hands of Fortune, but in man's own hands. Antiquity had taught resignation; Christianity salvation; the *philosophes* taught emancipation—man's moral autonomy, the courage to rely on himself, the motto which Kant proposed for the Enlightenment in a tag of Horace's: '*Sapere aude: Incipe*'—'Dare to know—start!'

The *philosophes'* confidence in science was borne out by the progress made in every branch during the eighteenth century and by a series of technical inventions, culminating in James Watt's (1736–1819) invention of the steam engine, on which the Industrial Revolution of the nineteenth century was based. Apart from their more mathematical parts, scientific ideas and experiments were not yet closed to the ordinary educated man by the barriers of specialization. It was the age of the scientific amateur and collector. Voltaire had his own laboratory; Joseph Priestley (1733–1804), who identified oxygen, was a Unitarian minister; and scientific societies, as well as a proliferation of scientific journals, allowed the whole educated world—educated in the humanities—to follow the latest scientific discoveries. The split into two cultures had not yet taken place. An illustration of this is the amount of space devoted by the *Encyclopédie,* the bible of the Enlightenment, to science and industry as well as ideas; another the fact that Buffon's *Histoire naturelle,* published in 1749, was one of the century's best sellers.

2

SCIENCE AND THE AMERICAN EXPERIMENT

John Patrick Diggins

In the winter of 1786, only ten years after declaring independence from England and four years after concluding the war that underscored that declaration, America was falling apart. The single thing the thirteen former colonies seemed to have in common was a penchant for squabbling among themselves. Religious differences separated the Calvinists of New England from the Baptists of the South. The economic interests of northern merchants clashed with those of southern slave owners. Border disputes were common and periodically led to skirmishes. Atlantic states such as South Carolina envied their landlocked neighbors' proximity to the public lands of the Northwest Territories, and states such as New Jersey, with no seaports, were unhappy about paying import tariffs to New York and Philadelphia, whose harbors were well suited for shipping.

To make matters worse, the Articles of Confederation, ratified in 1781, had placed most of the nation's power with the states. Consequently, Congress was too weak to address broad domestic problems, the most troubling of which was a public debt of sixty million dollars, a legacy of the War of Independence. Small farmers, whose financial problems were especially acute, pressed state legislatures to issue paper money with which to pay their creditors. Though it undermined the value of hard currency, several states complied with the farmers' demands out of fear. And with good reason: when the Massachusetts legislature refused, armed bands forced a number of courts to halt foreclosures and imprisonment for debt. Though the rebels were soon subdued by state militia, their brief uprising, along with the other troubles brewing throughout the colonies, awakened leaders to the growing crises: the confederation was on the verge of collapse.

At first, discussion about how to restore unity seemed destined to degenerate into bitter disputes, as well. A handful of former loyalists, who had opposed the war, and representatives of New England's upper classes called for a return to monarchy. Desperate and disgruntled, members of the military thought they could put the country back on course by installing themselves as its new rulers. But the most fundamental and far-reaching disagreement existed between the federalists, who desired a strong central government, and the anti-federalists, who were reluctant to relinquish even a fraction of state autonomy. Nevertheless, the gravity of the situation was sufficient to persuade the various factions to set aside their differences; Congress and every state save Rhode Island accepted the federalists' invitation to a general convention to revise the Articles of Confederation.

The fifty-five individuals who gathered in Philadelphia in May of 1787 constituted the most outstanding group of American statesmen ever to have assembled in one room. Representing Virginia was George Washington, a hero of the war; James Madison, one of the greatest political intellects in the country's history; Edmond Randolph, the state's governor; and George Mason, author of Virginia's bill of rights. From Pennsylvania came Benjamin Franklin, spokesman for the colonies in their debate with Great Britain about self-government, and James Wilson, an exceptionally gifted lawyer. And the New York delegation included Alexander Hamilton, a talented champion of centralized government.

The group proved to be as bold as it was brilliant. Scarcely had the delegates cleared their throats when Randolph presented fifteen specific resolutions (almost certainly authored by Madison), whose scope greatly exceeded the charter of the convention; included was a proposal to create a national authority with sovereignty over the states; rather than fiddle with the Articles of Confederation, they would begin again, to frame a new constitution. And of what would this constitution consist?

Besides freeing the colonies of England's control, the War of Independence had sundered America's ties to the governmental traditions that had dominated England until the eighteenth century. The framers now aligned themselves with the intellectual movement that had recently swept across Europe—the Enlightenment; they rejected the political ideas of the past, turning elsewhere for models after which to pattern government. One of the most important of these models was nature, whose laws were seen as templates for social laws. And the interpretation of nature considered most valid during the Enlightenment was that offered by such men as Isaac Newton, the English physicist. True, the U.S. represented the confluence of several intellectual, social, and political trends, but of these, one of the most powerful and lasting was the growing popularity of science itself.

In turning toward science, the framers spurned two traditions that had shaped political thought before the Enlightenment. The first was Christianity, which defined man's nature in terms of a spiritual destiny that lay beyond history. Whether that destiny was fulfilled by prayer or work, government was considered a divinely ordained institution to be obeyed as much for salvation as for maintaining social order. The second tradition was classical republicanism, a political system with roots in ancient Greece and Rome, as well as in Renaissance Italy. In its purest form, a republican government is one in which power is exercised by elected representatives who are directly responsible to a body of citizens. Classical republicans sought to elevate people into patriots devoted to civic virtue and felt this could be achieved best when government officials lived close enough to their constituents to exhort them to correct behaviour and, in turn, to be accountable to them. Thus it was presumed that republicanism worked only for small-scale governments, such as those that existed in sixteenth-century Florence, Milan, and Genoa.

To many of these scientifically oriented thinkers of the Enlightenment, many of these traditions, emphasizing as they did the repression of self-interest in the name of church and state, were unrealistic. The architect of this critique was the Scottish philosopher, David Hume. Taking Newton's empiricism as his model, Hume held that there could be no knowledge of anything beyond experience. He conceived of philosophy in general, and of political thought in particular, as inductive, experimental sciences. Sound government must be based on the *science of politics*—on the direct observation of human behaviour.

Such observations led Hume to conclude that human nature is uniform, that even in the face of social and economic differences, invariant rules can be drawn from men's actions. The most important of these is that, since reason is a slave to the passions, political thinkers must be all the more scientific because they cannot expect the people to be so. Noting that, for centuries, the condition of the human race remained miserable under religious and classical authority, Hume argued that the aim of government should be not to exhort citizens to attain grace or virtue but to accept man as a pleasure-seeking creature. Rather than leading to political instability, man's pursuit of material gain will induce productive work habits and thereby contribute to the creation of wealth and progress, as long as government is designed to offset opposing passions. This picture of mankind accorded well with the world view of eighteenth-century science, which was based largely on Newton's three laws of motion, in particular, the third; for every action there is an equal and opposite reaction.

Both Hume's ideas about government and Newton's outlook on nature came together in early American political thought. Hamilton, Madison, and the other framers were particularly impressed with Hume's essay "That Politics Be Reduced to a Science." From Hume they learned that if government concerns itself with institutions and political structures, rather than with manners and morals, a right and powerful republic need not succumb to corruption. The clearest and most forceful articulation of this lesson is found in *A Defence of the Constitutions of Government of the United States of America,* composed in 1787 and 1788 by John Adams, later to become the second president, and in *The Federalist,* a series of eighty-five essays by Hamilton, Madison, and John Jay, then the secretary of foreign affairs, which appeared in New York newspapers, in support of the Constitution, between October of 1787 and August of 1788. It is no accident that these documents, brilliant expositions of the political theory that underlies American government, are studded with the language of natural science.

Adams wrote the *Defence* in response to French political thinkers who had criticized the American states for having governments whose branches were designed to reflect class divisions as a means of controlling them. Because post-revolutionary America had no monarchy, aristocracy, or peasantry, the French felt the country could dispense with its system of checks and balances and simply vest all authority in a single, national assembly.

Adams faulted the French for failing to realize that governmental abuse cannot be eradicated merely by entrusting power to an active citizenry. He argued that a strong executive branch was necessary to mediate between the rich and the poor, the powerful and the weak. Whereas the French believed that class differences could be abolished along with the executive branch, which remained for them a symbol of monarchial tyranny, Adams, like the skeptic Hume, was convinced that potentially explosive divisions of one kind or another would always exist in society and that democracy must be controlled to prevent the tyranny of any particular faction.

"All nations, from the beginning, have been agitated by the same passions," Adams observed. To him, there was only one solution to political power conceived as a force that expands until met by a counterforce: "Orders of men, watching and balancing each other, are the only security: power must be opposed to power, and interest to interest." Proof for the idea came from the classical mechanics of Newton (for every action, a reaction).

The laws of physics, as well as the maxims of geometry, were also used to support the political ideas in *The Federalist*. In number thirty-one, for example, Hamilton cited a variant of the laws of mechanics (the means should be proportionate to the end) to defend the constitutional clause that authorized the new government to make any laws necessary to carry out its objectives. (For example, the Constitution says that the government shall regulate commerce, but it fails to mention banking. Nonetheless, according to Hamilton, the government can create a banking system to regulate commerce.)

Elsewhere in *The Federalist,* Hamilton and Madison advanced the Newtonian principle that an effect cannot exist without a cause, to show why factions are inevitable. Since the differences that give rise to factionalism are "sown" into human nature, government should abandon any hope of abolishing the causes of factionalism and attend, instead, to the establishment of political structures that will counterbalance natural conflicts, thereby preventing them from erupting into civil strife. Extending this line of reasoning, both authors invoked the Euclidean theory that the whole is greater than the parts to arrive at one of the most astounding conclusions in modern political philosophy: a good and stable government can be constructed from defective human parts.

The framers also appealed to science to support their theories about the size of government. One of the main concerns of the anti-federalists was that the Constitution would create an extended government designed to rule over a vast territory, a dangerous departure from the classical principle that republics must remain small for citizens to exercise control. Hamilton responded that the science of politics makes possible "the enlargement of the orbit of government." In this new, scientific scenario, liberty was to be preserved not by citizen participation—which, more often than not, yielded governments too parochial to be fair—but by fragmentation of power within a mosaic of countervailing devices and by a distancing of government from the people. To achieve these ends, the framers installed two key features in the Constitution: a separation of powers between the executive, legislative, and judicial branches of the federal government and a division of power between the federal and state governments.

That these features were linked so intimately to Newtonian theories of motion and force is only one of many signs that, in the late eighteenth century, the West was entering that period of history in which the scientific ethos would redefine all aspects of human endeavor. The Newtonian cosmology gave the framers confidence that the Constitution should accord with the ways of nature. If a government proportions its parts, Hamilton declared, its power will never constitute a threat to the security of its citizens. Balance and counterpoise bring stability and equilibrium. Liberty is preserved not by civic virtue but by the design of government itself, which, in turn, rests on the principles of physics and geometry. Unlike the systems of the past, the American government would be one of *mechanisms* rather than of men—"a machine that would go for itself," in the words of the nineteenth-century American poet James Russell Lowell.

Later generations were not uniformly overjoyed with a government conceived mechanistically. Woodrow Wilson, for one, believed that the Constitution had been so delicately balanced that it failed to allow for executive leadership. He felt that the framers had been mistaken in conceiving of politics as a branch of mechanics, because government "is a living thing." Thus, he called for a new constitution, one that would be open to adaptation, a government "accountable to Darwin, not to Newton." Yet, when one considers that the framers not only balanced power but countervailed the irrational interests and passions from which power springs, it could be said that they gave us a government that went beyond Darwin, one accountable to Freud as well as to Newton.

3

THE INVENTION OF THE BALLOON AND THE BIRTH OF MODERN CHEMISTRY

Arthur F. Scott

The first manned balloon flights in France 200 years ago were inspired by basic research into the nature of gases by some of the leading chemical investigators of the day.

The first free flight by human beings was a balloon ascension from the gardens of the Chateau de la Muette in the Western outskirts of Paris on November 21, 1783. The passengers were Pilatre de Rozier, the young director of a museum of science in Paris, and the Marquis d'Arlandes, an army officer with good connections at the court of Louis XVI. In a hot-air balloon designed by the brothers Joseph-Michel and Jacques-Etienne Montgolfier the two passengers stayed aloft for some twenty-five minutes and came down unharmed in the open country near the road to Fontainebleau, having traveled about five miles.

The flight was remarkable in its own right, but it also epitomized a major achievement in chemistry, namely the fall of the phlogiston theory of chemical composition under the impact of the discovery that gases are distinguishable by weight. The names of four preeminent chemists—Joseph Black, Henry Cavendish, Joseph Priestley, and Antoine Lavoisier—are entwined in the records of the first balloon flights, manned and unmanned. Their work opened the way to the first clear understanding of the chemical nature of matter.

The Montgolfier brothers lived in Annonay, a town near Lyons. They had been fascinated by the idea of flight, and it occurred to them that a paper bag filled with smoke from a fire would rise in the air. Late in 1782 they carried out two preliminary experiments, which satisfied them that a bigger bag filled with a sufficiently large fire could be made to float. The brothers first demonstrated their idea publicly in Annonay on June 4, 1783. The balloon bag was a spherical sack made out of linen and lined with paper. It was 36 feet in diameter and weighed about 500 pounds. The balloon was inflated over a fire fed with small bundles of chopped straw. When it was released, it rose to a considerable height and came down in about ten minutes, having traveled a mile and a half. Great excitement ensued, and news of the experiment spread quickly throughout France and the rest of Europe.

A different group carried out the next balloon trial in Paris two months later. The experiment was supervised by a physicist, Jacques Charles. Exploiting his knowledge of recent discoveries in the study of gases, Charles had decided to inflate the balloon with hydrogen.

Since hydrogen would easily escape through a paper liner, the balloon bag was made out of thin silk fabric and coated with rubber. The hydrogen was obtained from the action of sulfuric acid on iron filings. Inflating the bag to its final diameter of 13 feet took several days and consumed nearly 500 pounds of acid and 1,000 pounds of iron. An immense crowd watched the ascension from the Champs de Mars on August 27. The balloon stayed up for 45 minutes, finally landing in a field near Gonesse, about 15 miles away, where it so terrified the inhabitants that they tore it to shreds.

Some three weeks later the Montgolfier experiment was repeated in Versailles, this time with Louis XVI and his court in attendance. Filling the fire balloon was a simple task compared with the preparation of the hydrogen ballon and within 10 minutes the balloon was ready to take off. For this demonstration the balloon was fitted with a small cage carrying a sheep, a rooster, and a duck. The balloon itself was not the plain bag of the first ascent but was brightly painted in oil colors. The flight ended in a wood about two miles away. The first aerial travelers were uninjured.

Once the feasibility of balloon flight had been established, the practical possibilities were quickly tested. In October, de Rozier was lifted to 80 feet in a tethered Montgolfier balloon and remained aloft for more than four minutes. A month later, de Rozier and d'Arlandes made their historic free flight across Paris. Not to be outdone, Charles embarked with a passenger from Paris on December 1 in a hydrogen balloon. This flight lasted for two hours and took them some 27 miles to the small town of Nesle. There the passenger was let off and Charles continued alone, ascending to an altitude of about two miles. In a span of six months, man had taken to the air and had learned how to fly.

In the years following 1783 there were many balloon flights all over Europe. Particularly noteworthy was an ascent by Joseph Montgolfier, the only one of the two brothers to have actually flown. He made his flight on January 10, 1784, from Lyons. The balloon, named *Flessellers,* was the largest one up to that date, standing more than 180 feet high and measuring 100 feet around. It was inflated from a straw fire in 17 minutes and rose to a height of 3,000 feet, carrying seven people.

Success followed success in ballooning. In August, 1784, a French chemist, Guyton de Moreau, accompanied by Abbé Bertrand, made a flight to more than 10,000 feet to collect data on the temperature and pressure of the atmosphere. In January of the following year the first crossing of the English Channel (from Dover to Calais) was achieved by Jean Pierre Blanchard, a French aeronaut, and John Jeffries, an American physician.

Following the first flight at Annonay, the French Academy of Sciences, at the request of the government, appointed a commission to report on that experiment and to plan future experiments. Lavoisier, the French chemist whose scientific discoveries were among those underlying the first balloons, was one of the commissioners and played a leading part in the work of the commission. The French government evidently regarded the balloon invention as a significant one, since it covered the expenses of some of the later flights directed by the commission.

The reaction of British scientists to the balloon was less enthusiastic. In November, 1783, King George III and the court at Windsor were treated to an exhibition of a hydrogen balloon. Impressed, the king wrote to Sir Joseph Banks, the president of the Royal Society of London, offering to subsidize further experimentation. The reply came back that since "no good whatsoever" could be expected from such experiments, the society was not interested.

The potential value of the balloon in warfare, however, was recognized quickly. A pamphlet on the subject was published in the same month as the demonstration at Windsor. Benjamin Franklin expressed the situation clearly in a letter dated soon afterward:

> The invention of the balloon appears, as you observed, to be a discovery of great importance. Convincing sovereigns of the folly of wars may perhaps be one effect of it, since it will be impossible for the most potent of them to guard his dominions. Five thousand balloons, capable of raising two men each, could not cost more than five ships of the line, and where is there a prince who could afford to cover his country with troops for its defense as that ten thousand men descending from the clouds might not in many places do an infinite amount of damage before a force could be brought together to repel them?

The spectacular developments in balloon flight were an inevitable consequence of a drastic change in the human understanding of matter. At the time the only science worthy of the name was mechanics, in particular celestial mechanics, the study of the motion of the heavenly bodies. Chemistry was just being freed from the dogma of alchemy, and biology and the other natural sciences were still in the early observational stage. It was a time when a scholar might still master all science and was properly referred to as a natural philosopher. Four of these natural philosophers greatly influenced the invention of the balloon: Black, Cavendish, Priestley, and Lavoisier, all of whom would today be called chemists.

To anyone familiar with modern scientific concepts, the primitive state of chemistry in the early 18th century is bewildering. The alchemical idea that all matter was compounded from four terrestrial elements—air, earth, fire, and water—was still widely held. This simple notion had first appeared in Aristotle's *Natural Science* some 20 centuries earlier and had led, among other things, to the belief that different kinds of matter could be transmitted into one another. One result was the illusory quest for the philosopher's stone, which was said to be capable of turning iron and lead into gold. Another descendant of Aristotle's ideas was also in vogue at that time, namely the phlogiston theory, which was to cloud and confuse the thinking of chemistry for most of the 18th century.

The phlogiston theory was developed to explain the nature of fire. From man's earliest prehistoric experience, it had been recognized that certain substances burn and others do not. The alchemists had enlarged on this observation, noting that with intense enough heat even the common metals would burn, leaving a calx, or ash, that could not be burned. Why was this so?

The explanation put forward by George Stahl in the first decades of the 18th century was based on an earlier idea of his teacher, Johann Becher. Becher had expanded the Aristotelian elements to include *terra pinguis* (fatty earth), which was supposed to be released from a substance when it burned. Stahl took the idea further, asserting that a metal was nothing more than a compound of its calx and fatty earth. Viewed from these perspectives, burning was the release of the stored fatty earth, which Stahl renamed phlogiston, from the Greek for "flammable."

The phlogiston theory was as versatile as it was successful. It explained, for example, why a calx heated with charcoal would revert to the original metal: the charcoal, a flammable substance, is rich in phlogiston, whereas the calx, which does not burn, has none.

Hence the charcoal transfers its phlogiston to the calx, thereby regenerating the metal and leaving charcoal ash. Successes such as this one propelled the theory into general acceptance, and the idea of phlogiston came to dominate chemical thought for most of the century that followed.

Black, Cavendish, Priestley, and Lavoisier were all confirmed phlogistonists when they embarked on their chemical careers. Indeed, the first three were engaged chiefly in making experimental discoveries they often interpreted in terms of the phlogiston theory. Lavoisier, however, had the genius necessary to organize the new findings, along with older facts, into a system of chemistry that had no place for phlogiston. Ironically, although the work of Cavendish and Priestley contributed as much as anything to the overthrow of the phlogiston theory, neither man ever gave up the theory. Priestley remained so convinced in 1800, well after oxygen had become accepted as the cause of fire, that he called his final book *The Doctrine of Phlogiston Established.*

The first break with the chemical ideas of Aristotle stemmed from the experiments of Jan van Helmont, who made the results of his studies known early in the 17th century. Although the alchemists were aware earlier that gases were produced in reactions such as fermentation or the burning of charcoal, they regarded the gases as a form of ordinary air. By means of simple chemical experiments, van Helmont produced gases he could distinguish from ordinary air. He gave them such graphic names (in translation) as windy gas, fat gas, and smoky gas. Van Helmont made no chemical tests of these gases, nor did he attempt to isolate them, but he is credited with introducing the word "gas" into the scientific vocabulary. The study and understanding of gases developed into a branch of chemistry known as pneumatic chemistry, and van Helmont is generally seen as its founder.

The field of pneumatic chemistry lay relatively dormant until the middle of the 18th century. Then it suddenly took on new life and new direction, with surprising results. In the words of Torbern Bergmann, the 18th century Swedish chemist: "During the past 10 years chemistry has not only soared into regions of invisible aerial substances, but it has dared to explore the nature of these substances, and to search for their constituent principles." Indeed, by 1779, when those words were written, the chemical composition of eight gases was already known with certainty.

Although Black, Cavendish, Priestley, and Lavoisier were not close associates, their scientific contributions built on one another and developed into what is now known as the scientific revolution. The chain of discoveries was initiated by Black. In the 1750's, while he was a medical student at Edinburgh, he undertook a careful examination of the gas released by the action of acids on solid magnesia (magnesium carbonate). His primary goal was to understand the antacid properties of magnesia, but in the process he established that the gas released was a chemical entity distinct from atmospheric air.

Black named this new substance "fixed air," since it seemed to be fixed or trapped inside the magnesia. At the time it was not understood that this gas was a compound of chemical elements, and several decades passed before it was renamed carbon dioxide after its atomic composition. By passing gas bubbles through limewater and looking for a milky precipitate, Black was able to show that fixed air was released in the burning of charcoal, in respiration, and in fermentation. He became one of the foremost chemical philosophers of his age, serving first as professor of chemistry at Glasgow and later returning to Edinburgh in the same capacity.

One of the first scientists to look at the properties of fixed air was Cavendish. He was the stereotype of the early natural philosopher: rich, eccentric, and reclusive. Having inherited vast wealth (at one time he was among the richest men in England), Cavendish chose to live his life alone and to devote himself to experiment. In 1766 he published three papers titled *Experiments on Factitious Air.* By factitious air Cavendish meant any kind of gas that is "contained in other bodies . . . and is produced from them" by chemical manipulations. Before Cavendish, only Black's fixed air was known to be factitious. Cavendish had followed Black's method of producing fixed air by adding acid to magnesia and had extended his work by trapping samples of the gas in animal bladders. By weighing the bladder filled first with atmospheric air and then filled with fixed air, Cavendish discovered that fixed air was 1.47 times heavier than normal air.

Propelled by curiosity, Cavendish went further. What would happen if the magnesia in Black's experiment were replaced with a common metal such as iron? Once again gas bubbles were observed and once again Cavendish collected the gas in a bladder. This factitious gas, however, did not give rise to a precipitate in limewater and turned out to be 11 times lighter than air. Moreover, instead of extinguishing a flame as fixed air did, it produced an explosion when a flame was brought near it. Cavendish had clearly discovered a second factitious gas, which he appropriately named "inflammable air."

The work of Black and Cavendish firmly established that gases were separate chemical entities. It was no longer possible to think of air as one of the elementary constituents of matter. But what about earth, fire, and water?

At about this time Lavoisier, a young French aristocrat, undertook a simple test that eliminated "earth" as an elementary substance. An old experiment, which had suggested that it might be, involved heating water for an extended period in a closed "pelican." (That was what the vessel, a retort, looked like.) In the end a small amount of solid was visible at the bottom of the vessel. This experiment had been interpreted as the conversion of water into "earth."

Lavoisier decided to test the accepted interpretation of this experiment with the chemical balance. He weighed the empty pelican and added purified water to it. After sealing the top he recorded the weight of the filled vessel and by subtraction ascertained the weight of the water. He then allowed the water to simmer for 101 days. At the end of the experiment he weighed the filled and empty pelican again. The combined weight had not changed, but a solid had appeared whose weight was equal to the loss in weight of the empty vessel. Obviously the "earth" had leached out of the glass pelican and had not come from the water. Combined with the work of Black and Cavendish, Lavoisier's experiment cast grave doubt on Aristotelian alchemical theory.

The final developments in the scientific revolution hinged on further discoveries in pneumatic chemistry, mainly by Priestley. He was a man of diverse talents and interests. Trained as a Non-conformist clergyman, he had several careers, including publicist, author (of 106 books), and chemist. In 1772 he published a paper titled *Observations of Different Kinds of Air,* in which he described the preparation of several new gases. In the next decade, which was the one just preceding the invention of the balloon, Priestley added eight more gases to his list of discoveries.

At the heart of Priestley's success lay a major improvement in the technique for recovering gases. Previously chemists had collected gases by bubbling them into a water-filled bell jar that had been carefully inverted and set in a pan of water. As gas collected at the top of the jar, water was displaced from the jar into the pan. If a gas was soluble in water, however, it could not be collected by this technique. By the simple device of substituting liquid mercury for water, Priestley could collect and analyze many new gases.

Priestley's most important discovery came in 1774. With sunlight and a 12-inch burning lens he heated the red precipitate of mercury, a powdery substance long known to alchemists. Just as Black had observed in the burning of charcoal, a gas was produced, but it was not fixed air. Indeed, this gas had remarkable properties all its own: it made a candle burn brighter, and a mouse could live in it for nearly twice as long as it could in the same amount of atmospheric air.

Since Priestley adhered to the phlogiston theory of combustion, it was natural for him to interpret these properties in terms of phlogiston. Remember that phlogiston was supposed to leave a substance when it burned. Since it had to go somewhere, Priestley reasoned that it was going into the new gas. Thus the gas must be deficient in phlogiston, and Priestley called it "dephlogisticated air." This name was not destined to last for long. Soon, in the laboratory of Lavoisier, the gas would be renamed oxygen and would figure as the cornerstone of modern chemical theory.

It was at about this time that Lavoisier first began to seriously question the phlogiston theory. In 1772 he had prepared a memoir on the burning of sulfur and phosphorus in air. Again making use of the chemical balance, he determined that both substances gained weight in burning. He attributed the gain to their combining with air. In his memoir Lavoisier went on to speculate that "what is observed in the combustion of sulphur and phosphorus may well take place in the case of all substances . . . and I am persuaded that the increase in weight of metallic calces is due to the same cause." In agreement with his conjecture, Lavoisier found on heating the calx of lead (lead oxide) with charcoal that "just as the calx changed into the metal, a large quantity of gas was liberated." These observations and speculations were in complete contradiction to the phlogiston theory, which taught that phlogiston escaped from a substance when it burned, with an accompanying loss of weight. The young Lavoisier, recognizing the heresy in these ideas, submitted his memoir as a sealed note to the French Academy, thereby ensuring his prior claim if such revolutionary thoughts were sustained by future work.

Lavoisier's mature thoughts on burning and the theory of combustion appeared in his famous memoir of 1783, *Reflexions sur le phlogistique* (Reflections on Phlogiston). There he summarized his many arguments against the validity of the phlogiston theory. The evidence was clear enough for him to write:

My only object in this memoir is to extend the theory of combustion that I announced in 1777; to show that Stahl's phlogiston is imaginary and its existence in the metals, sulphur, phosphorus and all combustible bodies is a baseless supposition, and that all the facts of combustion and calcination are explained in a much simpler and easier way without it.

Lavoisier's explanation was indeed simple. It was not phlogiston that was lost during the combustion of a substance; it was oxygen from the air that combined with it. Lavoisier's hypothesis could explain all the facts about combustion. This included the quantitative ones, such as the fact that the weight gained by a substance in combustion was precisely equal to the weight of the oxygen gas that had disappeared.

By this time the results of the research in pneumatic chemistry were being widely disseminated. Great progress in the understanding of matter was being made, and gases with unusual new properties were being discovered. Based on his familiarity with the properties of Black's fixed air, Priestley had dissolved it in water and found that the resulting concoction was pleasant to drink. The new "soda water" became an immediate hit in European society. The Montgolfier brothers were also learning of the work with gases and translating it into their ideas about balloons. One more great stroke was required, leaving in its wake both the scientific revolution and the balloon.

The final piece of the puzzle was discovered in England. Cavendish had taken up Priestley's use of the electric spark to examine the new gases. Cavendish was particularly interested in the light gas he had earlier called inflammable air, and he was sparking mixtures of it and common air. The spark caused a bluish flame accompanied by contraction of the volume of the gas and the formation of a small amount of liquid, which he called a dew.

It was the dew that attracted Cavendish's attention, and he set about designing a second experiment to collect larger quantities of it. The substance, he wrote, "had no taste or smell and . . . left no sensible sediment when evaporated to dryness; neither did it yield any pungent smell during evaporation; in short, it seemed pure water." Indeed, further examination proved it to be just that.

This famous experiment was completed in 1781 but not reported to the Royal Society until 1784. Formal publication was delayed primarily because Cavendish wanted first to investigate his observation that when dephlogisticated air was substituted for common air in this experiment, the water produced was acidic. The cause of the acidity he found to be nitric acid, the composition of which he was able to establish for the first time.

Cavendish had shown that water was produced from inflammable air and dephlogisticated air when a mixture of the two gases was ignited. The finding did not mean to him that water is a compound of hydrogen and oxygen. Not to a confirmed phlogistonist! He wrote: "There seems the utmost reason to think that dephlogisticated air is only water deprived of phlogiston, and that inflammable air, as was before said, is either phlogisticated water, or else pure phlogiston, but in all probability the former." In other words, Cavendish believed water existed as water in each of the two "airs" and that the reaction between them released it. In the process, the phlogiston was transferred from the phlogiston-rich inflammable air to the phlogiston-poor dephlogisticated air.

On November 12, 1783, Lavoisier read at a public meeting of the academy a memoir with the long title *Memoire dans lequel on a pour objet de prouver que l'eau n'est point une substance simple, un element proprement dit, mais qu'elle est susceptible de decomposition et de recomposition* (On the Nature of Water and on Experiments that appear to prove that this Substance is not properly speaking an Element, but can be decomposed and recombined). Although the methods and results were inferior to those of Cavendish, Lavoisier was bold enough to take the leap and assert that water was a compound of oxygen and hydrogen. Lavoisier had also devised a clever experiment showing that water could be broken down into its constituent elements. His idea exploited the fact that when steam reacts with red-hot iron (the iron was actually a gun barrel), the water decomposes to form hydrogen and iron oxide. Only when he found, in a side experiment, that copper at red heat did not react with water was he actually able to carry out the experiment he was seeking.

The successful experiment was set up in a copper tube containing small pieces of iron. A weighed sample of water was dropped into the red-hot tube. Any steam that remained undecomposed was condensed and weighed; the gaseous fraction (hydrogen) was then collected over water and measured; finally the iron in the copper tube was reweighed to determine its gain in weight. From this experiment Lavoisier concluded that water was made up of one part of hydrogen and 6 1/2 parts of oxygen by weight. (The correct value is 1:8.) These graphic demonstrations that water can be taken apart and put back together again fit so neatly into Lavoisier's conception of nature that they dealt a final blow to the phlogiston theory. More than that, the experiment marked the end of the four Aristotelian elements.

Buoyed by the success of his interpretation of this experiment, Lavoisier was in a position to construct a new, logical system of chemistry. He set it forth in his *Traité élémentaire de chimie* in 1789. In it, both oxygen and hydrogen appear among Lavoisier's list of 33 elements, all but two of which can be found in the modern periodic table. The publication of the book signified the beginning of the scientific revolution and the birth of modern chemistry.

Keeping in mind the story of the initial balloon ascents, the effect of the parallel revolution in chemistry on ballooning, and particularly on the hydrogen-filled balloons, seems obvious. Yet the interconnection of the two endeavors is even deeper. Although the story of the hydrogen balloon began in Cavendish's laboratory, where he first prepared his "inflammable air" and established that it is much lighter than atmospheric air, it was Black who applied the discovery to demonstrate for the first time the possibility of producing a lighter-than-air object. The following story by Thomas Thompson, the distinguished chemist who succeeded Black at Glasgow, sets forth Black's simple achievement:

> Soon after the appearance of Mr. Cavendish's paper on hydrogen gas, in which he made an approximation to the specific gravity of that body, showing that it was at least ten times lighter than atmospheric air, Dr. Black invited a party of his friends to supper, informing them that he had a curiosity to show them. Dr. Hutton, Mr. Clarke of Elden and Sir George Clarke of Pennicuik were of that number. When the company invited had assembled, he took them into a room. He had the allantois [the thin fetal membrane] of a calf filled with hydrogen gas, and upon setting it at liberty, it immediately ascended and adhered to the ceiling. The phenomenon was easily accounted for: it was taken for granted that a small black thread had been attached to the allantois, that this thread passed through the ceiling, and that some one in the apartment above, by pulling the thread, erected it to the ceiling, and kept it in position. This explanation was so probable that it was acceded to by the whole company; though, like many other plausible theories, it turned out wholly unfounded; for when the allantois was brought down, no thread was found attached to it.

Years later, in 1784, Black wrote a letter giving an account of his thinking:

> As you speak of the "birth" of aerostatic experiments, I beg leave to communicate to you more fully my thoughts on that subject. In the first place, although what I have

already informed you of is strictly true, I by no means set up my claim for merit in the inventing of machines for general flight and excursions. The experiment with the bladder, which I proposed as a striking example of Mr. Cavendish's discovery, was so very obvious that any person might have thought of it; but I certainly never thought of making large artificial bladders, and making these lift heavy weights, and carry men up into the air. I have not the least suspicion that this was thought of anywhere before we began to hear of its being attempted in France, and I do not doubt that what has been published in the newspapers is perfectly true, viz, that Mons. Montgolfier [*sic*] had sometimes before conceived the idea of flying up into the air by means of a very large bag or balloon of common air, simply rarefied by the application of Fire of Flame.

The idea being founded upon a principle which has long been known, and which has no connection with Mr. Cavendish's discovery, it is only surprising that Mons. Montgolfier should not have put it sooner in practice. I suppose, therefore, that though he might have formed the Project a long time before, he never was roused into an operation for making the trial until others began to think of flying by means of inflammable air. Who first thought of the method I cannot tell, for I confess I did not read the history of the Experiments; they never interested me in the least.

What speculations actually led the Montgolfier brothers to undertake their experiments with the hot-air balloon? This question is more difficult to answer, and what can be said is more in the way of speculation. James Glaisher, writing in the 1878 edition of the *Encyclopedia Britannica,* states: "The Montgolfier brothers imagined that the bag rose because of the levity of the smoke or other vapor given forth by the burning straw, and it was not til some time later that it was recognized that the ascending power was due merely to the lightness of heated air compared to an equal volume of air at a lower temperature." Evidently the Montgolfier brothers were under the impression that the vapor given off by the straw was inflammable air or something similar. Black, however, knew better. He made it clear in his letter that the hotter air was simply "rarefied."

There is other evidence that the Montgolfier brothers at the time of their experiment were laboring under a misapprehension regarding the nature of the smoke and vapors from fire. In the correspondence of Sir John Sinclair, a lawyer who was active in English politics at the time, one finds the following story:

Towards the conclusion of the year 1785, some circumstances occurred, which induced me to take a short excursion from London to Paris, and accidentally I went in company with three distinguished foreigners, namely, Argand, so well known for his improvements in the art of making lamps; Reveillon, the greatest manufacturer of paper hangings then known . . . and [Joseph] Montgolfier, so celebrated for his discovery of balloons. I was able to obtain much information from the conversation of these intelligent men; and I remember, in particular, that the latter gave an account of the origin of his discovery, of which the following is the substance.

Montgolfier said that he and his brother were paper manufacturers in Languedoc, but he had always felt a strong attachment to chemical inquiries. They were thence led to procure all the information they could regarding those subjects. It seems that Montgolfier and his brother had talked over the possibility of being able to ascend themselves, or to send up large bodies from the earth, at a very early period, without, however, having made any experiments to prove whether the idea was practicable or not; but happening to read an account of some experiments made by Dr. Black, which explained the nature of the various kinds of airs or gases, and, in particular, their differences in point of weight, he immediately said to his brother, "The possibility of effecting what we talked about some time ago seems to be proved by a foreign chemist." The point which should be generally known is this, that had it not been for Dr. Black's discoveries, no experiment would probably have been tried by the two Montgolfiers. This I can assert upon the evidence of the older Montgolfier, who was one of the most candid and able men I have met with, and who always mentioned Dr. Black with the respect to which he was so peculiarly entitled.

INDUSTRIAL REVOLUTION

The Industrial Revolution began in England in the 18th century, and brought with it changes so dramatic that they affected every sphere of life. From the first steam engines that pumped water out of mines to the machines that transformed the textile industry, the inventions of the 18th and 19th centuries created a mentality that led to more and more inventions and a constant striving to change the way people produced things, a mentality that continues to drive business and industry today.

The articles in this section cover developments in England and the United States. The first selection discusses the steam engine, its origins, and some of its consequences. The second examines the development of machine tools and their critical role in the growth of industry.

The Industrial Revolution spread from Britain to the United States in the late 18th and early 19th centuries. The American Industrial Revolution is often described as beginning with the inventions of Oliver Evans. Evans, an inventor ahead of his time, invented both a high pressure steam engine and an automatic flour mill. It is the flour mill that is most relevant to a discussion of the Industrial Revolution, for it anticipated the elimination of workers through the introduction of machines. In the United States, as in other countries, industrialization began in earnest with the textile industry. The American textile mills took a different form than their English counterparts. The most striking difference in the early textile mill was that the early American mill employed young women from New England farms to run the machines, while British mills employed first children, then women and men. This is the subject of the fourth article in this section.

Machines lay at the heart of the Industrial Revolution, and with each new machine the life of the worker changed. Sometimes work was made easier, sometimes it was made very boring, but whatever the impact on the worker, productivity almost always increased with new machinery. Often workers were put out of work by the introduction of new machines. Sometimes the work shifted from skilled male workers to less-skilled female and child workers. The next selection will show the impact of the sewing machine on the working population, and on fashion.

The final selection goes outside the countries that spawned the new industries to show how the Industrial Revolution affected other countries. "The Nemesis in China" tells the story of Western aggression against China, a country that simply wanted to keep to itself. The military technology that grew out of the Industrial Revolution made it easy for England to invade China, a feat that would have been nearly impossible without the steam engine.

THE ORIGINS OF THE STEAM ENGINE

Eugene S. Ferguson

Fifty years before James Watt came on the scene Thomas Newcomen built practical steam engines to pump water out of mines. What is known of these engines and how did they influence later ones?

If one had a handbook of human history with a synoptic chart that opened out at the back, one might expect the chart to reduce the industrialization of England in the 18th century to the words "James Watt," "steam engine" and "textile mills." This familiar view is misleading on two counts. Watt did not invent the machine that supplied power to the looms of the textile mills. Steam engines had been put to work 50 years before Watt appeared on the scene, and the industry that created the demand for them was not weaving but mining. At the beginning of the 18th century two Englishmen from Devonshire, Thomas Savery of Shilston and Thomas Newcomen of Dartmouth, built steam-powered pumping machinery for the drainage of mines. The need for a way to remove water from mines had become more and more pressing as the mineral resources of England were exploited during the 17th century. The operators of tin mines in Cornwall and lead mines in Derbyshire were waging a losing battle against water seepage as their mines were dug deeper, and many coal mines around Birmingham and Newcastle were threatened with flooding as the inflow of water overcame the pumps then available. Savery's engine never succeeded as a mine pump, although it was useful for other purposes; Newcomen's did provide the power to lift water from mines.

The Newcomen engine also succeeded, two generations later, in stimulating the curiosity and imagination of James Watt. In 1769 Watt patented an engine soon brought to commercial status by industrialists who realized that its superior thermal efficiency would enable them to make greater practical use of steam power. The Newcomen engine should not, however, be considered a mere taking-off point for the genius of Watt. Its impact on the technology and economics of mining is today symbolized by the monotonous bobbing of the pivoted "walking beams" of oil-well pumping rigs, a familiar sight in the southwestern U.S. The vertical pump shaft is guided at its upper end by an odd protuberance on the beam called, in the graphic language of the industry, a horsehead. Whether or not the builder of the first such oil-pumping rig was aware of his source, he had borrowed these elements from a Newcomen engine originally used to pump water. In 250 years the power unit has evolved from a steam cylinder to an electric motor, but its function—to pull one end of the beam down—has not changed at all.

In Newcomen's design, one end of the beam was secured to the pump shaft and the other end was chained to a piston that fitted into a vertical steam cylinder. When steam supplied to the cylinder from a boiler directly below it was condensed by the injection of water, the resulting vacuum enabled the pressure of the atmosphere to force the piston down, thus drawing the beam down on one side and the pump rod up on the other. Long after the steam engine was being used for purposes other than pumping, it retained the overhead beam of Newcomen's design. Watt himself experimented in 1770 with turning the cylinder upside down in order to eliminate the beam, but he quickly and permanently abandoned the idea.

Little is known about Thomas Newcomen, the man whose innovations were so original, influential, and enduring. He was born in Dartmouth in 1663, made a living as a seller and perhaps small-scale manufacturer of iron products, and died in London in 1729. The recent tricentennial of his birth gave impetus to the study of his life and work; such study, including this critical review of the Newcomen engine, would scarcely have been possible were it not for the dedicated men who in 1920 in London organized the Newcomen Society for the study of the History of Engineering and Technology. The members of this group, the first to take a serious interest in Newcomen as an individual, combed the records for the origins and later history of the steam engine, publishing their findings in the *Transactions* of the society.

The source materials they uncovered tell us more about the state of technology at the time than about the events of Newcomen's life; nothing is revealed of his formal and informal education, the actual sources of his ideas, and the steps by which his major innovations were thought out. It is unlikely that we shall ever learn the details of the steps taken by Newcomen during the 10 years he spent developing his engine. He was not prominent during his lifetime, and although his engine won immediate acceptance, it was seldom linked with his name, being known merely as the "fire engine" or "atmospheric engine." In this article I shall review the antecedents of the engine he designed and, as far as I am able to reconstruct it, the period of development immediately preceding its appearance.

A glance at the dozens of well-illustrated books devoted to machines that were published in Italy, France and Germany from the time of Georgius Agricola's *De Re Metallica* (1556) onward indicates that the problem of water-raising was one that occupied many mechanics and mechanical philosophers in the advanced countries of Europe. Except for Agricola's treatise on mining, which gave details of 14 kinds of pumps for removing water from mines, the books were concerned less with mine drainage than with pumping water for town and castle water supplies and for the operation of fountains. Nevertheless, the techniques of pumping were well known and widely discussed. Some of the devices employed were an endless chain of buckets, the Archimedean screw and the rag-and-chain pump, in which a series of rag-wrapped balls, spaced a foot or two apart on a continuous chain, were drawn vertically upward through a wooden pipe, each forcing some water ahead of it. There were many alternative machines using manpower or horsepower for the hoisting of ordinary tubs of water. During the 17th century, the possibility of using steam or gunpowder as a motive power was also being explored.

It has been said that science owes more to the steam engine than the steam engine owes to science. Such a generalization seems particularly inappropriate with respect to a machine that exemplifies the overlap between the empirical and the theoretical stages of the Industrial Revolution. Although it is true that a clear understanding of the thermodynamic phenomena in the steam engine was not attained until around 1860, it is equally true that the sequence of ideas apparent in the work of Galileo, Torricelli, and Pascal in establishing the fact of atmospheric pressure, and of von Guericke, Huygens, and Papin in devising ways to make atmospheric pressure do work, was an indispensable prerequisite of the Newcomen engine.

Close to the Newcomen engine chronologically but not conceptually was the steampowered machine patented by Thomas Savery in 1698. This engine, which promised to solve the problem of mine flooding, incorporated elements and principles not shared by the Newcomen engine and can be traced to a wholly different line of development. Savery, a gentleman of leisure and Fellow of the Royal Society of London, exhibited a model before the society in 1699. His engine consisted of a vessel in which steam was condensed to produce a vacuum, whereupon the vessel was filled by water rising through a suction pipe. Steam at high pressure was then admitted to the same vessel, forcing the water to a higher elevation. The machine was a combination of steam pumping devices built or suggested earlier by Salomon de Caus and R. d'Acres and probably well known in Savery's circle.

In 1702, Savery expanded his patent application in a small book entitled *The Miner's Friend*. Here he addressed himself to the "Gentlemen Adventurers in the Mines of England":

> I am very sensible a great many among you do as yet look on my invention of raising water by the impellent force of fire a useless sort of a project that never can answer my designs or pretensions; and that it is altogether impossible that such an engine as this can be wrought underground and succeed in the raising of water, and dreining your mines. . . . The use of the engine will sufficiently recommend itself in raising water so eaise and cheap, and I do not doubt but that in a few years it will be a means of making our mining trade, which is no small part of the wealth of this kingdome, double if not treble to which it now is.

In spite of Savery's optimism, the metalworking techniques at his command were inadequate to solve the problem of containing steam at several atmospheres of pressure. Hence the Savery engine was practical only in situations other than the one for which it was originally intended. The most successful application of the engine was in pumping water into building or fountain reservoirs that were no higher than about 30 feet, which called for only moderate steam pressure.

The Newcomen engine soon preempted the role of draining the mines, but the Savery engine was the first to be employed (around 1750) to turn machinery. For this purpose the engine pumped water into a reservoir some 15 or 20 feet above that supplied a conventional water wheel. Throughout the latter part of the 18th century, the Savery engine was built in considerable numbers and used by manufacturers who could not or would not afford the larger, more efficient, but initially more expensive Newcomen and Watt engines. As late as 1833 at least five Savery engines were at work in France; the engine was reinvented about 1870 in Germany, perhaps also in England. Now known as the pulsometer, it went on to a new career of pumping water containing solids in such applications as the drainage of shallow excavations.

The problem of following the sequence of events in the development of the Newcomen engine points up the meagerness of available source materials. What little information

Newcomen's contemporaries have left us requires careful interpretation. One popular scientific lecturer of the early 18th century, John Theophilus Desaguliers, described him as an "ironmonger" and "Anabaptist." This is the way he has been described by modern writers oblivious to the fact that "ironmonger" has come to imply "peddler," or perhaps "junkman," and that "Anabaptist" suggests the outlandish. Thus Newcomen is likely to be thought of as a ragged, gaunt pusher of a handcart, waiting for Dickens to be born so that he could get into one of his books.

The background of his assistant, John Cawley, is even less distinct. Desaguliers called him a glazier; another man who could have known him said he was a plumber. Elsewhere he is referred to as a brazier or coppersmith. This description seems proper because an ironmonger was a dealer in hardware and industrial supplies, sometimes manufacturing what he sold. He might have had an iron foundry as part of his establishment; he usually employed braziers and tinsmiths; he was likely to have a lathe and a smithy. It has been suggested, I think reasonably, that the ironmonger rather than the millwright (who generally built in wood) was the predecessor of the mechanical engineer. So we can forget the picture of Newcomen the indigent peddler and accept the more plausible likeness of a man well skilled in the machinery trade.

As for the significance of the work Newcomen did in developing the steam engine, Desaguliers states:

> If the reader is not acquainted with the History of the several Improvements of the Fire-Engine since Mr. *Newcomen* and Mr. *Cawley* first made it go with a Piston, he will imagine that it must be owing to great Sagacity, and a thorough knowledge of Philosophy, that such proper Remedies for the Inconveniences and difficult Cases mention'd were thought of: But there as been no such thing: almost every Improvement has been owing to Chance.

Further detraction—or inverted praise—came from Marten Triewald, a Swedish engineer who took plans for a Newcomen engine back to Sweden with him in 1726, attributing the design to the Almighty, who "presented mankind with one of the most wonderful inventions that has ever been brought into the light of day, and this by means of ignorant folk who had never acquired a certificate at any University or Academy." Triewald did mention, however, that Newcomen worked on his machine "for ten consecutive years."

Since Desaguliers and Triewald, our principal sources, were contemporaries of Newcomen's, it is perhaps presumptuous to question their judgment. But contemporaneousness does not ensure accuracy, and Desaguliers is known as a kind of press agent of science and the arts. He was the first to publish the absurd story about Humphry Potter, the boy who, while attending a manually controlled Newcomen engine, invented the automatic valve gear in order to keep the engine running when he went fishing. The work of both authors shows them to be vain and opinionated, and it is natural to wonder on what occasion Newcomen had pricked their pompous balloons.

The scant biographical information does not tell us unequivocally that Newcomen's design was complete when the engine was set to work near Birmingham in 1712. L. T. C. Rolt has recently assembled evidence that suggests the existence a few years before 1712 of one or more unsuccessful Newcomen engines in Cornwall, near the inventor's home in Dartmouth. This would certainly make more credible the appearance of a definitive machine in 1712. In any case, a virtually anonymous ironmonger working in Dartmouth would hardly travel 175 miles to Birmingham, as Newcomen apparently did, to erect an engine unless he had connections farther afield than his home city. Although I cannot be certain, it seems probable to me that Newcomen was no stranger to London and that he quite possibly had traveled to the Continent, where he might have seen some of the great water-driven pumping engines around Paris. Just as Americans in the early 1800s went to England to learn the latest techniques in engineering, so in the 1700s Englishmen went to the Continent.

The design of the engine built by Newcomen in Birmingham in 1712 was, if not definitive, remarkably near completion. Certainly by 1717 it had been given its final form; we have an engraving made of the engine in that year. Fifty years later John Smeaton was to improve Newcomen's machine by determining after methodical empirical investigation the optimum operating conditions and proportions of parts of the engine, but Smeaton did not tamper with the inventor's essential design.

Even in its earliest manifestations the Newcomen engine was simple enough so that observers could understand its operating principle and cyclical sequence of events as soon as an explanation was provided. A vertical steam cylinder, fitted with a piston, was located under one end of the large, pivoted working beam; the piston rod was hung on a flat chain secured to the top of the arch-shaped head of the beam. Steam was supplied to the cylinder by the boiler directly below it. A vertical lift pump was located under the other end of the beam and the pump rod hung on a flat chain secured to the arch head just above it. Thus the piston rod and the pump rod moved vertically, always tangent to a circle whose center was at the pivot of the beam.

A working stroke began after the steam cylinder had been filled with steam, at a pressure just slightly above atmospheric, from the boiler. The pump end of the working beam was held down by the weight of the reciprocating pump parts, which extended down into the mine. The steam-admission cock was closed, and water was then injected into the cylinder in order to condense the steam and produce a vacuum. The atmosphere, acting on the top of the piston, pushed the piston down into the evacuated cylinder, which caused the pump rod to be lifted by the other end of the cylinder in order to allow the pump end of the working beam to go down. As soon as the cylinder pressure reached atmospheric, the spent injection water was discharged into a sump.

The cylinder was large. The first engine cylinder was 21 inches in diameter and had a working stroke of more than six feet. The effective vacuum was about half an atmosphere, enabling a 21-inch piston to lift unbalanced pump parts and water weighing one and a quarter tons. Operating at 14 working strokes a minute, the engine would develop about six horsepower. Later engines increased in size to a cylinder diameter of seven feet and a stroke of 10 feet and developed well over 100 horsepower.

The late Henry W. Dickinson, author of the current standard history of the steam engine and a principal founder of the Newcomen Society, recognized that Newcomen's contribution was the "first and greatest step" in the development of the modern steam engine, but he diluted the effect of this judgment by writing: "When we look into the matter closely, the extraordinary fact emerges that the new engine was little more than a combination of known parts."

This statement brings to mind a remark made in 1853 by a correspondent of *Silliman's Journal*:

It appears that the human mind cannot arrive at simplicity except by passing through the complex; it is like a mountain more or less elevated, whose heights must be overcome before the plain at the opposite base can be reached: and when reached, the level seems to be that of the plain left behind. So when a simple solution of a problem is arrived at, we think it an easy natural thought and almost self-evident.

This, it seems to me, describes the problem we have in looking at the innovations of Thomas Newcomen from a 20th-century vantage point. In retrospect the idea of the steam engine is a natural thought, modified only by our occasional impatience with Newcomen's inability to see some obvious further development, such as the addition of a crank and fly-wheel, which came two generations later (shortly after having been rejected as impractical by so capable and forward-looking an engineer as John Smeaton). It is not easy for the human mind to put what is now obvious back into the box labeled "Unknown."

In discussing Newcomen's achievement with reference to the "known parts" of the engine, it should be noted that he was not simply a clever compiler of mechanical elements. He did not employ many devices, including the crank and flywheel, that were vastly better known than some he made use of in his "combination of known parts," and most of those he did use he modified in such a way as to make the distinction between adaptation and invention seem artificial.

Consider Newcomen's use of the steam cylinder and piston. The line of development leads straight from von Guericke through Huygens and Papin to Newcomen. The cylinder fitted with a piston and evacuated by the condensation of steam was clearly present in Papin's design published in 1690 and republished in 1695, and we ought to assume that Newcomen knew at least as much about Papin's work as had been published. The steam in Papin's cylinder, however, was to be condensed by cold water dashed on the outside wall. Newcomen's essential improvement was to inject water directly into the cylinder, which sped the condensation and enabled the engine to operate at 12 or 14 strokes a minute instead of three or four.

One of Newcomen's experimental engines had employed a water jacket around the steam cylinder for cooling, and it may be, as Triewald reported, that the change from external to internal cooling resulted from the accidental leakage of jacket water into the cylinder, which "immediately condensed the steam, creating such a vacuum that . . . the air, which pressed with a tremendous power on the piston, caused its chain to break and the piston to crush the bottom of the cylinder as well as the lid of the small boiler." Even if this report is accurate, Newcomen was still faced with the nice diagnostic problem of determining from the wreckage what had caused the sudden smash. Serendipity in no way diminishes Newcomen's role in the innovation of injection condensation.

In his use of the boiler, Newcomen was adopting a thoroughly developed "known part." Made of copper, the boiler probably was derived directly from the brewer's kettle. Since the steam pressure was low—Newcomen set his safety valve to open at about 1.5 pounds per square inch above atmospheric pressure—the difficulties of design and construction were few. Indeed, the boiler was similar to the one built by Savery.

The full synthetic ability of Newcomen, and his judicious critical sense, are revealed in his treatment of the working beam, the pump and the valve gear. The working beam and pump can be examined together, because their appearance is that of a greatly enlarged pump handle or well sweep attached to a common reciprocating lift pump. Before Newcomen's day few, if any, mines in England were drained by lift pumps attached to beams, pump handles, or sweeps. Where the topography of the mining district permitted, long drainage tunnels, called adits, were dug from the lowest mine level to a lower open valley in the vicinity. Although the adits were small in cross section, some of them extended for two miles or more. Even after a mine was deepened beyond its adit level, water had to be pumped only as high as the adit. When surface water was available, an underground water wheel, receiving its water from ground level and discharging into the adit, would operate a lifting device of some kind, usually a chain of buckets.

In some larger works, where horses could be used, the water was lifted in great tubs by a whim, or horse gin. The hoisting rope was wound on a horizontal drum geared to a vertical shaft. The vertical shaft, fitted with a hub with radiating arms, was dragged around by horses hitched to the ends of the arms. In smaller mines, where only manpower was available, a horizontal drum turned by hand cranks was used to hoist buckets or drive a rag-and-chain pump.

If Newcomen had seen a copy of Agricola's mining book, he would have found reciprocating lift pumps in profusion, but he would have come away from the treatise with the distinct impression that the proper way to move the rod of the lift pump up and down was to hang it on a crank arm, that is, to employ a crank and connecting rod. There is one simple beam pump in Agricola, but it is a small one operated by the power of a single man.

Among the actual devices that Newcomen might have seen was a large overhead pivoted beam, without arch heads, in the horse-driven water pump at York House in London. The London Bridge waterworks, although they employed cranks and connecting rods, had the lower third of a large pulley cut away in a manner that faintly suggests the arch heads at the ends of the Newcomen engine beam. The almost complete absence of the arch head from pump beams in the illustrations that Newcomen might have seen is most striking. A sketch in Leonardo da Vinci's notebooks could hardly have been known to Newcomen because the notebooks were effectively buried until the 19th century. Only one illustration remains as the possible—or probable—source of Newcomen's arch heads. In a book by Venturus Mandey and James Moxon—*Mechanick-Powers: or, the Mistery of Nature and Art Unvail'd,* published in London in 1696—there is a cam-operated pumping device that clearly shows the sector-and-flat-chain arrangement adapted by Newcomen, who changed the shape of the beam from curved to straight. The drawing in the Mandey and Moxon book was copied directly from an earlier work edited by Philippe de la Hire, a French mathematician and member of the Académie des Sciences, who had directed the building of such a pump to supply water to a castle near Paris.

Thus the working beam of the Newcomen engine appears to be an elegant adaptation, not a copy, of ideas that existed before he designed his engine. I have labored this point in order to emphasize the fact that Newcomen was not merely adapting the steam cylinder to a widely used system of water-raising. His engine was a new and original system in itself.

The origin of the valve gear, which enabled the engine to operate automatically—opening and closing valves as required for the sequence of operations—is similarly obscure. The idea may have been suggested to Newcomen by a control mechanism of the automata—knights, maidens, and animals—that performed at an appointed hour in the great medieval clocks. The Newcomen engine valve gear was a sequential control; it remained for Watt to supply a regulatory feedback control system. Newcomen's system, however, was much more involved than, for example, the control of the rate of a common clock.

Even after all the elements of the steam pumping engine had been settled on, however, there was still the problem of the physical arrangement of the elements. Pictures of the gaunt and unsymmetrical profile of the Newcomen engine set against the English landscape, with its awkwardly tall stone enginehouse and its outlandish protruding beam threatening to topple the whole assemblage, make it difficult to believe that there was anything about the arrangement that could not have been built differently if the "right way" had not been shown boldly by Newcomen. As an assemblage of elements, some adopted but most adapted, the engine was a clear statement of the builder's personal style of invention.

The genius of James Watt was of a different kind, and to discuss the difference in terms of superiority smacks of useless historical partisanship. Newcomen selected the components of a steam engine and gave to each its proper place and function. Watt, on the other hand, originated at least two new major components, and in making a brilliant adaptation of a third, he introduced the world to the notion of feedback for automatic control.

Watt began his work on steam engines in 1763, when, as an instrument maker at the University of Glasgow, he undertook the repair of a teaching model of a Newcomen engine. His careful and sustained study led him in 1765 to recognize that he might increase the thermal efficiency of the engine, as well as its capacity and operating speed, by condensing the steam in a chamber attached to, but separate from, the main steam cylinder. This was the first of his most important innovations.

His earliest patent, which included the separate condenser, was granted in 1769, but his first successful full-sized engine was not completed until 1775, the year in which Matthew Boulton became his partner. Parliament granted a patent extension to Watt that year, providing a virtual monopoly on the condensing steam engine for 25 years.

After Watt had devised a double-acting engine, in which steam moved the piston first in one direction and then in the other as it was admitted alternately to each end of the cylinder, the arch head and flat chain no longer sufficed to guide the upper end of the piston rod, because the chain transmitted force in tension only. Accordingly, in 1783 Watt brought forth his second major innovation: the straight-line linkage that bears his name. Refining further his first idea, Watt combined the straight-line linkage with a pantograph, a linkage system in parallelogram form, to produce the so-called "parallel motion."

In these two inventions we find a measure of Watt's capacity: the separate condenser was neither anticipated nor invented independently by anyone else, and the parallel motion solved a problem whose existence was not even suspected until Watt overcame it. For the next 100 years mechanics and mathematicians occupied themselves in a search for alternative solutions.

Finally, in 1788 Watt adapted the centrifugal "flyball" governor to control the speed of his engine by linking the governor to the steam-inlet valve. The flyball governor had been used in grain mills to increase the distance between the flat grinding stones as their speed increased. Watt's use of the governor, however, added the far-reaching principle of feedback that made possible self-regulating, rather than merely automatic, machines. The ordinary steam engine and the Watt engine were built, in the words of Boulton, "with as great a difference of accuracy as there is between the blacksmith and the mathematical instrument maker." Thus, the few astonishingly sophisticated Boulton and Watt engines in service toward the end of the century hurried a generation of machine builders to a higher order of accuracy, which in turn called for a whole new array of large, rugged, and precise machine tools. The influence of the new tools on mechanizationt was profound and can be traced directly to the present. The effect of the separate condenser and self-regulating speed control on the direction of industrial technology can be appreciated if we recognize that their invention was an essential step toward the modern steam turbine. Undeniably, Watt opened doors whose very existence might have gone unnoticed for 100 years after his time.

The Watt steam engine was twice as efficient, from the standpoint of fuel consumption, as even the best Newcomen engine. A recent study by two English economic historians, A. E. Musson of the University of Manchester and E. A. G. Robinson of the University of Cambridge, has shown, however, that both Savery and Newcomen engines were being built long after they had been made obsolete by Watt's improvements, and that Boulton and Watt supplied only about a third of all steam engines built during the 25-year period of the patent monopoly (1775–1800). It is also clear that a two-cylinder Newcomen engine capable of turning machinery was in existence, and that the high-pressure engines operating without condensers of any sort were soon to be built by Richard Trevithick in England and Oliver Evans in the U.S.

Since hindsight is one of our best-developed faculties, it has been possible for writers for more than 200 years to dismiss the appearance of the Newcomen engine of 1712 as well as the Watt engine of 1775–1788 as being merely normal responses to industrial demands. The well-established axiom of simultaneous but independent discovery, which can be interpreted to mean that a particular invention is inevitable, has been applied to suggest that if Thomas Newcomen had not built his engine, somebody else would have done so at about the same time.

This seems no more accurate in the case of Newcomen than in the case of Watt. In looking carefully at the Newcomen engine, it has become increasingly evident to me that it represents a unique solution to the problem the inventor set out to solve. There was no anticipation of the completed engine, and nobody came forward to contest Newcomen's priority of invention. The first radical modification occurred no sooner than 50 years later, when Watt conceived the separate condenser.

Newcomen was not the first man to "discover" the correct way to build a steam engine; there is no correct way. It is conceivable, for example, that he might have made the cylinder horizontal rather than vertical, that he might have supplied steam above atmospheric pressure (only eight pounds per square inch would have sufficed to do the work), or that he might have used a crank, connecting rod, and flywheel. Any of these variations would have been possible if he had approached the problem differently. But by producing a machine that was a pumping engine, not easily adapted to the turning of wheels, Newcomen limited the options that lesser engineers could exploit in the future. He did the job his way, and he gave the world such a convincing statement of rightness in the machine he put together that he exerted an enormous influence on the direction in which English technology would proceed for the next several generations.

5

THE DEVELOPMENT OF MACHINE TOOLS

L. T. C. Rolt

The early British engineers were masters of precise machinery; sophisticated mass-production overtook them from America.

Even if a layman has occasion to visit an engineer's machine shop, he emerges with no very clear idea of what is going on. His walk down a long machine-lined aisle while his guide shouts incomprehensible explanations above the roar and chatter of the machines leaves him stunned and bewildered. But for all their bewildering complexity, most modern machine tools are either adaptations, or greatly refined versions, of three tools: the lathe, the drilling machine, and the grindstone, whose origins go back into pre-history. It is broadly true to say that until the eighteenth century the lathe and the drilling machine were used to shape or to bore wood or the softer stones and were powered either manually or by foot treadle. The only significant exception to this generalization was the water-powered cannon-boring mill which was introduced about 1540. The so-called 'hammer ponds,' which today remind us of the vanished iron industry of the Sussex Weald, were in most cases used, not to power hammers, but to drive primitive boring mills.

With hindsight, we can now appreciate the true significance of these early cannon-boring mills. Their message was that for working the harder and more stubborn iron the old man-powered tools were not good enough and that something more massive and power-operated would be demanded by the second Iron Age. But this Industrial Revolution would demand something more than mere power; it would call for power combined with increasing accuracy.

Whereas a version of the primitive cannon mill succeeded in boring cylinders for the early Newcomen or 'atmospheric' steam engine, it was quite incapable of producing a cylinder of sufficient accuracy for James Watt's improved engine. The engine would not work, and its frustrated inventor had to wait for ten years before John Wilkinson, the famous iron-master of Bersham, near Wrexham, developed a new type of boring mill expressly for the purpose and succeeded where others had failed. Watt was delighted. "Mr. Wilkinson," he wrote to a friend, "has improved the art of boring cylinders so that I promise upon a 72-inch cylinder being not further from absolute truth than the thickness of a thin six-pence in the worst part." The success of Watt's engine was now assured.

This was the first, and certainly the most notable, illustration of the truth that even the most promising invention must remain a paper dream if the tools are not available to make it. When we remark that a particular engineer or inventor was 'born before his time,' what we really mean is that in his enthusiasm he failed to recognize this simple truth. Extending, as they do, the power and the cunning of the human hand, the engineer's machine tools are the true arbiters in the progress of technology.

It was no accident that an ironmaster should have been responsible for the first historic advance in machine tool design. Because of transport difficulties, until the last decade of the eighteenth century, iron was fashioned where it was made and the initiative lay with the ironworks; with Wilkinson's works at Bersham, Broseley and Bradley; with the Darby family's famous works at Coalbrookdale; with the Butterley Company in Derbyshire and the Carron Ironworks in Scotland. The historic firm of Boulton & Watt made only a few small parts for their steam engines at their works at Birmingham; the major components they brought in a finished state from Wilkinson.

This situation lasted until 1795 when Wilkinson's industrial empire broke up as a result of a family disagreement. Because no other supplier proved capable of meeting their exacting standards, Messrs Boulton & Watt resolved to build the Soho Foundry, a new works specifically designed for the manufacture of steam engines. For ease of transport, this revolutionary new plant was built beside the Birmingham Canal. Unlike the earlier ironworks, when it opened its doors in 1796 it was the first specialized engineering plant of modern type in the world. This large claim can be made with confidence, thanks to the remarkable completeness of the Boulton & Watt records that have come down to us.

The new works was divided into the following departments: Drilling Shop, Heavy Turning Shop, Nozzle Shop, Fitting Shed, Parallel Motion and Working Gear Shop, Light Fitting Shop, Pattern Shop, Casters' Shop and Smiths' Shop. As in modern practice, in laying out the plan of these different workshops, much thought was devoted to ensuring the most efficient and economical production flow from the raw material entering forge and foundry to the machined and fitted sub-assemblies that passed into the Fitting Shed where they were built into complete steam engines. The original machine tools with which these works were equipped were almost certainly built on the spot. Although they would appear remarkably crude to modern eyes, it is clear from contemporary inventories that some of them at least were special-purpose tools, designed to machine particular components such as the nozzles (valves) and the parallel motion. Such specialization of machines reflected a remarkably highly organized application of the principle of division of labour, not only among machine-operators but also among those responsible for fitting and sub-assembly. Piecework rates were determined for all these specialized operations.

If Messrs. Boulton & Watt were pioneers of workshop organization and method, the pioneer of workshop precision was undoubtedly the Londoner, Henry Maudslay (1771–1831). Born at Woolwich, Maudslay first worked at Woolwich Arsenal, where his remarkable aptitude as a metal-working craftsman attracted the notice of Joseph Bramah, the inventor of the hydraulic press and the water closet. In 1797, Maudslay left Bramah's employ to set up on his own account in a small workshop in Wells Street, off Oxford Street, and it was here that he built the first of his famous screw-cutting, slide-rest lathes (now preserved in the Science Museum), the acknowledged ancestor of the modern machine tool. It is significant that in making this first lathe Maudslay had to cut by hand, with infinite labour and care, an accurate lead-screw for it. It was upon the accuracy of this part that the precision of his machine depended; once it had been achieved, the machine became capable of reproducing with great facility similar screws of a like accuracy. Having thus built his skill into the tool of his creation, that tool has perpetuated it with ever greater accuracy down to the present day. For it is an important characteristic of all the engineer's machine tools that they are self-propagating; that they create their own successors and are capable of reproducing a design improvement in a whole generation of those successors. Thus the engineer's ingenuity initiated a mechanical process of technological evolution far more rapid than that of natural selection.

Maudslay's success was such that in 1810 he founded the business of Maudslay, Sons & Field on Westminster Road, Lambeth, an engineering works that maintained throughout the nineteenth century a reputation for quality of workmanship second to none. Moreover, the firm became a school for budding engineers and in this way Maudslay's teaching and his methods were handed down to future generations. Of the four celebrated mechanical engineers and machine tool makers who served under Maudslay at Lambeth, only Joseph Clement remained in London. The other three, Richard Roberts, James Nasmyth, and Joseph Whitworth, headed north where each founded a business of his own in Manchester. The other "great mechanics" and tool-makers of this period, Matthew Murray, James Fox, and George Bodmer, likewise established themselves in Leeds, Derby, and Manchester respectively. This was no coincidence. It was the textile industry that induced all these men to set up in business where they did.

Because the manufacture of textiles was the first to be mechanized on the factory system, it was the first industry to rely heavily upon the services of skilled mechanics to build and to service its complex machinery. Consequently, it was in the shadow of the textile mills that Britain's new engineering industry was born and grew up. It soon ceased to rely exclusively on the mills for its custom. In order to meet the needs of the textile trade, this new industry had to equip itself with machine tools and, as Boulton & Watt and Maudslay had earlier done, it had perforce to design and build these machines itself. Having done so, however, it soon discovered that there was an expanding market for such tools. In this way the machine tool industry began.

Roberts, Nasmyth, Murray, Fox, and Bodmer all designed some outstanding machine tools and manufactured them for sale. But in each case, their business grew into large, unspecialized, general engineering firms in which such tools were only one of a wide variety of products, ranging from looms to locomotives. They thus perpetuated upon a large scale the tradition of the small craft workshop prepared to tackle any job that came its way. Only Joseph Whitworth abandoned this tradition.

If any man can be said to have inherited the mantle of Henry Maudslay and to have spread abroad his perfectionist standard of precision, it was Joseph Whitworth (1803–1887). In 1805, Maudslay had made a micrometer capable of measuring to 1–10,000th of an inch. He called this instrument his Lord Chancellor because it became the ultimate arbiter of accuracy in his works. In 1856, Whitworth produced a machine capable of detecting differences of a millionth part of an inch. Where Maudslay devised a standard range of screw threads for use in his own works, Whitworth was responsible for the first national standard range of threads which became known by his name. At his works at Chorlton Street, Manchester, Whitworth decided to specialize in the manufacture of machine tools of the highest quality and accuracy which, by 1850, had become famous throughout the world. He achieved this success not only by the brilliant design and precision of Whitworth machines but also because, by specializing, he was able to reduce costs, to give speedier and more reliable delivery and service than were his less specialized competitors.

Unlike the textile industry, the new industry of engineering was never stigmatized by radical reformers, although, somewhat ironically, it was responsible for the textile machinery that caused so much human suffering and provoked so much social protest. The reason for this was that the motives behind the mechanization of the two industries were quite different. Mill-owners adopted machinery to save costs and so maximize their profits. The new machinery enabled them to perform more quickly, by unskilled child labour, operations that had hitherto required skilled craftsmen. The great pioneer mechanics, on the other hand, built their skill into their tools because they aimed to make entirely novel products of an accuracy that would satisfy their own exacting standards of craftsmanship. To achieve this end in any other way was impossible. It was not a question of economics; the necessary pool of manual skill did not exist.

Quite a number of the machine tools built by Whitworth and his contemporaries have survived and are to be seen in the Science Museum and elsewhere. They were built to last, and the superb quality of their design and construction is a tribute to the craftsmanship of their makers. No wonder that within two decades Britain could boast that she had become the workshop of the world. Yet this same tradition of craftsmanship, in engineering in general and tool-making in particular, helps to explain why Britain lost her pre-eminent position. Because labour in Britain was relatively cheap compared with other countries, her pioneer machine tool-makers saw no reason to pursue to its logical conclusion the process of building the skill into the tool which Henry Maudslay had begun. The lesson of Boulton & Watt's Soho Foundry, with its special purpose machines operating under an equally specialized labour force, was ignored. Instead, British engineers concentrated upon the production of general purpose tools of great flexibility and high quality. Tools of this type continued to make up the bulk of the population of the average British engineering machine shop as late as the 1920s.

By contrast, in the United States the process of building the skill into the tool continued unabated due to the very different social conditions prevailing. It has been said that the American manufacturer suffered from an acute shortage of labour which supplied him with the incentive to make the machine take the place of the skilled mechanic. This is not strictly true. What he did have to contend with was a very high turnover of labour as wave after wave of immigrants from the old world reached the eastern seaboard of America. These were men of every trade from labourers to highly skilled craftsmen, but they were also men of enterprise whose ambition it was to earn enough money to enable them to move west, acquire land or property, and set up in business on their own account. In these circumstances the mechanization of production suited both sides. It enabled the manufacturer to maintain a high rate of production despite the disadvantage of the large labour turnover. It suited his employees because high productivity enabled him to offer higher wages than they had been accustomed to in Europe. Some American manufacturers of the period went so far as to say that they actually preferred unskilled to skilled labour in their new plants because skilled men were more set in their ways and therefore less adaptable to new methods.

As pursued in America, the process of building the skill into the tool enabled components to be produced with such accuracy that, with the minimum of costly hand fitting, they became completely interchangeable, a process that first became known in Europe as the "American system" but which we now call mass production. It was first applied in America to the manufacture of rifles and revolvers and subsequently to such things as clocks, agricultural machinery, typewriters, sewing machines, bicycles, and finally to motor cars. The first example of the new system to be seen in England was a display of sets of interchangeable rifle parts in the American Section of the Great Exhibition of 1851. This won the manufacturers, Messrs. Robbins & Lawrence of Windsor, Vermont, a medal. What was much more important, it led directly to the adoption of American machine tools and American methods in the new British Government Armoury at Enfield. Other European armouries soon followed suit. To have thus seized the technical initiative from Britain after only seventy years of independence was a very significant achievement, especially when we remember that since 1783, Britain had done her utmost to prevent by legislation the export of machine tools and any "brain drain" of her skilled men to the dissident colony.

Armaments manufacture was a special case. It was not by reason of financial economy that the armaments industry of Europe adopted the American system; the great advantage of interchangeability of parts was the sole consideration. But when it came to applying the system to normal commercial production for the civil market, the British engineer mistakenly dismissed it as a shoddy, second-best device, a desperate expedient which the American manufacturer had adopted in the effort to overcome a chronic labour shortage. Writing in 1915, Alfred Williams, that remarkable author, poet, and blacksmith from Swindon Works, had this to say of American and British machine tools:

> The chief features of American machinery are—smartness of detail, the maximum of usefulness of parts, capacity for high speed and flimsiness, styled 'economy' of structure; everything of theirs is made to 'go the pace.' English machinery, on the other hand, is at the same time more primitive and cumbersome, more conservative in design and slower in operation, though it is trustworthy and durable; it usually proves to be the cheaper investment in the long run. One often sees American tackle broken all to pieces after several years' use, while the British-made machine runs almost *ad infinitum*.[1]

To this a contemporary American engineer would have replied by asking: "Who wants a machine tool to run *ad infinitum* when developments in design efficiency will have made it obsolete in ten years?"

Yet the view expressed by Alfred Williams was commonly held by both masters and men in Britain until 1930, when the great trade depression forced the widespread adoption of the American system as the only alternative to commercial extinction. Perhaps the most significant examples of engineering philosophies so long divergent were the famous 'Silver Ghost' Rolls-Royce and the equally famous Model T Ford. The former was a costly and superb creation of engineering craftsmanship which Henry Maudslay or Joseph Whitworth would have been able fully to appreciate because it was built by conservative methods and machines not dissimilar from those with which they were familiar. By comparison, the

---

1. Alfred Williams, *Life in a Railway Factory,* Duckworth, 1915.

Model T Ford appeared so crude to British eyes that it became the butt of many jokes; yet the fact that this ridiculed "tin lizzy" was the product of the most sophisticated mass-production plant in the world was the secret of its reliability and its fantastically low cost. By adopting the American system, it was Henry Ford who first made motoring for the millions possible, for good or ill.

One of the many jokes circulated by Henry Ford quoted him as saying that his customers could have their cars in any colour they wished, provided it was black. Unconsciously, perhaps, this emphasized the fault of the American system of mass-production. By the process of building the skill into the tool, the machine can be made to perform feats of speed and accuracy that no human hands can match, but only at the expense of the craftsman's versatility. Hence, the introduction of mass production methods means that the consumer of the goods so produced must be educated to accept uniformity in the product in the place of a former diversity.

There is also another problem. The immense capital cost of tooling-up a modern plant for mass production tends to make a manufacturer cling to his product for too long because of his natural reluctance to scrap, or to make fundamental changes in, his plant. Hence, he endeavours to introduce minor changes in the "styling" of the product, designed to delude the customer into thinking he is buying lamb instead of the old mutton. Thus, the philosophy of continuing obsolescence that inspired the American system proved ultimately self-defeating. Modern machine tools, with their cybernetic control systems, represent attempts to overcome this problem by combining the high output and accuracy of the mass production system with the quality and versatility of the general purpose machine tool which Maudslay and Whitworth pioneered.

THE UNCOMMON MILL GIRLS OF LOWELL

Helena Wright

In the early nineteenth century the "ladies of Lowell," Mass., were enlightened mill girls who spent their leisure in cultural pursuits.

"Acres of Girlhood," Whittier called them, "beauty reckoned by the square rod." These were the famous ladies of Lowell, the literary mill girls who spent their leisure in the pursuit of culture and enlightenment. They were famed for their education and talents, and also for their attractive bearing and deportment, as evinced in the descriptions of their pageant in honour of the visit of President Andrew Jackson to Lowell in June 1833.

Although Jackson's politics were not those of the owners of Lowell's corporations, nothing was spared to make this day a festive occasion. Two hickory trees were transplanted to a more prominent position to honour "Old Hickory," victor of the Battle of New Orleans. A parade was planned which included the mounted volunteer infantries of surrounding towns, some 500 schoolchildren with flowers, and the girls. Citizens flocked to the streets of Lowell, as much to view the famous operatives as to see the President.

For the procession, the girls were ranked by the corporations for which they worked, in order of the founding of the companies. They carried banners of green and white silk inscribed "Protection to American Industry," and each division of girls was accompanied by the overseer of their department in the mill. The two columns of 2,500 Yankee beauties stretched out for two miles. All dressed in white, with sashes and parasols of bright colours, the girls, in twos, filed past the balcony where Jackson stood to review them. The President had been ill in nearby Boston during the previous weeks; and it was said that the sight of all those fresh, young, intelligent countenances visibly revived him.

Political motives prompted Jackson's tour in the spring of 1833. Yet what brought him twenty-five miles out from Boston to the mud and board streets of a new town? What, indeed, brought Charles Dickens, Harriet Martineau, Michel Chevalier (representing the French Government), and a variety of other travellers, European and American, to this small manufacturing city during its second decade of existence? Surely it was not to observe the manufacture of cotton cloth, for that could be viewed in Manchester or Lille. Jackson might have viewed the process at far less distance from Washington. Yet he spent the afternoon of his visit to Lowell in the mills of the Merrimack Corporation, where the girls, still in their parade costume, demonstrated to him their respective parts in the process of the cotton manufacture. There must have been something special in Lowell's manner of operation to attract such notice.

Lowell was the direct outgrowth of a venture known as "the Waltham experiment"—an endeavour that successfully introduced the power-loom to America and combined in one mill all operations of textile manufacturing. Waltham, Massachusetts, was the town chosen in 1813 for the Boston Manufacturing Company, established by a group of enlightened New Englanders with capital to invest and a desire to assist the burgeoning economy of the United States. The brain-child of a wealthy merchant turned entrepreneur, the Boston Manufacturing Company was conceived by Francis Cabot Lowell, a Boston exporter who had turned from foreign trade with sufficient capital to enable him to indulge an interest in other forms of speculation and investment.

While on a visit to England and Scotland in 1810–1812, Lowell had become curious about the power-loom, then in use in Britain but not yet in successful operation in America. Lowell's interest was great enough, and his mind keen enough, to enable him, upon his return to the United States, to engage a mechanic and attempt to reconstruct a workable loom. There were strict laws against allowing the secrets of the British textile industry to be carried to America by workmen able to implement them; but there was apparently no suspicion attached to a wealthy American merchant who, to all intents and purposes, was merely an observer.

Lowell was able to interest certain wealthy friends in his idea for a manufacturing establishment; and, a factor that would add greatly to the success of the venture, he was able to perfect a working loom. The first power-loom in the United States was patented by Lowell and his investing partner, Patrick Tracy Jackson, in 1815. By that time, it was already in operation at Waltham and had proved itself invaluable to the experiment it had inspired.

The Boston Manufacturing Company was incorporated in 1813 to produce cotton, woolen, and linen cloth, although only cotton was ever actually fabricated. It was the beginning of a factory system in America where all operations were carried out under one roof, and where all major phases of textile manufacturing were performed by power-operated machinery. It was also the proving ground for the Waltham system, wherein the social and moral implications of manufacturing were given as much thought as the industrial and financial.

While in Britain, Francis Cabot Lowell had not failed to notice the ill effects that the factory produced on its operatives and their environment. In many areas, spinning only was concentrated in the factory, while weavers worked at home on the yarn provided for their warp and weft. They were dependent on factory production of yarn, and therefore moved close to the mills. The introduction of the power-loom into the factory, in many cases against the will of the weavers, led to the rapid development and urbanization of manufacturing centers, and eventually, to the untenable conditions of the nineteenth-century industrial slum.

This system was inaugurated in America by Samuel Slater, who, in 1790, in Pawtucket, Rhode Island, had begun spinning mills based on English inventions. Here, as in England, whole families were employed to tend the carding and spinning machinery, with the children working long hours doffing and slubbing. The yarns were sent out to be woven into cloth, but manufacturing villages were created, as families with large numbers of children were recruited and crowded near the spinning mill. The more children a family had, the more eagerly they were sought by the factory, for they provided a constant supply of cheap labour. Often, only the children were regularly employed, and the whole family lived on their small wages plus what the parents could earn by weaving or farming.

It was the creation of conditions such as these that Francis Cabot Lowell was anxious to avoid. At Waltham, and as continued at Lowell, the boarding-house or Waltham system was established as an alternative to the Rhode Island or English system. The majority of operatives employed were women in their late 'teens and twenties. Their welfare was solicitously provided for in the boardinghouse, under the capable direction of a matron, usually a widow, who represented the company and its interests in strict adherence to regulations of behaviour, hours, and attitude.

The girls were required to take residence in the boarding-houses, where the doors were locked at ten o'clock each night. They were also required to be constant in attendance on religious worship, either in town or a neighbouring parish. The Boston investors were concerned that as owners they should direct and influence the education, morals, and general beliefs of their operatives. They established schools for the children of the town, who here did not work full-time in the mills; a savings organization was incorporated so that the operatives would be encouraged to save their wages and receive interest on their earnings; and in 1826 the Rumford Institute was established in Waltham, a combined library, lyceum, and hall for social affairs and the improvement of the working population.

This unique system, first put into operation at Waltham, came to full flower at Lowell, another investment of the successful capital interests of the Boston Manufacturing Company. Further expansion of the factories at Waltham was limited by the water-power capacity of the Charles River after completion of the third mill on that site in 1820; and so the investors turned to the Patucket Falls of the Merrimack River near the town of Chelmsford, thereby expanding their enterprise and creating the city of Lowell.

An agent for the corporation, Paul Moody, who in his youth had been connected with the first American cotton mill at Beverly, Massachusetts in 1787, and whose mechanical skill had assisted Francis Lowell's memory in the making of the power-loom in 1814, had explored the area surrounding Boston for a suitable mill privilege, preferably in an undeveloped place that would permit further expansion. He found the desired site at the confluence of the Concord and Merrimack Rivers on the border of the states of Massachusetts and New Hampshire. Here the Patucket Falls, with a descent of thirty feet, provided motive power for the industrial development planned, including possible future requirements. Proximity to the port of Boston was another favorable aspect, as well as the connection to Boston by water provided on the Middlesex Canal.

The land was purchased from unsuspecting farmers in 1821, and construction began on the first mills in 1822. The venturesome company planned not merely a single mill this time, but an entire community, integrated to complement its own members' production and that of its predecessor at Waltham, producing several types and grades of cotton cloth. The new community was named after Francis Cabot Lowell, who, although he had died in 1817, was the true guiding spirit behind the enterprise.

The first mill completed was the Merrimack Manufacturing Company, which began producing cloth in 1823; bleaching and printing operations were probably commenced in 1824. Lowell was designed in addition to Waltham, as another type of manufacturing endeavour, to give more depth and new possibility to the investors and their system. The products of the two did not compete on the market, but complemented each other: Waltham made plain serviceable sheetings; Lowell was established to make decorative goods, such as calicoes, and to print them.

The success of the new venture was due in large part to the capabilities of the manager of the mills, Kirk Boott. Boott, the American-born son of an English merchant who prospered in Boston in the export trade, had been educated in England and served in the British Army, although never against America. After resigning his commission in 1813, Boott studied engineering at Woolwich. He returned to Boston in 1817 to join his brothers in their father's business. Happening to make the acquaintance of Patrick Tracy Jackson in 1821, when the company was looking for an agent to take charge of the new city on the Merrimack, Boott proved to be just the candidate for the position. He had real managerial skills and was well suited to his task. He knew how to operate the new mills efficiently, and he produced excellent results for the investors. In addition to supervising the building of the mills, Boott extended the small existing Patucket Canal, providing the necessary water-power flow from the river to the mills; and he planned the general layout of the city.

Fortunately for the corporation, the services of Paul Moody, chief mechanic and head of the machine shop at Waltham, were also available to the new enterprise. He took charge of the installation of the power-loom, fruit of his collaboration with Francis Lowell, and the implantation of other machinery he had designed or adapted, namely a cotton spinning frame, a double-speeder, and a dressing frame for sizing the warp.

The interests of the stockholders of the new corporation, known as the Proprietors of Locks & Canals (the name of the existing local corporation whose shares they had purchased), were not in conflict with the earlier investment at Waltham. In fact, many of the same individuals were involved, Patrick Tracy Jackson, Nathan Appleton, Benjamin Gorham, and Warren Dutton among them. Moody, Boott, and Boott's brother, John, also took shares in the company, but in smaller amounts, and they were definitely regarded as high-ranking employees rather than as partners. The result, then, was not a conflict of interest between the two investments; rather, a spirit of compromise prevailed.

The success of the corporation was evident not only in its financial and mechanical aspects, but also in the effects of the paternalistic system on the social and moral environment provided for the labouring force. It was the operatives, really, that the foreign visitors flocked to see. To begin with, the employment of women as a majority of the labour force in the new city was unusual. The Rhode Island and English systems had depended on unskilled children and a few skilled adults, largely trained men, as overseers and operators of specialized machinery, such as spinning mules. In the Waltham system, and as it was enlarged upon at Lowell, girls were employed to tend the roving and spinning frames, to draw in the warps, and to mind the looms. Men were engaged primarily as overseers, machinists, teamsters, and in other heavy occupations, or those requiring a definite skill, such as calico printing.

The greatest difference was in the calibre of the individuals employed. The girls at Lowell were not part of a permanent working class as were their counterparts in Rhode Island or England. They were generally of rural middle-class New England stock (as good as that of the capitalists!) and as well-educated as any girl might be in that day. They were recruited and encouraged to come to Lowell, but they were not expected to remain. Most girls worked only a few years, saving their money and building a small amount of capital with which to start married life or to assist a brother in furthering his education. Wages averaged about two dollars per week above what was paid for board, more than could be earned by teaching in school or dressmaking, the most popular of the few alternative occupations open to women at that time. By 1843, over $100,000 had been invested by the girls in Lowell banks, this amount not including what was sent home or saved elsewhere.

The girls came, however, for more than financial independence; they reaped the benefits of association with their peers and engaged in literary and cultural activities unknown to the farms from which many had come. Lucy Larcom, a mill girl whose poetry and prose received no small attention in her day, describes this consciousness quite clearly in the following passage from *A New England Girlhood* (1889):

> For what were we? Girls who were working in a factory for a time, to be sure; but none of us had the least idea of continuing at that kind of work permanently. Our composite photograph, had it been taken, would have been the representative New England girlhood of those days. We had all been fairly educated at public or private schools, and many of us were resolutely bent upon obtaining a better education. Very few were among us without some distinct plan for bettering the condition of themselves and those they loved. For the first time, our young women had come forth from their home recruitment in a throng, each with her own individual purpose. For twenty years or so, Lowell might have been looked upon as a rather select industrial school for young people. The girls there were just such girls as are knocking at the doors of young women's colleges today. They had come to work with their hands, but they could not hinder the working of their minds also. Their mental activity was overflowing at every possible outlet.

The corporation had planned well, so that the operatives could better their situations through social and cultural intercourse. Schools were built, and churches, some with the assistance of the girls, for they were required to be regular in their attendance at the church of their choice and to pay 37 1/2 cents per quarter for the support of public worship of the denomination each chose to join. In 1825, $500 was devoted by the corporation to the purchase of books for the nucleus of a library, which was completed by later appropriations. The Lyceum, built at company expense, provided an opportunity for the price of fifty cents per season of twenty-five lectures for the girls to hear such leading lights as Ralph Waldo Emerson and Edward Everett, and so distinguished a speaker as former President John Quincy Adams. Night-school courses were offered for the more ambitious, among them Lucy Larcom and her sister.

Attracted by the educational opportunities and the chance to earn a wage, the girls were drawn by the prospect of companionship as well. Many were farmers' daughters, tempted by the tales of neighbours who had experienced city-life for a year or two. The independence of earning some money with which to buy finery and save for the future, in combination with the prospect of close friends and worthwhile pursuit of knowledge, must have been irresistible to most girls, familiar only with small Yankee villages and farms, and yet educated enough to know what was lacking in their lives.

Harriet Hanson Robinson, mill girl and daughter of a boarding-house matron, later wife of a publisher with whom she worked ardently for women's suffrage, recorded much of her early experience in an account she entitled *Loom and Spindle*. She speaks of the positive connotations of being a factory girl:

> At the time the Lowell cotton-mills were started, the factory girl was the lowest among women. In England and in France, particularly, great injustice had been done to her real character; she was represented as subjected to influences that could not fail to destroy her purity and self-respect. In the eyes of her overseer she was but a brute, a slave, to be beaten, pinched, and pushed about. It was to overcome this prejudice that such high wages had been offered to women that they might be induced to become mill-girls, in spite of the opprobrium that still clung to this "degrading occupation". . . . But in a short time the prejudice against factory labour wore away, and the Lowell mills became filled with blooming and energetic New England women . . . If they returned to their secluded homes again, instead of being looked down upon as "factory girls" by the squire's or the lawyer's family, they were more often welcomed as coming from the metropolis, bringing new fashions, new books, and new ideas with them.

Whatever the particular reason that drew a girl to Lowell, it was the desire and intent of the corporation to attract her. Labour was in short supply in the early years of American industry: men were involved in clearing and settling the country, and New Englanders in particular had a reputation for preferring the independence and rewards of working for themselves, on their own land or at sea. There was no industrial working class as such, and the girls had to be persuaded by the benefits of working in the mills before any great number left their homes. This was another factor in favour of the establishment of the boarding-house system: God-fearing New England families had to be convinced of a correct moral atmosphere before dispatching their daughters to Waltham and Lowell and the other corporation towns that developed after their example.

From all parts of New England they came, lured by the recruiting agents of the corporation or the reports of friends and neighbours who had gone before. A new girl was soon put wise to the ways of city-life with the helpful advice of her fellow boarders. Homely country expressions and mannerisms gave way before the assault of new shawls, worldly companions, and intellectual opportunities. Some boarding-houses had joint-stock pianos; most had subscriptions to leading literary magazines such as the *Edinburgh Review, Blackwood's,* and the *North American Review,* to less serious, more popular periodicals, such as *Ladies' Pearl* and *Godey's,* and memberships to circulating libraries as well.

The two centers around which the New England culture revolved were education and religion. The society of mill girls at Lowell was no different; for in creating the social, moral, and cultural environment, the corporation had developed a model that drew entirely on existing customs. They established not a new, ideal, synthetic atmosphere, but rather approximated as closely as possible the religious and mental values of a New England town or family.

Insistence on church attendance was a feature of this attitude, regarded not as a restrictive rule, but as an already-accepted guideline of behaviour. The churches were, in fact, the center of much of the social and intellectual activity of the girls. It was out of the Improvement Circles of the Second Universalist and First Congregational churches that were developed the literary magazines for which the operatives became so famous. These circles of girls met under the direction of the ministers and read to each other pieces they had composed especially for the edification and enjoyment of their peers, in the manner of contemporary periodical literature. This similarity became an identity, for in October of 1840, several pieces written by members of the Second Universalist Church improvement circle were published under the title *The Lowell Offering*.

This periodical, containing stories, poems, and essays by the operatives, was published from 1840 to 1845. Two publications actually sprang up at about the same time, but were eventually consolidated into one magazine. It gained wide acclaim for the literary mill girls and brought them attention, attention as people, just as the novelty of their whole system had been advertised by the corporation at every opportunity. Some of the best pieces from various issues of the *Offering* were collected and published in London in 1844 as *Mind Amongst the Spindles*.

Among the foreign visitors who were favourably impressed with the literary mill girls was the Rev. William Scoresby, Vicar of Bradford, Yorkshire, who visited Lowell in the summer of 1844. Scoresby recorded his impressions and presented them in a series of lectures on America, two of which were enlarged upon and published in 1845 as *American Factories and Their Female Operatives*. His book is almost entirely devoted to his descriptions of Lowell, wherein he discusses the "general superior tone of moral principle and propriety of behaviors prevalent among the young women of the operative classes of New England." Gratifying to Scoresby was the "watchful consideration and moral care for the young women taken by their employers and others." His final chapter is devoted to suggestions for the improvement of the condition of English factory operatives—"especially that of females."

The corporations were not slow to capitalize on the fame and publicity the operatives earned for themselves. Glowing accounts such as Scoresby's, and the literary activity of the girls, were to the advantage of the owners and put Lowell high in public esteem. The experimental city that visitors had flocked to see was proving its merits again—or, at least, the merits of those wise investors who had engineered the system. Every effort by the girls served the interests of their masters equally as well as their own.

A note of cynicism? Perhaps, for by 1845 the *Lowell Offering* had been criticized as the paid organ of the corporation, working against the best interests of the operatives. Censure was voiced in the Lowell newspapers by a most articulate adversary, a young woman named Sarah Bagley, an editor of a well-written paper on the side of labour, the *Voice of Industry*, and a mill girl herself since 1836.

The criticism was not far from the mark, for by 1845 the *Offering* was dead, its circulation having dwindled and its contributors having been somewhat enlightened to their exploitation. Never a financial success, the widely-acclaimed magazine was in fact supported and printed by the newspaper known to be the mouthpiece of the corporations. Contributions of written material, and subscription among the Lowell girls themselves, began to decrease as early as 1843. Revived briefly as the *New England Offering* in 1848, the publication was no longer the product of the operatives. There were still subscribers in other cities and the mill agents bought many copies, but the girls themselves were becoming more interested in labour reforms than in transitory literary fame which brought them little respite from their tedious tasks in the factory.

What had happened in the utopia that was Lowell? The town held up as a model now suffered strikes, walk-outs, and the problems of any manufacturing city. How did such a change occur, in only twenty-odd years? Benevolent despotism can hold sway only while the tools of the system are unaware of their exploitation, and while the despots are sincere in their benevolence. Papers such as the *Voice of Industry* and other organs of the labour reform movement made the operatives cognizant of the inequities of long hours and low wages. By 1845, these intelligent, high-spirited girls were working fifteen minutes per day longer under less agreeable working conditions, producing more cloth for less pay than in the 1820s.

The absence of a market for domestically-produced cloth had been an early fear of the original investors. Their fears disappeared as the growth and westward expansion of the American population created a huge demand for the types of cloth produced by the New England mills. Coarsely-woven sheetings and shirtings and cheap calicoes found ready buyers in a society of pioneers and immigrants. Finer goods continued to be imported, but these did not compete for the same market as the domestic goods.

The great success of the corporations and their model towns had led to their expansion throughout New England. Manchester, Chicopee, Holyoke, Lawrence, all had followed the Lowell pattern, even down to a literary magazine in some cases, although all but the *Lowell Offering* were partially staffed and edited by men. In most cases, these new textile enterprises were financed by the profits first gained by the stockholders of Lowell and Waltham. The great returns on investment had inevitable results: more stockholders were attracted to the prospects, and they wanted greater returns—higher production, wider markets, and more profit. The effects on the operatives were noticeable.

Working conditions had altered radically since the early, friendly days when the girls had chatted and read on the job, tending an extra machine so that a friend might have a few days at home with her family. New machinery had been introduced which operated at a significantly faster rate. Girls formerly had tended one loom, two at the most, while now four was normal. Paid by the piece, girls were forced to compete under a new system of premiums whereby the overseer received a bonus for production above and beyond the normal quota. This affected the relations of the girls with their superiors, with whom they had previously been on pleasant terms, almost as fathers and daughters. New men took advantage of their positions to threaten the girls with lower pay and dismissal if production rates were not kept high.

In the light of increasingly restrictive and unpleasant circumstances, it was small wonder that the girls, educated and independent as they were, became involved in striking for higher wages and in the movement for a ten-hour day.[1] Under the able leadership of Sarah Bagley, the Lowell Female Labour Reform Association was formed. Miss Bagley, the vociferous opponent of the *Lowell Offering,* wrote stirring appeals for the *Voice of Industry* and *Factory Tracts,* the paper of the Lowell Female Labour Reform league, for the operatives to join forces against the "driveling cotton lords." She spoke in many of the corporation towns and assisted in the formation of branches of the Female Labour Reform Association. Her Lowell group was the leader and encouraged the support of the ten-hour movement, initiated by the

---

1. Not until 1874 did a ten-hour day become law for women and children in Massachusetts. Men, who had the vote and could influence politicians and legal procedure, had received ten-hour benefits since the eighteen-fifties, the dates varying with individual trades.

English-born male operatives of the Fall River–New Bedford area, which had not developed along the lines of Lowell's female operative system.

Ironically, as Hannah Josephson notes in *The Golden Threads* (1949), the oft-maligned English system, by 1845, had four to six fewer hours in the working week, two more holidays per year, and most British operatives were required to tend but two looms. In 1847, the ten-hour day became law in Great Britain, even though the Acts of 1850 and 1853 were necessary to establish and further define actual protection under the law.

The inequities that existed in what had been the most widely-praised manufacturing town of its day had permeated the corporate structure. Management no longer took a benevolent attitude toward the welfare of the operative. What had been the showplace of the industry was in ferment, the laborers speaking out against the owners, clamouring for shorter hours and higher piece rates.

The development and spread of the corporation system, and its attendant push for profit and production, spelled the end of the experiment begun at Waltham in 1813. The original investors were perhaps more sincerely moral than their successors, but the fact remains that as the philosophy of manufacturing was altered, when the operatives felt the pinch and began to rebel, Lowell lost the place it had held in the public eye, and the system as originally envisaged was finished. The newer investors wanted fast and large returns with no trouble from the workers. By chance, the agitation for better working conditions coincided with great famine in Ireland, which brought to the United States large numbers of immigrants more willing to work under worsening conditions than were the militant Yankees.

A rather rapid transformation took place in Lowell, as later in many other corporation towns. By 1850, fifty percent of the working population of Lowell was of Irish birth. The boarding-house residency requirements were generally ignored, and by the 1870s the boarding-houses were sold to private landlords. And, as the Irish and those who followed them began to chafe and strike under the management's dictum, there were always successive waves of new immigrants from other lands to fill their places.

The concept that had been put into practice with such promise at the Boston Manufacturing Company in 1813, that had enjoyed such success at Lowell in the 1820s and 30s, had been put to the test and failed. As a long-term achievement, the Waltham experiment and its flowering at Lowell did not make a permanent, positive contribution to labour practices in the textile industry in America. The operatives, however, the literary ladies who were the paragons of their day, made history for themselves on their own merits.

7

THE *NEMESIS* IN CHINA

Daniel Headrick

For several centuries, China and Europe had coexisted at arm's length, having only limited contact. Each side knew a great deal about the other. The Chinese imported European clocks and instruments, and respected Western astronomy and mathematics. Europeans, in turn, purchased the silks, porcelain, tea, and objets d'art of China, and admired some of her customs and institutions.

Yet the exchange was quite restricted and showed little promise of growth, even after two and a half centuries of direct contact. This was especially galling to the British, who by the eighteenth century were the dominant European power in the Far East and had developed a national craving for Chinese tea. In exchange for this tea, Britain had little to offer, for China was economically self-sufficient. Hence the tea trade caused a serious drain of gold and silver to China. The Chinese government, interested mainly in keeping the "sea barbarians" under control, deliberately confined the trade to certain merchants of Canton and resisted the entreaties of such distinguished ambassadors as Lord Macartney (1793) and Lord Amherst (1816).

The situation began to change, however, at the end of the eighteenth century, when the British discovered that their Indian possessions could produce a commodity for which China had a large and fast-growing demand: opium. As a result, there arose a triangular trade; India produced the opium, the Chinese exchanged the opium for tea, and the British drank the tea. From the British side of the triangle, there was not so much a flow of goods as a political and military power.

Opium, as Michael Greenberg pointed out, "was no hole-in-the-corner petty smuggling trade, but probably the largest commerce of the time in any single commodity."[1] At the center of this commerce stood the Honourable East India Company. The opium was grown mostly on company lands in Bengal, and though private merchants carried out the trade to China, they had to purchase their ware from the company, which was the sole opium manufacturer after 1797. Furthermore, the company's main business, outside of administering and taxing Indians, was the export of Chinese tea to England.

The company's monopoly of the China trade ended in 1834, and relations with China were soon exacerbated by the activities of private British traders. The Chinese government attempted several times to curtail the drug traffic, but with little success. What Chinese officials considered law enforcement against smuggling and narcotics, the traders saw as unjustified interference with free enterprise. William Jardine of the trading firm Jardine Matheson and Co. wrote anonymously to the *China Repository* in 1834:

> Nor indeed should our valuable commerce and revenue both in India and Great Britain be permitted to remain subject to a caprice, which a few gunboats laid alongside this city would overrule by the discharge of a few mortars. . . . The result of a war with the Chinese could not be doubted.[2]

That same year Jardine, Matheson, and sixty-two other British merchants in China petitioned the king to send three warships and a plenipotentiary to China, and "expressed the opinion that there would be no difficulty in intercepting the greater part of the internal and external trade of China and the capture of all the armed vessels of the empire."[3]

Even after the loss of its trade monopoly, the East India Company kept an interest in China through its import of tea and especially its manufacture of opium. Indeed opium yielded one seventh of the total revenue of British India in the nineteenth century. The China trade was essential to the prosperity of the British Empire. It is no surprise, then, that the East India Company became involved in the war with China.

If the tension between China and Britain was commercial in origin, its persistence was a consequence of the state of military technology. Like an elephant and a whale, China and Britain evolved in two different habitats. At sea, Britain was invincible and could destroy any Chinese fleet or coastal fort. China, on the other hand, was a land empire with few interests beyond her shores and few cities along her coasts. As long as the Europeans were incapable of pushing their way inland, the Celestial Empire was invulnerable.

The steamer, with its ability to navigate upriver and attack inland towns, ended the long Anglo-Chinese stalemate.

The first steamer to reach China in 1830 was the 302-ton *Forbes,* a seagoing ship built in India for the Calcutta-Macao trade. In 1835, Jardine purchased a 115-ton steamer with two 24-horsepower engines, which he named *Jardine.* He and other foreign merchants then petitioned the senior Hong merchant, their Chinese counterpart, for permission to operate the *Jardine* on the Pearl River between Canton and Macao. The acting governor-general of Canton rejected their request:

> . . . if he presumes obstinately to disobey, I, the acting governor, have already issued orders to all the forts that when the steamship arrives they are to open a thundering fire and attack her. On the whole, since he has arrived within the boundaries of the Celestial Dynasty, it is right that he should obey the laws of the Celestial Dynasty. I order the said foreigner to ponder this well and act in trembling obedience thereto.[4]

When the *Jardine* steamed upriver in defiance of this order, she was fired on and forced to retreat.

This setback notwithstanding, the foreigners, who now possessed steamers, refused to submit to threats of thundering fire. The British merchants continued to petition their government to send a punitive expedition to China. The British government, in particular the redoubtable Palmerston, also believed a war with China was inevitable. The only question was how to carry it out. Jardine, writing to Palmerston in November 1839, advised sending two line-of-battle ships, four frigates, two or three sloops, two large steamers, and "two small flat bottomed Steamers for River work, which it may be necessary to take out in frame and set up in China."[5] Palmerston, who hoped to bring China to her knees by seizing an offshore island and stopping her coastal trade, passed on this advice to the lords of the Admiralty.[6] Sir Gilbert Elliott, Lord Minto, at the time first lord of the Admiralty, had a clearer idea of the difficulties involved. On February 16, 1840, he wrote to his nephew Lord Auckland:

> I hope you will be able to send a respectable land force with the expedition. The mere occupation of an Island would not require much, but I think it very probable that the possession of one or two of their towns or great commercial Depots on the line of inland communication, but which are approachable from the sea may be very desirable, and to effect this a considerable force in troops would be necessary. However you are accustomed to work upon so great a scale that I feel no apprehension of your stinting this operation of whatever you think likely to secure and expedite its success and shall not be much surprised if I receive a letter from Emily dated the Imperial Palace of Peking. For after all it is nothing more or less than the conquest of China that we have undertaken. I believe I have already told you that we turn to the Indian Government for such steamers as it may be able to furnish, we have none fit for such a voyage except some giants of great draught of water, which would be of little use in inshore and river operations, and consume an enormous quantity of fuel.[7]

The parties involved in planning the war with China—Jardine, Palmerston, Hobhouse, Minto, and Auckland—relied mainly on the traditional tools of war (that is, sailing warships and marine infantry) to defeat their enemy. If they thought of river steamers, it was at most as small auxiliary vessels that would have to be assembled in China, a lengthy and complicated process. Peacock, however, had other plans, as John Laird explained:

> The China war having commenced it was decided by the Secret Committee of the East India Co, on the recommendation of Mr. Peacock, instead of sending all these Vessels out in pieces, and putting them together at Bombay, to send 4 of them under Steam round the Cape, an experiment at the time considered very hazardous, especially as the "Nemesis" and "Phlegethon" (two Vessels built by Mr. Laird at Birkenhead) had to carry two 32 pounders on pivots, one at each end of the Vessel.[8]

We know a great deal about the *Nemesis* as a machine and as a protagonist, thanks to two sources. One is a report to the Admiralty by the naval architect Augustin Creuze, who at the Royal Navy Dockyard at Portsmouth examined the ship after she hit a rock off the Bay of St. Ives on the Cornish coast.[9] The other was a book based on the notes of Captain William Hutcheon Hall, who recounted the ship's history after she left England.[10]

Creuze gave a detailed technical description of the *Nemesis*. She measured 660 tons burthen, 184 feet long overall (165 between perpendiculars), 29 feet wide, 11 deep with a draft of 6 feet when fully loaded and less than 5 in battle trim. She was powered by two 60-horsepower Forrester engines and had two masts. The armament she carried was heavy for a boat her size: two pivot-mounted 32-pounder guns powerful enough to blast a hole in a fortress wall. In addition, she had five brass 6-pounders, ten smaller cannons, and a rocket launcher. Her interior was separated by bulkheads into seven watertight compartments. She also had two sliding keels and an adjustable rudder. During trials she tore a gash in her hull; the safety offered by her bulkheads and the ease with which she was repaired impressed Creuze.

He also discussed the inaccuracy of compasses, which had bedeviled iron ships from their inception. An iron hull deflects the earth's magnetism, making uncorrected compasses unreliable on board. In 1838, the Astronomer-Royal, Professor George Airy, discovered a method of compensating for the influence of the hull, and applied it to several ships. Although he did not adjust the compass of the *Nemesis* himself, the ship was deemed fit to go to sea.[11] Creuze concluded, in his report to the Admiralty, that iron was a better material for shipbuilding than timber.

To command the *Nemesis* the Secret Committee chose Hall, a master in the Royal Navy. As a young man, Hall had accompanied Lord Amherst's 1816 mission to China. In the late 1830s, he became interested in steamers and spent two years studying them in Glasgow and along the Clyde and the Mersey. In June 1839, he crossed the Atlantic on the *British Queen,* one of the first steamships belonging to Macgregor Laird's British and American Steam Navigation Co. While in America, he paid close attention to the steamboats on the Hudson and Delaware rivers, then returned to England just as the Birkenhead Iron Works was putting the final touches on the *Nemesis.* Thus prepared, Hall joined the *Nemesis* in December 1839. On February 14, 1840, Peacock officially requested the Admiralty's permission to appoint him captain of the ship. The request was granted on February 26.[12]

The *Nemesis* left Portsmouth on March 28, 1840. Her journey east was long and difficult. She was the first iron ship to round the Cape of Good Hope and almost sank in the Indian Ocean when heavy seas caused her hull to split open next to the paddle-boxes. After some improvised repairs at Delagoa Bay, she steamed for Ceylon, arriving October 6. There Hall received orders to proceed to China. Peacock meanwhile was exultant: "I am in high spirits about my iron chickens; having excellent accounts of them from Maderia [*sic*]. I have accounts of 'Nemesis' from the Cape, where she arrived in fine order, and literally astonished the natives."[13]

By the time the *Nemesis* reached Macao on November 25, 1840, the war had been going on, desultorily, for five months. The British fleet had harassed coastal towns like Amoy and made preparations for an offensive against Canton. On January 7, 1841, strengthened by the arrival of the *Nemesis* and some seagoing steamers, the British launched their first attack on the Bogue forts defending the Pearl River below Canton. The Chinese, whose defense strategy was static, had hoped to hold off their enemy, but the broadsides of the British men-of-war, towed into position by the steamers, quickly breached their defenses. Marine infantry troops soon stormed the fortifications.

The Chinese fleet was equally vulnerable. The war junks were half the size of the *Nemesis,* or one tenth that of a first-rate British battleship. They were armed with small cannons that were hard to aim, and with boarding nets, pots of burning pitch, and handguns. Without much difficulty the *Nemesis* sank or captured several junks; the rest were frightened off with Congreve rockets. The Chinese also relied on fire-rafts filled with gunpowder and oil-soaked cotton that were set ablaze and pushed toward enemy ships. The steamers, however, quickly grappled them and towed them out of reach. The previous year Commissioner Lin

Tse-Hsü had purchased the 1,080-ton American merchantman *Cambridge,* but for lack of sailors who knew how to handle the ship, she was kept idle behind a barrier of rafts. She was soon lost to the *Nemesis.*[14]

In a few days the river route to Canton was clear and the sailing fleet began its slow ascent. As the fleet approached the city in early February, the *Nemesis* entered the inner passage, a labyrinth of narrow shallow channels that paralleled the main channel of the river, a place where no foreign warship had ever dared venture. While approaching Canton from the rear, she destroyed forts and junks at will and terrorized the inhabitants. Commodore J. J. Gordon Bremer, commander in chief of the Expedition Fleet, described the role of the *Nemesis* in a letter to the earl of Auckland:

> On proceeding up to Whampoa, three more dismantled forts were observed, and at four P.M. the Nemesis came into that anchorage having (in conjunction with the boats) destroyed five forts, one battery, two military stations, and nine war junks, in which were one hundred and fifteen guns and eight ginjalls, thus proving to the enemy that the British flag can be displayed throughout their inner waters wherever and whenever it is thought proper by us, against any defence or mode they may adopt to prevent it.[15]

Hall was exultant. On March 30,1841, he wrote to John Laird:

> It is with great pleasure I inform you that your noble vessel is as much admired by our own countrymen as she is dreaded by the Chinese, well may the latter offer a reward of 50,000 dollars for her . . . but she will be difficult to take, they call her the devil ship and say that our shells and Rockets could only be invented by the latter. They are more afraid of her than all the Line-of-Battle ships put together.[16]

And two months later he wrote Peacock:

> With respect to the Nemesis I cannot speak too highly in her praise she does the whole of the advanced work for the Expedition and what with towing Transports, Frigates, large junks, and carrying Cargoes of provisions, troops and Sailors, and repeatedly coming in contact with Sunken Junks—Rocks, Sand banks, and fishing Stakes in these unknown waters, which we are obliged to navigate by night as well as by day, she must be the strongest of the strong to stand it . . . as far as fighting goes we have had enough of that being always in advance, and most justly do the Officers as well as the Merchants of Macao say "that she is worth her weight in gold."[17]

Technically, the British campaign of 1841 was a huge success, and Hall may be forgiven for his enthusiasm over the performance of his boat. But the political results of the campaign were nonetheless disappointing. The British fully expected the government of China to sue for peace following the destruction of the Chinese fleet and the capture of the Bogue forts and of Canton. The Chinese, though, were persuaded neither by these victories nor by the subsequent British capture of Amoy, Tinghai, Chinghai, and Ningpo. The British commander in chief, Admiral George Elliott, therefore decided to strike at the Grand Canal—the jugular vein of China—the principal north-south trade route along which boatloads of rice from Szechuan province were sent to feed the population of Peking, the capital. The idea may have originated in a letter which Samuel Baker, tea inspector for the East India company, wrote in February 1840 and which was transmitted to Palmerston:

> The Yang coo kiang as far as its junction with the Grand Canal ought to be examined and regularly surveyed. This might be done with the aid of a steamer . . . The island of Kiu Shan would be a strong position and enable us to distress the internal commerce greatly by cutting off the communication between the Northern and Southern Provinces by means of the Grand Canal.[18]

Palmerston reiterated the proposal in a secret instruction to the lords of the Admiralty dated February 20, 1840.[19]

By the start of the 1842 campaign, the British fleet had been reinforced by several additional steamers. An Indian Navy sent its steamships *Atalanta, Madagascar, Queen,* and *Sesostris.* The gunboats destined for the Indus also appeared on the scene: the 510-ton *Phlegethon,* sister of the *Nemesis,* and the smaller *Medusa, Ariadne, Pluto,* and *Proserpine.* Altogether the fleet that advanced upon the Yangtze in May 1842 included eight sailing warships, ten steamers, and over fifty 20 transports, troopships, and schooners.[20]

The Chinese had a vague idea of how steamers worked. Commissioner Lin called them "wheeled vehicles which use the heads of flames to drive machines, cruising very fast," and Ch'i-shan, governor-general of Chihli, called them "ships with wind-mills" and "fire-wheel boats."[21] An anonymous Chinese source, whose translated account of steamers appeared in *The Nautical Magazine,* described the *Nemesis* in these terms:

> On each side is a wheel, which by the use of coal fire is made to revolve as fast as a running horse. . . . Steam Vessels are a wonderful invention of foreigners, and are calculated to offer delight to many.[22]

In June 1842, the British fleet entered the Yangtze. The Chinese were ready to receive their enemy, having assembled a considerable fleet of sixteen war junks and seventy merchantmen and fishing vessels requisitioned for naval duty. In the forts of Woosung, near the mouth of the river, they had placed 253 heavy artillery pieces.

The Chinese also unveiled a secret weapon: paddle-wheelers armed with brass guns, gingals, and matchlocks, and propelled by men inside the hull operating treadles. Nin Chien, governor-general of Nanking, wrote of them:

> Skilled artisans have also constructed four water-wheel boats, on which we have mounted guns. They are fast and we have specially assigned Major Liu Ch'ang . . . to command them. If the barbarians should sail into the inland waterways, these vessels can resist them. There is not the slightest worry.[23]

The battle of Woosung was swift. The British ships of the line soon silenced the guns of the forts. The *Nemesis,* towing the eighteen-gun *Modeste,* led the fleet into the river, firing grape and canister at the Chinese crafts, which fled. The *Nemesis* and the *Phlegethon* there-upon chased the fleeing boats, captured one junk and three paddle-wheelers, and set the rest on fire.

The British were astonished to discover that their opponents had paddle-wheelers. Some saw them as proof of the Chinese imitative ability.[24] In actuality, the Chinese took the idea of paddle-wheels from their own history—the paddle-wheel boat was a Chinese invention of the eighth century or earlier. Under the Sung dynasty, paddle-wheelers played a celebrated role in the battles against pirates in 1132 and against the armies of Digunai in 1161. From these examples, the hard-pressed Nin Chien and other Chinese officials drew inspiration in 1841 and 1842.[25]

Even more ironic is the appearance of the paddle-wheel in the West. The first paddle-wheel steamer was built in 1788 by Patrick Miller and William Symington, after Miller recalled having read somewhere "that the Chinese had, in the long-distant past, tried paddle-wheels fitted to certain of their junks with the cranks turned by slaves. . . .[26] Like so many other Chinese inventions, the paddle-wheel was to haunt China in later centuries when her innovative spirit had flagged and her technology was surpassed by that of the Western barbarians.

After the one-sided battle of Woosung, the British fleet encountered little resistance from the Chinese. Instead, its lumbering journey upriver was marked by a constant struggle against currents, sandbars, and mud. Every one of the sailing ships had to be towed by the steamers again and again. Finally in July 1842, the fleet reached Chinkiang, at the intersection of the river and the Grand Canal. This time the court at Peking realized its precarious situation and a few days later sent a mission to Nanking to sign a peace treaty. Steam had carried British naval might into the very heart of China and led to the defeat of the Celestial Empire.

After the Opium War, small armed steamers continued to serve in the Far East. The *Nemesis* was assigned to chase pirates in the Philippine and Indonesia archipelagos. In the Second Anglo-Burmese War of 1852–53, the British advanced up the Irrawaddy with an entire fleet of steamers, many of them veterans of the Opium War. During the Second Opium War (1856–60), the Royal Navy brought up more than twenty-five gunboats and other small steamers to attack Canton and the Taku forts near Peking. Gunboats also figured prominently in the French conquests of Tonkin (1873–74) and Annam (1883), and in the Third Anglo-Burmese War of 1885.[27]

The gunboat had become not just the instrument, but the very symbol of Western power along the coasts and up the navigable rivers of Asia. One protagonist of the colonial wars of that time, Colonel W. F. B. Laurie, put it succinctly: Steamers, he declared, were " 'a political persuader,' with fearful instruments of speech, in an age of progess!"[28]

The early history of the gunboat illustrates the interaction between technological innovation and the motives of imperialism. Because his father had an iron foundry and a shipyard, Macgregor Laird could turn his interest in Africa into an exploring expedition on the Niger. Peacock's classical erudition and Russophobia led him to translate the Anglo-Indian concerns with rapid communications into a steamboat expedition on the Euphrates. Their combination of interests persuaded the East India Company to become the first major purchaser of gunboats. In turn, the company's habit of acquiring gunboats led to Britain's victory in the Opium War. Thus, in the case of gunboats, we cannot claim that technological innovation caused imperialism, nor that imperialist motives led to technological innovation. Rather, the means and the motives stimulated one another in a relationship of positive mutual feedback.

NOTES

1. Michael Greenberg, *British Trade and the Opening of China, 1800–42* (Cambridge, 1951), p. 104.
2. K. M. Panikkar, *Asia and Western Dominance* (New York, 1969), p. 97.
3. William Conrad Costin, *Great Britain and China, 1833–60* (Oxford, 1937), p. 27.
4. On the *Forbes* and the *Jardine,* see George Henry Preble, A *Chronological History of the Origin and Development of Steam Navigation,* 2nd ed. (Philadelphia, 1895), pp. 142–45; H. A. Gibson-Hill, "The Steamers Employed in Asian Waters, 1819–39," *Journal of the Royal Asiatic Society, Malayan Branch,* 27 pt. 1 (May 1954): 127 and 153–56; H. Moyse-Bartlett, *A History of Merchant Navy* (London, 1937), p. 229; Arthur Waley, *The Opium War Through Chinese Eyes* (London, 1958), pp. 105–06; and Peter Ward Fay, *The Opium War, 1840–42: Barbarians in the Celestial Empire in the Early Part of the Nineteenth Century and the War by Which They Forced Her Gates Ajar* (Chapel Hill, N.C., 1975), p. 51.
5. India Office Records, L/P&S/9/1, pp. 411–12.
6. India Office Records, L/P&S/9/1, pp. 487–88.
7. National Maritime Museum, Greenwich, ELL 234: Letters from Sir Gilbert Elliot, Lord Minto, on China 1839–41.
8. John Laird, "Memorandum as to the part taken by the late Thomas Love Peacock Esq in promoting Steam Navigation" (1873), MS Peacockana 2 in The Carl H. Pforzheimer Library, New York.
9. "On the Nemesis Private Armed Steamer, and on the Comparative Efficiency on Iron-Built and Timber-Built Ships," *The United Service Journal and Naval and Military Magazine,* part 2 (May 1840): 90–100.
10. This book went through three editions: The first two are William Dallas Bernard, *Narrative of the Voyages and Services of the Nemesis from 1840 to 1843,* 2 vols. (London, 1844 and 1845); the third edition is Captain Wiliam H. Hall (R.N.) and William Dallas Bernard, *The Nemesis in China, Comprising a History of the Late War in That Country, with a Complete Account of the Colony of Hong Kong* (London, 1846). The book was reviewed in "Voyages of the 'Nemesis'," *The Asiatic Journal Monthly Miscellany* 3, 3rd series (May–Oct 1844): 355–59. For a recent look at the subject, see David K. Brown, "Nemesis, The First Iron Warship," *Warship* (London) 8 (Oct. 1978): 283–85.
11. "Mr. Airy, Astronomer-Royal, on the Correction of the Compass in Iron-Built Ships," *The United Service Journal and Naval and Military Magazine* part 2 (June 1840): 239–41. See also Stanislas Charles Henri Laurent Dupuy de Lôme, *Mémoire sur la construction des bâtiments en fer, addressé à M. le ministre sur la mirine et des colonies* (Paris, 1844), pp. 36–41; Edgar C. Smith, *A Short History of Naval and Marine Engineering* (Cambridge, 1938), pp. 99–100; and Hall and Bernard, p. 4.
12. India Office Records, L/P&S/3/6, p. 167. On Hall's career, see "William Hutcheon Hall," in William R. O'Byrne, *A Naval Biographical Dictionary: Comprising the Life and Servies of Every Living Office in Her Majesty's Navy, from Rank of Admiral of the Fleet to that of Lieutenant, Inclusive* (London, 1849), pp. 444–46; and "Hall, Sir William Hutcheon," in *Dictionary of National Biography,* 8: 978.
13. Edith Nicolls, "A Biographical Notice of Thomas Love Peacock, by his Granddaughter," in Henry Cole, ed., *The Works of Thomas Love Peacock,* 3 vols. (London, 1875), 1: xliii. On the eastward journey of the Nemesis, see Hall and Bernard, ch. 1.
14. On Chinese defenses, see John Lang Rawlinson, *China's Struggle for Naval Development, 1839–1895* (Cambridge, Mass., 1967), pp. 3–5 and 16–18; Fay, pp. 123–24, 207–09, 218, and 289; and G. R. G. Worcester, "The Chinese War Junk," *Mariner's Mirror* 34 (1948): 22.
15. Reprinted in *The London Gazette Extraordinary* 19984 (June 3, 1841): 1428.
16. India Office Records, L/Mar/C 593, pp. 543–44.
17. India Office Records, L/P&S/9/7, pp. 59–60.
18. India Office Records, L/P&S/9/1, p. 519.
19. India Office Records, L/P&S/9/1, p. 591.
20. The Yangtze campaign of 1842 is described in Gerald S. Graham, *The China Station: War and Diplomacy 1830–1860* (Oxford, 1978), ch. 8; G. R. G. Worcester, "The First Naval Expedition on the Yangtze River, 1842," *Mariner's Mirror* 36 (1950): 2–11; Hall and Bernard, pp. 326–27; Rawlinson, pp. 19–21; and Fay, pp. 313 and 341–45.

21. Lo Jung-Pang, "China's Paddle-Wheel Boats: Mechanized Craft Used in the Opium War and Their Historical Background," *Tsinghua Journal of Chinese Studies*, NS no. 2 (1960): 190–91. For a different translation of Lin's description, see Waley, p. 105.

22. Letter from Willam Huttman, *The Nautical Magazine and Chronicle* 12 (1843): 346.

23. Lo, p. 190.

24. Lo, p. 194; Worcester, "War Junk," pp. 23–24; and Fay, p. 350.

25. Lo, pp. 194–200; and Rawlinson, pp. 19–21.

26. George Gibbard Jackson, *The Ship Under Steam* (New York, 1928), p. 26.

27. On the last assignment of the *Nemesis*, see *Parliametary Papers* 1851 (378.) vol. LVI part 1, pp. 149–52. On the Second Anglo-Burmese War, see Col. W. F. B. Laurie, *Our Burmese Wars and Relations with Burma: Being an Abstract of Military and Political Operations, 1824–25–26, and 1852–53* (London, 1880), pp. 86–92. On gunboats in the Second Opium War, see Anthony Preston and John Major, *Send a Gunboat! A Study of the Gunboat and its Role in British History, 1854–1904* (London, 1967), ch. 4. On French gunboats in Indochina, see Joannès Tramond and André Reussner, *Eléments d'histoire maritme et coloniale (1815–1914)* (Paris, 1924), pp. 344–49, and Frédérick Nolte, *L'Europe maritime et diplomatique au dixneuvième siècle 1815–1884* (Paris, 1884), p. 521. On the Third Anglo-Burmese War, see A. T. Q. Stewart, *The Pagoda War: Lord Dufferin and the Fall of the Kingdom of Ava, 1885–6* (London, 1972), ch. 5.

28. Laurie, p. 109.

INVENTION AND PROGRESS

The articles in this section ask questions about engineering and invention in the late 19th and early 20th centuries. By the second half of the nineteenth century, technology and industry had become part of the language of everyday life. How did people feel about inventors and their new inventions that were changing life at an ever increasing pace?

The first article examines an issue that is often overlooked by historians of the railroad—popular criticism. This is an amusing look at the fears that people developed around riding trains.

The second piece is about Nikola Tesla, an inventor who, in his lifetime, was as famous as Thomas Edison. Edison invented the light bulb but Tesla invented the means to harness and transmit electricity. Many of his patents form the basis of much of our current technology. The essay describes Tesla's life and the unpredictable life of the inventor.

The last article in the section raises interesting questions about the meaning of the Industrial Revolution and the industrial age that followed. Leo Marx asks "does improved technology mean progress?" What do you think?

THE NEUROSES OF THE RAILWAY

Ralph Harrington

From the beginnings of their development in the early nineteenth century, railways inspired deep anxieties and provoked strong opposition. The common factor in much anti-railway discourse—whether couched in environmental, medical, or social terms—was a perception of railways as fundamentally unnatural, as intrinsically at odds with the established order embodied in the rural landscape, the social structure of traditional communities, and the constitution of the human mind and body.

It was claimed that trains would blight crops with their smoke and terrify livestock with their noise, that people would asphyxiate if carried at speeds of more than twenty miles per hour, and that hundreds would yearly die beneath locomotive wheels or in fires and boiler explosions. Many saw the railway as a threat to the social order, allowing the lower classes to travel too freely, weakening moral standards and dissolving the traditional bonds of community; John Ruskin, campaigning to exclude railways from the Lake District, warned in 1875 of "the certainty . . . of the deterioration of moral character in the inhabitants of every district penetrated by the railway."

The more extreme fears did recede as the railways spread, becoming established as an economic and social necessity and proving their ability to function safely and reliably; yet below the superficial acceptance, deep disquiet remained. Rather than disappearing altogether, the fear and anxiety provoked by the railway changed in nature as the nineteenth century progressed, becoming a fear of internal rather than external disruption.

The reasons for this change lay in the unique potency of the railway as a symbol of modernity. In the scale and sophistication of its engineering, the order and complexity of its operation, the speed and power of its technology, the railway embodied all the forces of mechanization, organisation and industrialised progress which lay behind modern civilisation. This quality could inspire wonder and admiration, and many artists and writers saw the railway as a natural subject for artistic treatment; as Zola wrote of Paul Bourget,

> You, modern poet, you detest modern life. You go against your gods, you don't really accept your age. Why do you find a railway station ugly? A station is beautiful.

Similar sentiments inspired the Italian Futurists in the first years of the twentieth century to celebrate "greedy railway stations that devour smoke-plumed serpents" and "deep-chested locomotives whose wheels paw the tracks like the hooves of enormous steel horses bridled by tubing"; but the images of the railway in Futurist paintings such as Boccioni's "Train in Motion" and his "States of Mind" series, and Carrá's "Milan Station" (all from 1911) reveal the darker forces behind the promise of technological advancement, depicting the disorientation and confusion of rail travel as well as its excitement.

Such works recognised that if the railway represented the triumph of mechanisation and the embodiment of progress, it was also inherent with danger, bearing all the threatening ills of neurosis, destruction, and degeneration which lay behind the facade of modernity. The railway carried people at unheard-of speeds, and forced them to place complete trust in its technology; it trapped them in noisy, unsteady, claustrophobic wooden boxes, isolating them from the world beyond the carriage window; it subjected them to violent jolts and constant vibrations, and assaulted their ears with rattles, roars, and deafening shrieks; it reshaped their physical environment with its tracks, vast structures and earthworks, and increasingly dominated their mental world with the demands of its timetables, connections, and bureaucratic procedures; in short, it is little wonder that so many saw themselves as the victims of a technology which, rather than serving human needs, forced human beings to conform to its own requirements, and that the belief that the railway posed an insidious degenerative threat to the human mind and body became steadily more widespread from the 1860s onwards.

Among contemporary medical practitioners, nerve specialists, and psychiatrists, including such figures as Freud, Oppenheim, and Charcot, the manifestations of railway-related fear and nervous disorder comprised a recognised and important medical phenomenon; they found themselves dealing with ever more victims of "railway phobia" and came to the conclusion that there was indeed something about the railway, something to do with the speed, the nature of the motion, the vibration, the risk of accident, perhaps even with the blurred view from the carriage window, that was damaging to human health.

The peculiar physical motion and the jolts and vibrations associated with railway travel were an early focus of medical concern. In 1857, a French physician, E. A. Duchesne, claimed to have identified a *"maladie des mécaniciens"* characterised by "generalised, continuous and persistent pains, accompanied by a feeling of weakness and numbness," suffered by train drivers and firemen as a result of the constant vibration they experienced in the footplate. A German medical survey of 1860 also referred to the nervous and muscular pains to which locomotive crews were prone because of the constant "mechanical tremor" they experienced, and drew attention to the fact that similar vibrations could be felt by passengers in the train itself.

Similar concerns were expressed in Britain, where between January and March 1862 the medical journal *The Lancet* published a detailed investigation of "The Influence of Railway Travelling on Public Health," in which much attention was paid to the possible medical effects of the "rapid, short vibrations and oscillations" to which railway travellers were subjected. These vibrations, according to the medical experts consulted by *The Lancet*, caused "a considerable number of muscles [to be] called into action, and maintained in a condition of alternating contractile effort throughout the journey", causing a feeling of fatigue to afflict the railway traveller. Nor was this the only cause of nervous, muscular, and mental exhaustion associated with travel by train; among the other influences considered by *The Lancet* were:

> . . . the impression on the brain produced by the rattle affecting it through the nerves of hearing; the rapid succession of objects presented to the sight, and the vibrations actually transmitted by the movement of the carriage to the very substance of the brain and spinal cord . . . the effects of hurry and anxiety to catch trains, and the frequent concentration of effort required to compress business matters at the last moment into the strict limits imposed.

All these factors, concluded *The Lancet,* combined to create a degree of mental and physical "wear and tear" unique to railway travel. A general medical textbook from 1884 made the same point:

> The eyes are strained, the ears are dinned, the muscles are jolted hither and thither, and the nerves are worried by the attempt to maintain order.

The fatiguing nature of railway travel was seen as one aspect of the wider phenomenon of "neurasthenia," the supposed exhaustion of the body's nervous energy by the pressures and demands of modern life. The American psychiatrist, George M. Beard, a specialist in neurasthenia, saw the jolts and rattles of railway travel as one cause of the "molecular disturbance" in the nervous system which produced neurasthenic symptoms, while the medical writer, Max Nordau, asserted in his highly influential work of 1985, *Entartung (Degeneration)*, that "Even the little shocks of railway travelling, not perceived by the consciousness . . . cost our brains wear and tear." Nordau saw the railway neuroses as:

> . . . exclusively a consequence of the present condition of civilised life . . . The terms "railway-spine" and "railway-brain", which the English and American pathologists have given to certain stages of these organs, show that they recognise them as due partly to the effects of railway accidents, partly to the constant vibrations undergone in railway travelling.

As Nordau's words suggest, the significance of the railway accident in theories of rail-related neuroses was considerable. Railway disasters possessed a uniquely potent horror for the late nineteenth-century public; a fact exploited by Thomas Love Peacock when he used the image of a train collision in his last novel, *Gryll Grange* (1860), to question the value of technological progress:

> *I see long trains of strange machines on wheels,*
> *With one in front of each, puffing white smoke*
> *From a black hollow column. Fast and far*
> *They speed . . .*
>
> *But while I look, two of them meet and clash,*
> *And pile their way with ruin. One is rolled*

Down a steep bank; one through a broken bridge
Is dashed into a flood. Dead, dying, wounded,
Are there as in a battle-field. Are these
Your modern triumphs? Jove preserve me from them.

On the railway journey, fear of the accident, although repressed, was always present. *The Lancet,* considering the "mental influences" of railway travel in its 1862 survey, referred to the "often experienced condition of uneasiness, scarcely [i.e. almost] amounting to actual fear, which pervades the generality of travellers by rail." In 1873, the same journal commented that:

Accidents have been so frequent of late . . . that we may be said to have supped full of railway horrors, and railway travelling has become almost insupportable to persons of a nervous temperament, whose thoughts are solely occupied during a journey by speculations on possible dangers.

The significance of the railway accident was that it marked a catastrophic failure of human control over the dangerous forces inherent in mechanised progress. "Without rigorous surveillance at all points," stated a French technical encyclopedia of 1844:

the most powerful and perfected industrial means, that is, steam engines and railway trains, can cause the most grave and fatal mishaps . . . their very power, once halted or turned from its proper objective, is transformed into a terrible agent of destruction.

Man's use of steam power, it was suggested, placed him "in a position best compared to that of a man who is walking along the edge of a precipice and cannot afford a single false step." This sense of human helplessness and fragility before the vast forces precariously harnessed by industrial technology underlies the pathology of the railway accident and of the railway journey.

Railway accidents subjected their human victims to unprecedented violence and shock; in addition to the physical injuries they inflicted, they also produced previously unknown and puzzling psychological and nervous reactions in those who were otherwise unharmed. *The Lancet* examined many cases in which healthy people who had sustained no physical injury in railway accidents subsequently suffered nervous disorders, physical sickness, loss of the use of limbs, impaired vision, and other symptoms. In 1862, the journal described the case of a healthy man who escaped from a major railway accident shaken but unhurt, and was able to return to normal work after a short rest. All was well until three weeks later, when he suddenly fell very ill and retired to bed "in a state of coma. He died the following day, from serious effusion on the brain."

Another accident victim "did not complain of any special injury at the time, and was able to walk about the scene of the accident and to examine the defective arrangement of the rails . . ." yet collapsed the next day at work suffering from severe nervous disorder. His chief complaint was "a feeling of nervous depression, and particularly that the countenances of his fellow-passengers, with terrified eyes" would seem constantly to come before him.

Many such cases involved sufferers experiencing "disturbed and diminished sleep, frequent starting when dozing, dreams of collision, noises in the ears, feverishness. . . ."

The case of Charles Dickens, who was involved in a railway accident in June 1865, provides an interesting illustration of the phenomenon. Immediately after the accident, Dickens was calm and collected, according to his own account; but a few hours afterwards he began to feel "faint and sick" in the head and to suffer from a general nervousness. He subsequently found continuing his railway journey distressing, having to travel on a slow train rather than an express, and even the noise of his London hansom cab was too much for his nerves. Even four days later, Dickens was unable to complete an account of the accident in a letter to a friend, breaking off abruptly with the words "in writing these scanty words of recollection I feel the shake and am obliged to stop." Dickens suffered fear and anxiety when travelling by train for the rest of his life.

The medical discussions of the nervous disorders which followed railway accidents comprise an extremely involved chapter in medico-legal history which need not be examined in detail here. What is significant, in terms of the history of the railway as an agent of the degenerative forces of industrial civilisation, is the stress laid on the unparalleled horror and violence of the railway accident, and the slow establishment of the importance of psychological factors alone in bringing about post-traumatic nervous collapse. Initially, it was believed that some kind of physical damage to the spinal cord was responsible; thus John Erichsen, a professor of surgery and author of the first (1866) full treatment of the subject (and populariser of the term "Railway Spine" for the condition, despite calling it "an absurd appellation"), sought a purely organic explanation in "concussion of the spine . . . due to molecular changes in its structure."

Subsequently, however, Erichsen acknowledged the importance of psychological factors, specifically fright, in railway accidents; in the second (1875) edition of his book *On Concussion of the Spine,* he accepted that the terrifying nature of a railway collision must "of necessity greatly increase the severity of the resulting injury to the nervous system." Seeking to explain the nervous disorders suffered by railway accident victims, Erichsen conceded that "terror" was a significant cause:

> The crash and confusion, the uncertainty attendant on the railway collision, the shrieks of the sufferers, possibly the sight of the victims of the catastrophe, produce a mental impression of a far deeper and more vivid character than is occasioned by the more ordinary accidents of civil life.

Ten years later, the rejection of an organic explanation for "railway spine" is much more explicit in the work of Herbert Page, a railway company surgeon. In his *Injuries of the Spine and Spinal Cord Without Apparent Mechanical Lesion* (1895), Page asserted that there were "few or no facts" to support the theory of actual injury to the spine in cases of post-accident neurosis, and introduced the concept of general nervous shock to account for the phenomenon in terms of "some functional disturbance of the whole nervous balance or tone rather than any structural damage to any organ of the body." The cause of this nervous shock was the level of "fear and alarm" associated with the railway accident:

Medical literature abounds with cases where the gravest disturbance of function and even death . . . have been produced by fright and by fright alone.

Page himself describes a particularly compelling case of "an apparently strong and healthy girl" of nineteen, who was involved in a railway accident:

She received no bodily injury, but the night of the accident she woke screaming that the engine was rushing into her room . . . and she died in five weeks, no structural disease whatever being found after death.

It appeared to contemporaries, as George F. Drinka puts it in his history of Victorian neuroses, that the railway could dissolve the human nervous system in an instant, "a cataclysmic split second of fright."

The theory of the power of ideas, and particularly of the idea of imminent injury or death, in bringing about medical symptoms of the severest nature had its genesis very largely through the study of the consequences of railway accidents, and proved very influential on the developing sciences of the human mind. The work of the great French neurologist Jean-Martin Charcot in particular demonstrated the power of an idea or emotion—fear, anxiety, anger—in bringing about attacks of hysteria. In the mid-1880s, Charcot developed his view that the terror felt by a subject during some form of physical trauma, such as involvement in a railway accident, was translated into an electrical shock which tore through the nervous system, bringing about its collapse; fright served as an *agent provocateur* provoking the manifestation of a latent heredity disposition towards hysteria. Many of the experiences which provoked this "traumatic hysteria" in the cases studied by Charcot were connected with work accidents on or near the railways; significantly, even where the forces of nature alone were responsible for bringing about a hysterical attack, there was often an underlying connection with technology and civilization. One case, cited by Dr. Drinka, involved a sufferer whose collapse had occurred when he had been caught in a thunderstorm while walking along a country road.

in the same instant that I heard the thunder and saw the lightening, I saw . . . a brilliant spinning fire [which] gave forth three clouds of smoke which resembled the smoke coming out of the chimney of a locomotive . . . I lost consciousness.

One did not have to be involved in an accident to suffer "railway phobia"; even a mental association with railways could be enough. The acceptance of the importance of the psychological, rather than the physiological, causes of nervous disorder was a recognition that the origins of railway phobia lay deeper than in the physical consequences of constant vibration or jarring of the spine. The nervous symptoms which the railway provoked represented a psychological reaction to the forces of civilisation and industrialisation embodied in the railway, forces which expressed themselves in the unnatural jolts and vibrations experienced by railway passengers, but also in the speed, disorientation, and noise of railway travel, the disconnection of passengers from their surroundings, their helplessness in the event of accident, and the fragility of the technical means by which the potentially disastrous forces of fire, steam, and mechanical energy were controlled.

These concerns are present in many contemporary literary works. In Dickens' *Dombey and Son* (1848), the railway is relentless and destructive, "the power that forced itself upon its iron way—its own—defiant of all paths and roads, piercing through the heart of every obstacle," tearing apart and reshaping the fabric of the city. In George Gissing's *In the Year of Jubilee* (1894), the "subterranean din and reek" of King's Cross underground station is vividly portrayed:

> This way and that sped the demon engines, whirling lighted waggons full of people. Shrill whistles, the hiss and roar of steam, the bang, clap, bang of carriage-doors, the clatter of feet on wood and stone. . . .

In Gissing's novel, in which the polarisation between corrupt city and virtuous country is sharply drawn, the railways, and especially the tangle of lines under London, express the frenetic, exhausting chaos and confusion, and the ugly commercialisation, of city life. In Tolstoy's *Anna Karenina* (1874–76) the railway has a profound significance as an agent of change, but also as an agent of inescapable destiny, dramatised by such moments of crisis as the death of a drunken porter beneath a train, and ultimately in the climactic scene of Anna's own death; while in Tolstoy's short story "The Kreutzer Sonata" (1889), the central figure, Pozdnyshev, recounts his story during a long train journey, and another such journey features at a crucial point in his own narrative. This story illustrates the threatening feeling of enclosure inherent in railway travel; whereas the journeys in pre-railway age novels such as Fielding's *Tom Jones* involve constant interaction between the travellers and the surrounding world, the occupants of the railway carriage are almost entirely isolated from the regions through which they pass. This point was well understood by Ruskin, who saw travel by train as analogous to being "sent" from one place to another, with no real experience of a "journey" in between; railway travel, he wrote, "transmutes a man from a traveller into a living parcel."

The moving railway carriage could be seen as imprisoning its passengers in a self-contained world from which there was no escape, either from others or from oneself; hence Pozdnyshev's outburst, "Oh, I'm so afraid, so afraid of railway carriages; I get stricken with horror in them." The same theme is present in Emile Zola's novel *La Bête Humaine* (1894), in which the central event is a brutal murder committed aboard a moving train, the victim trapped with his murderer in an isolated railway compartment, unable either to escape or to call for help. In Zola's novel the significance of the railway as both an agent of progress and an inexorable force of destruction is unforgettably dramatised in the final scene of a packed troop-train, driverless and uncontrollable, plunging onward to certain disaster:

> But the train, like a wild boar in the forest, held to its course, heedless of red lights and detonators . . . What did the victims matter that the machine destroyed on its way? Wasn't it bound for the future, heedless of spilt blood? With no human hand to guide it through the night, it roamed on and on, a blind and deaf beast let loose amid death and destruction. . . .

It is difficult now to recapture the impact that the railway had on those experiencing it for the first time, or to comprehend the extent to which the fears it provoked remained powerful, even as it became an accepted part of modern life. In his 1907 poem "The Sons of

Martha," Rudyard Kipling celebrated the sophisticated systems of transport and communication which underpinned modern technological society; but beneath the outward show of
confidence lies an unease born of fear, an awareness of the risks inherent in the merchanised
progress which, threatening as well as beneficial, was transforming human existence:

> *It is their care, in all the ages, to take the bullet and cushion the shock,*
> *It is their care that the gear engages—it is their care that the switches lock.*
> *It is their care that the wheels run truly*
> *—it is their care to embark and entrain,*
> *Tally, transport, and deliver duly the Sons of Mary by land and main.*

Kipling's words, as much as the writings of the nineteenth-century physicians involved in
investigating the medical consequences of railway travel, represent a process of evolution in
human consciousness; the neuroses of the railway reflect the breakdown of human nervous
systems under the assault of modern civilisation, the civilisation of which the railway, with
its power, speed and danger, was perhaps the most dramatic symbol.

9

THE WORK OF THE WORLD

Curt Wohleber

Tesla was missing. The American Institute of Electrical Engineers had just awarded Nikola Tesla its Edison Medal at New York City's Engineers' Club in May, 1917. The group was now gathered at a nearby auditorium for speeches. But the guest of honor had somehow slipped away.

B. A. Behrend—who had pleaded long and hard with Tesla before the sixty-year-old inventor finally agreed to accept an award named after a bitter rival—took to the streets. He found Tesla in Bryant Park, behind the New York Public Library. He was standing there, tall and handsome, dressed in crisp white tie and tails, covered from head to toe with pigeons. The birds snatched feed from his hands, perched serenely on his head, and milled about in a gray mass at his feet. Tesla saw Behrend approach and raised a finger to his lips. The pigeons scattered.

Tesla followed Behrend back to the auditorium. Behrend composed himself and addressed his colleagues: "Were we to seize and eliminate from our industrial world the results of Mr. Tesla's work, the wheels of industry would cease to turn, our electric cars and trains would stop, our towns would be dark, our mills would be dead and idle. . . . His name marks an epoch in the advance of electrical science. From that work has sprung a revolution. . . ."

For a time, around the turn of the century, the reputation of Nikola Tesla very nearly eclipsed that of Thomas Edison. Edison had invented the practical incandescent lamp, but Tesla had devised the means to bring the electricity that would light those lamps to millions of homes in America and around the world, cheaply and efficiently. He was the toast of New York's high society, throwing lavish dinner parties at Delmonico's and the Waldorf-Astoria. After those dinners he would adjourn to his laboratory to entertain celebrity guests such as Mark Twain with demonstrations of electrical wizardry. In his hands glass tubes glowed to life wirelessly. He passed a million volts harmlessly through his body. Great electric coils gave off terrifying sparks. Balls of electric fire danced eerily.

Even a highly abbreviated list of Tesla's achievements is impressive. There was the polyphase system, which made practical the large-scale electrification of America, and the Tesla coil, which produced high-frequency, high-voltage currents and later became an integral component of radio and then television equipment. His work with high-frequency electrical oscillations yielded crude prototypes of the cyclotron, the electron microscope, and neon and fluorescent lighting. He demonstrated a radio-controlled robot boat in 1898. He predicted global communications, computer science, and robotics with startling clarity.

Perhaps more than any other man, Tesla fitted the Hollywood stereotype of the eccentric scientist. His laboratory blazed and hummed with strange energies, and he himself had an otherworldly air about him. During electrical storms he liked to sit before a large window and, with childlike glee, watch the heavens rage. He eschewed romance, declaring it an unfit distraction for a man of science.

He had endless idiosyncrasies. An exaggerated fear of germs led him to demand his dinners be served accompanied by exactly eighteen napkins, with which he would meticulously polish his silverware; he could not enjoy a meal without first calculating its volume; the sight of pearl earrings made him ill. And he loved pigeons.

Nikola Tesla was born, it is said, during a thunderstorm at the stroke of midnight between July 9 and 10, 1856, in the village of Smiljan, Croatia. He was the son of Milutin, a minister, and Djouka, who was illiterate but had a prodigious memory and could recite vast amounts of poetry. It was from her, he maintained, that he inherited his inventive abilities; she had contrived many useful household devices.

As Tesla remembered his childhood, it was filled with many narrow escapes from death: on several occasions he nearly drowned; once he was almost boiled alive in a vat of milk; and he survived perilous encounters with dogs, hogs, and angry crows.

The phenomenon of static electricity entranced him. He once stroked the family cat and saw that its "back was a sheet of light, and my hand produced a shower of crackling sparks loud enough to be heard all over the place." His mother told him to stop before he started a fire. His father explained that it was electricity, just like lightning.

Nikola was fascinated. "Is nature a giant cat?" he asked himself. "If so, who strokes its back?"

Mechanical things interested him early on. He took apart his grandfather's clocks, though he had trouble putting them back together. At the age of five he built a bladeless waterwheel. (Interestingly, one of his last inventions of note was a bladeless turbine.) He also fashioned popguns, and arrows that he said could bore through an inch-thick pine plank.

Once he built a tiny motor powered by June bugs glued to a cross-shaped assembly mounted on a spindle. When the bugs tried to fly away, they turned a pulley, which drove the engine. The experiment ended when a local boy came by and began to eat his power supply.

He wanted to fly, and he noticed a peculiar buoyant sensation whenever he breathed deeply. From that he reasoned that if he hyperventilated enough, he might actually be able to float like a balloon. He tried this while leaping from the roof of a barn and holding an open umbrella. Neither deep breathing nor the improvised parachute prevented his plummeting to the ground and knocking himself out.

When he was twelve, he performed a slightly more sophisticated aeronautical experiment. The idea was to build a motor powered by atmospheric pressure, which would act on a cylinder partially enclosed by a box from which air had been evacuated—essentially a perpetual-motion device. He hoped to attach a propeller to this motor and fly away. When he assembled his engine and pumped the air out of the box, the cylinder indeed turned a little. He was thrilled, then dismayed when, rather than speeding up, the cylinder slowed to a halt. He later realized, much to his disappointment, that the cylinder's feeble rotation had resulted from air leaking into the box.

In the classroom Tesla was a star pupil, especially—almost alarmingly so—in mathematics. He would blurt the answers to involved problems without putting pen to paper. In his autobiography, *My Inventions,* Tesla boasts of an amazing mental ability: if a particular object or figure came to his mind, he would see a vivid image of it before his eyes. This gift disturbed him, because sometimes particularly distressing scenes, such as a funeral, would suddenly intrude on his vision. But this odd capacity also enabled him to carry out complex arithmetic operations without a blackboard and later to design whole machines solely in his mind. From time to time he would also see strange flashes of light. "In some instances," he wrote, "I have seen all the air around me filled with tongues of living flame."

In 1870 the fourteen-year-old Tesla went off to school in the city of Karlovac, where he stayed with an aunt and uncle. He finished the four-year term at the Higher Real Gymnasium in three years. He also caught malaria, and he was still weak from it when he returned to his family in Gospic, Croatia, where they had moved when he was six. He came down with cholera. Things looked bleak on all fronts. Even if he recovered from the cholera, Tesla faced a compulsory three years of military service. Worse still, his father insisted that he enter the ministry instead of studying engineering. The predicament sapped his will to live. "I was confined to bed for nine months with scarcely any ability to move," he recalled.

His father tried desperately to rouse him from his malaise. Then, when it looked as if he was going to die, Nikola whispered, "Perhaps I may get well if you will let me study engineering." Overcome, Milutin Tesla told Nikola that he would go to the best technical institution in the world. That promise, along with "a bitter decoction of a peculiar bean," restored Tesla's health: "I came to life like another Lazarus to the utter amazement of everyone."

At the advice of his father, Tesla spent the next year roaming the mountains, regaining his strength and, not incidentally, evading the draft. During this time he conceived a number of audacious inventions, including an ocean-spanning hydraulic tube for transporting mail at high speeds and an elevated ring circling the earth at the equator that would remain stationary as the earth turned within it, thus providing a simple means of rapid travel.

When his *Wanderjahr* was over, he entered the polytechnic institute in Graz, Austria, in 1875. Fiercely determined to penetrate the mysteries of electricity, he studied with an intensity that alarmed the dean of the engineering faculty, who wrote to Milutin that his son was working too hard.

During his second year in Graz, the school acquired a Gramme machine, a device consisting of a rotating conductive coil mounted between the ends of a horseshoe magnet. It could function as either a motor or a generator. If one turned the coil, its movement through the magnetic field would induce a current. Conversely, supplying an electric current to the coil would magnetize it, making it rotate within the field, thus providing mechanical power.

When it was functioning as a generator, the strength and direction of the current induced in the coil changed according to the coil's orientation to the magnetic field. As the coil turned, the current increased to a maximum, decreased to zero, then began to increase again, but in the opposite direction.

What was created, then, was an alternating current (AC). A commutator—a hollow cylinder split lengthwise, with each segment connected to one end of the coil—enabled a set of brushes to exchange connections with the coil terminals twice per rotation, resulting in an intermittent current of constant direction.

The device intrigued Tesla, but the violent sparking where the commutator and brushes met struck him as intolerably inefficient. He raised his objections to his professor, a German named Poeschl, who replied that the problem with the sparking was "inherent in the nature of the machine. It may be reduced to a great extent, but as long as we use commutators it will always be present to some degree. As long as electricity flows in one direction, and as long as a magnet has two poles, each of which acts oppositely on the current, we will have to use a commutator to change, at the right moment, the direction of the current."

"That is obvious," said Tesla. "The machine is limited by the current used. I am suggesting that we get rid of the commutator entirely by using alternating current."

Poeschl devoted his next lecture to demolishing Tesla's proposal. "Mr. Tesla will accomplish great things, but he certainly never will do this. It would be equivalent to converting a steady pulling force like gravity into rotary effort. It is a perpetual motion scheme, an impossible idea."

Tesla experienced an uncharacteristic moment of self-doubt. Was his idea really just a repeat of the flying-machine folly of his childhood? Before long, though, his confidence returned: "I could not demonstrate my belief at that time, but it came to me through what I might call instinct, for lack of a better name. But instinct is something which transcends knowledge."

Using his visualizing ability, he designed and mentally tested numerous AC motors. He slacked off on his studies to devote himself to the problem. He also took up card playing and billiards, which got him kicked out of the institute.

What happened next is unclear. He lost a great deal of money at cards, including some his parents had given him so that he could enroll at the University of Prague. He managed to win back the money and go to Prague, but there is no record that he ever enrolled at the university. One biographer suggests that he merely audited courses there for two years.

In any event, Testa went to Budapest in 1881. The telephone was coming to Hungary, and he hoped to be part of this new cutting-edge technology. Instead he had to settle for a low-paying position as a draftsman with the government's Central Telegraph Office. Once again Testa became gravely ill. Physicians were mystified by the affliction. For lack of a better term, they called it a nervous breakdown.

"I could hear the ticking of a watch with three rooms between me and the time-piece," Testa wrote. "A fly alighting on a table in the room would cause a dull thud in my ear. A carriage passing at a distance of a few miles fairly shook my whole body. The whistle of a locomotive twenty or thirty miles away made the bench or chair on which I sat vibrate so strongly that the pain was unbearable." Sunlight on his brow struck him with the force of a blow to the head.

But this illness passed as well, and soon Testa took up the AC motor problem with renewed vigor. He took long walks through Budapest. Testa recounted one such walk, through a city park with a friend named Anital Szigety, a mechanic, in memoirs he published in 1915. At one point Testa gazed at a particularly beautiful sunset and remembered some lines from Goethe's *Fauist*:

*The glow retreats, done is the day
of toil,—
It yonder hastes, new fields of life
exploring,—
Ah, that no wing can lift me from
the soil;
Upon its track to follow, follow
soaring!*

He stopped suddenly and fell into a trance. He had the key to building an AC motor; he could see it right in front of his eyes. He began sketching it in the dirt with a stick.

"Watch me," he told Szigety. "Watch me reverse it."

Szigety gestured toward a nearby bench and suggested that he sit down and rest.

"Don't you see it?" said Testa. "See how smoothly it is running? Now I throw this switch—and I reverse it. See? It goes just as smoothly in the opposite direction. Watch! I stop it. I start it. There is no sparking. There is nothing on it to spark!"

Szigety was baffled. "Are you ill?" he asked.

"It is my alternating-current motor I am talking about. I have solved the problem. Can't you see it right here in front of me, running almost silently? It is the rotating magnetic field that does it. See how the magnetic field rotates and drags the armature around with it? Isn't it beautiful? Isn't it sublime? Isn't it simple?" He smiled beatifically. "Now I can die happy. But I must live, I must return to work and build the motor so I can give it to the world. No more will men be slave to hard tasks. My motor will set them free, it will do the work of the world."

Whether or not he really had such a glorious moment of inspiration, Tesla had finally figured out how to build an electric motor that dispensed with the commutator and brushes. His solution was to run two or more out-of-phase alternating currents through the stator, or stationary outer portion of the motor. These currents would induce currents in the rotor, or armature—the inner, rotating portion. With a properly controlled phase relationship, the currents in the stator would create a rotating magnetic field. The induced currents in the rotor would create another magnetic field, at an angle to the one created by the stator currents. This would cause the rotor to turn, as the opposite poles of the two magnetic fields attracted each other. This breakthrough became known as the polyphase system.

Retreating again to his mental laboratory, Tesla built a series of imaginary motors, dynamos, and transformers. He later said that he was able to test his prototypes by running them for weeks on end and periodically checking them for signs of wear.

Soon afterward he got a job with the Continental Edison Company in Paris. He tried to interest his employers in the polyphase system, but Edison's antipathy to alternating current was well known. Tesla nevertheless distinguished himself as a crack troubleshooter, directing the repair of Edison power stations in France and Germany. While on assignment in Alsace he built his first actual prototype, a two-phase AC induction motor. It worked beautifully, but the only person who expressed any commercial interest in it was the mayor of Strasbourg, who tried without success to recruit some local investors.

Back in Paris, Charles Batchelor, a friend and close business associate of Edison, told Tesla that he ought to seek his fortune in America. Tesla arrived in the United States in 1884.

He had lost his luggage on his way to the steamship, so he arrived in New York with just the clothes on his back, a few coins, and a bundle of papers, mostly technical articles and poems he had written. He earned twenty dollars on his first day by fixing a machine for a grateful Manhattan shopkeeper. The next morning, armed with a letter of introduction from Batchelor, he called on Edison at his laboratory on Pearl Street. The great inventor, impressed with Tesla's credentials, hired him to repair a malfunctioning electrical system on a steamship.

The cultured, fastidious Tesla and the slovenly, folksy Edison were uniquely mismatched. Unable to find Croatia on a map, Edison once asked Tesla if he had ever eaten human flesh. They differed in inventive philosophy as well as personality. Edison took an almost perverse pride in his plodding trial-and-error approach to problem solving. Tesla, whose inventions existed fully formed in his head before he began to build them, found Edison's "empirical dragnets" distasteful. "If Edison had a needle to find in a haystack," he said later, "he would proceed at once with the diligence of the bee to examine straw after straw until he found the object of his search. I was a sorry witness of such doings, knowing that a little theory and calculation would have saved him ninety percent of his labor."

Despite their differences, Tesla impressed Edison with his skill and hard work. For months the young immigrant worked from 10:30 A.M. to 5:00 A.M. the next day, seven days a week. He presented a plan to improve the efficiency of Edison's dynamos. Edison said he would give him $50,000 if he could make the scheme work. Tesla labored feverishly on the project, and the improved dynamos did everything he said they would.

Then he asked Edison for the $50,000 he had been promised. Edison was taken aback. "Tesla, you don't understand our American humor," he said. Tesla was unamused. Edison made a counter offer: a ten-dollar-a-week raise. Tesla quit on the spot.

Soon afterward a group of investors approached Tesla with a proposal to form a new company to develop and market arc lights. As head of the Tesla Electric Light Company, he devised a safer, more reliable arc lamp than the ones generally in use at the time. For his effort, the investors paid him in stock certificates, which were virtually worthless because the United States was in the grip of the economic crisis that followed the Panic of 1884. He was forced out of the company, and he spent the next year working as a laborer on the streets of New York.

The foreman of his ditch-digging gang was moved and impressed by Tesla's story and introduced him to a Mr. A. K. Brown of Western Union, who helped Tesla form a new firm, the Tesla Electric Company. With financial backing and his own lab just a few blocks from Edison's, Tesla set to work building motors, dynamos, and transformers. In addition to his polyphase system, he developed single- and split-phase AC motors, which were less efficient but useful for special applications, or where a polyphase current was unavailable or impractical. Over the next several years Tesla received forty patents related to his AC system.

In May 1888 he lectured to the American Institute of Electrical Engineers. His address, "A New System of Alternate Current Motors and Transformers," created a sensation within the profession. Among those impressed by Tesla's vision was George Westinghouse, the Pittsburgh businessman and inventor of the Westinghouse air brake for trains. Westinghouse had secured American rights to a transformer, patented by Lucien Gaulard and John Gibbs, which was used to supply high-voltage alternating current for arc lighting.

William Stanley had greatly improved the Gaulard and Gibbs transformer, and in 1886 Stanley electrified eighteen businesses in Great Barrington, Massachusetts. (See "William

Stanley's Search for Immortality," by George Wise, *Invention & Technology,* Spring/Summer 1988.) Westinghouse declared that AC had arrived. Alternating current had a great advantage over the direct-current system marketed by Edison. Low-voltage direct currents dissipated rapidly, limiting the transmission radius of every generating station to a few miles. Stanley's transformer made it feasible to step up an alternating current to a high voltage, at which it could be transmitted efficiently across long distances.

But the system suffered from the lack of a practical motor it could power. Tesla's key patents filled that void. Westinghouse visited Tesla at his laboratory and nodded appreciatively as the inventor demonstrated his quietly humming machines. The two men made a deal: Tesla would get approximately $60,000 in cash and stock, plus a $2.50 royalty for every horsepower of motor or generating capacity sold.

As word of Westinghouse's plans spread, Edison, sensing a threat, prepared to strike back. The "War of the Systems" was one of the most down-and-dirty public battles in the annals of American business. Edison set out to convince the American people that alternating current, with its high voltages, represented a menace to anyone who dared let it into his home, a tactic he had used with considerably more justification when persuading people to give up gas-lighting for DC power and incandescent bulbs.

In West Orange, New Jersey, the home of his sprawling new invention factory, Edison offered local children a twenty-five-cent bounty for stray dogs and cats. Pets suddenly disappeared. Edison had hired a New York engineer named Harold Brown to document the menace of alternating current and explore its use as a means of execution. One corner of Edison's renowned center of beneficial innovations became a chamber of horrors as Brown "Westinghoused" dogs and cats and later calves and horses.

In 1888 New York State adopted electrocution as its official mode of capital punishment. Brown surreptitiously secured a license on several Tesla patents, and two years later William Kemmler, a convicted murderer, was the first man to be executed in Sing Sing prison's new electric chair. It was a grisly, protracted affair. Kemmler survived the first jolt, and the current had to be administered again. "They could have done better with an axe," commented Westinghouse.

The American public accepted alternating current anyway. And eventually so did Edison's company. A ruthless price war forced Edison to merge with Thomson-Houston, which used AC for arc lighting, and a new company known as General Electric was born.

In 1893 Westinghouse underbid General Electric and won the contract to light the Chicago world's fair. Working on short notice, Tesla cobbled together a dozen 1,000-horsepower AC generators. Celebrating (a year late) the 400th anniversary of the discovery of America, twenty-five million visitors mobbed Chicago and beheld such technological wonders as Thomas Edison's early motion-picture system, music transmitted live from New York via telephone, and an early prototype of the zipper. More courageous visitors enjoyed the thrill of riding G. W. G. Ferris's 250-foot wheel.

Tesla, nattily dressed as always, amazed audiences with an electric clock, glowing phosphorescent tubes, and spectacular discharges from mammoth electric coils. He sent 200,000 volts of high-frequency current through his body. A newspaper reporter wrote that Tesla was surrounded by "dazzling streams of light."

That same year, Westinghouse won the contract to build three AC generators at Niagara Falls (the distribution contract went to GE). Years earlier Tesla had daydreamed about harnessing the enormous power of that thundering curtain of water. Now it was to become a reality. Huge turbines were built, and in 1895 the first three 5,000-horsepower two-phase generators went on-line. One of the first customers was the Pittsburgh Reduction Company, which later became the Aluminum Company of America (now Alcoa). Cheap, plentiful electric power from the Falls made possible the large-scale commercial production of aluminum, and in the years that followed Niagara Falls became the center of the electrochemical industry. By the end of 1896 a twenty-six-mile transmission line carried current to power the lights and streetcars of Buffalo.

Alternating current was going to take over the world, but Tesla himself would profit little from that conquest. Westinghouse extended himself perilously in pushing the system. When Charles Coffin, a crony of J. P. Morgan and president of Thomson-Houston, tried to enlist him in a price-fixing scheme, Westinghouse refused. Rumors of mismanagement and imminent bankruptcy circulated on Wall Street, and his stock plummeted. The company had to merge with several smaller firms. Westinghouse Electric would be saved, but the bankers who had put the deal together pointed to one fatal liability: Tesla's $2.50-per-horsepower royalty. It would have to go.

Westinghouse went to Tesla's laboratory in 1896 to deliver the bad news in person. He explained the situation: Tesla must give up the royalties or the company would go under, taking his polyphase system with it. Tesla tore up the original contract and let Westinghouse buy his system outright for $216,000. He probably could have struck a deal satisfactory to the bankers while still ensuring himself lifelong prosperity, but Tesla most likely believed there would be plenty more money from other sources.

The last decade of the century saw Tesla at the zenith of his creative powers. In 1891 he had demonstrated the Tesla coil, an air-core step-up transformer and capacitor capable of converting high currents at low voltage to low currents at high voltage, all at high AC frequencies. He also began to experiment with ways of transmitting electricity wirelessly. A few years before, Heinrich Hertz had discovered the propagation of electromagnetic waves through space, and in his own lab Tesla noticed that sending a current through a coil of a specific frequency would elicit sparks from other coils tuned to either the same frequency or one of its harmonics. He foresaw a day when telegraph signals and electric power would be transmitted all over the world without wires, and he filed several key patents describing wireless transmitters and receivers.

Tesla's experiments were interrupted in 1895, when fire reduced his laboratory to a smoking, half-melted ruin. He had no insurance. Fortunately Edward Dean Adams, whose Cataract Construction Company had awarded Westinghouse the Niagara Falls generator contract, came through with $40,000 and suggested forming a new company with Tesla, capitalized at $500,000. Tesla, prizing his independence, declined the offer. He set up shop on East Houston Street and quickly returned to work, agonizing as the new equipment trickled in by rail.

Three years later, at the Electrical Exhibition in New York City's Madison Square Garden, 15,000 people watched Tesla demonstrate a remote-control model boat, an astounding feat considering that radio technology was still embryonic. War had broken out with Spain earlier that year, and Tesla hoped to sell his "tele-automatic" system to the government, but the military men found the idea of robot boats too exotic.

His work with wireless transmission intensified. With funding from John Jacob Astor and others, Tesla built a research station in Colorado Springs, where he promised to send a wireless signal from Pikes Peak to Paris in time for the 1900 Paris Exposition. He stayed in Colorado Springs for eight months, generating huge voltages and making the skies above the sleepy town crackle and flash. He asserted that before long he would be in communication with the intelligent beings that undoubtedly inhabited Mars, but he never even reached Paris.

There is a famous photograph of Tesla at Colorado Springs. It shows him sitting among his huge coils, reading calmly, as enormous jagged electrical discharges writhe about him. The picture was typical Tesla showmanship: not pure hokum, but not quite what it seemed to be either. The shot was a double exposure, Tesla's image added to the photograph while the coils were safely dormant.

Back in New York Tesla persuaded J. P. Morgan to provide $150,000 to finance another attempt at intercontinental wireless communication. He built a 187-foot tower called Wardenclyffe near Shoreham, Long Island. Stanford White helped with the design. As it was going up, Guglielmo Marconi managed to beat Tesla in sending a wireless telegraphic signal across the Atlantic. "Let him continue," Tesla said. "He is using seventeen of my patents."

Morgan's $150,000 ran out before Wardenclyffe was complete. Tesla blamed the banker's financial machinations. "You have raised great waves in the industrial world," he wrote, "and some have struck my little boat. Prices have gone up in consequence twice, perhaps three times higher than they were. . . ." Morgan refused to extend any more money, despite a series of increasingly desperate pleas from Tesla. The project had to be abandoned.

The "World System" he had hoped to pioneer at Wardenclyffe was Tesla's last large-scale endeavor, his final opportunity to sustain his reputation as one of the towering figures of American invention. But he had been too ambitious, too impractical. His scientific knowledge failed to keep up with the times. Revelations about atomic structure, relativity, and quantum theory passed him by. Even his knowledge of electrical phenomena was largely empirical; when he conceived his polyphase system in the 1880s, J. J. Thomson had yet to describe the electron.

Though Tesla would survive into the 1940s, his important scientific work was largely completed by the turn of the century. In the last decades of his life he faced mounting financial hardship. He was evicted from his beloved Waldorf-Astoria and took up residence in a series of progressively less fashionable hotels. Growing old and desperately in need of money, he turned his hand to some less visionary projects and enjoyed modest success with an improved locomotive headlight and a speedometer. His bladeless turbine showed great promise, but it never caught on. In the past two decades, however, interest in his turbine has grown, and it may soon find application in generators and jet aircraft.

Late in life Tesla's eccentricities grew ever more pronounced, particularly his almost fanatical devotion to pigeons. He spent hours feeding them in the park behind the library. If he came across one that was sick or injured, he would take it back to his hotel room, much to the dismay of the management.

John O'Neill, a young science writer and friend of the aging Tesla, once visited him at the Hotel New Yorker with William L. Laurence, a fellow journalist. In the hotel lobby Tesla, O'Neill recalled, told them a story about a white pigeon.

"I have been feeding pigeons," he began, "thousands of them, for years. Thousands of them, for who can tell—"

There was one pigeon of which he was particularly fond: pure white, with light gray wing tips. "No matter where I was, that pigeon would find me; when I wanted her I had only to wish and call her and she would come flying to me. She understood me and I understood her."

"I loved that pigeon.

"Yes, I loved her as a man loves a woman, and she loved me. . . . As long as I had her, there was purpose in my life." One night, he continued, the white pigeon flew through the window and landed on his desk. He knew that she was dying. "And then . . . there came a light from her eyes—powerful beams of light. Yes, it was a real light, a powerful, dazzling, blinding light, a light more intense than I had ever produced by the most powerful lamps in my laboratory.

"When that pigeon died, something went out of my life. . . . I knew my life's work was finished."

When O'Neill and Laurence left him that night, they walked for many blocks without speaking. Years later O'Neill wrote, "It is out of such phenomena as Tesla experienced"—in his hotel room and in that park in Budapest—". . . that the mysteries of religion are built."

Tesla died alone in his hotel room in January 1943. Less than a year later the U.S. Supreme Court voided Marconi's primary wireless patent in favor of a 1900 Tesla patent.

Today Tesla's name, while hardly forgotten, is unknown to many. His accomplishments, significant as they were, are not concretely present in everyday life the way Thomas Edison's light bulb is. Yet Tesla's voice can still be heard, on quiet nights when the sounds of traffic recede and one can hear the steady hum of power lines, carrying on the work of the world.

DOES IMPROVED TECHNOLOGY MEAN PROGRESS?

Leo Marx

Understanding the historical distinction between two contradictory concepts of progress helps explain the current disenchantement with technology.

Does improved technology mean progress? If some variant of this question had been addressed to a reliable sample of Americans at any time since the early nineteenth century, the answer of a majority almost certainly would have been an unequivocal "yes." The idea that technological improvements are a primary basis for—and an accurate gauge of—progress has long been a fundamental belief in the United States. In the last half-century, however, that belief has lost some of its credibility. A growing minority of Americans has adopted a skeptical, even negative, view of technological innovation as an index of social progress.

The extent of this change in American attitudes was brought home to me when I spent October 1984 in China. At that time the announced goal of the People's Republic was to carry out (in the popular slogan) "Four Modernizations"—agriculture, science and technology, industry, and the military. What particularly struck our group of Americans was the seemingly unbounded, largely uncritical ardor with which the Chinese were conducting their love affair with Western-style modernization—individualistic, entrepreneurial, or "capitalist," as well as scientific and technological. Like early nineteenth century visitors to the United States, we were witnessing a society in a veritable transport of improvement: long pent-up, innovative energies were being released, everyone seemed to be in motion, everything was eligible for change. It was assumed that any such change almost certainly would be for the better.

Most of the Chinese we came to know best—teachers and students of American studies—explicitly associated the kind of progress represented by the four modernization with the United States. This respect for American wealth and power was flattering but disconcerting, for we often found ourselves reminding the Chinese of serious shortcomings, even some terrible dangers, inherent in the Western mode of industrial development. Like the Americans whom European travelers met 150 years ago, many of the Chinese seemed to be extravagantly, almost blindly, credulous and optimistic.

Our reaction revealed, among other things, a change in our own culture and, in some cases, in our own personal attitudes. We came face to face with the gulf that separates the outlook of many contemporary Americans from the old national faith in the advance of technology and the basis of social progress.

The standard explanation for this change includes the familiar litany of death and destruction that distinguishes the recent history of the West: two barbaric world wars, the Nazi holocaust, the Stalinist terror, and the nuclear arms race. It is striking to know how many of the fearful events of our time involve the destructive use or misuse, the unforeseen consequences, or the disastrous malfunction of modern technologies: Hiroshima and the nuclear threat; the damage inflicted upon the environment by advanced industrial societies; and spectacular accidents like Three Mile Island.

Conspicuous disasters have helped to undermine the public's faith in progress, but there also has been a longer-term change in our thinking. It is less obvious, less dramatic and tangible than the record of catastrophe that distinguishes our twentieth-century history, but I believe it is more fundamental. Our very conception—our chief criterion—of progress has undergone a subtle but decisive change since the founding of the Republic, and that change is at once a cause and a reflection of our current disenchantment with technology. To chart this change in attitude, we need to go back at least as far as the first Industrial Revolution.

THE ENLIGHTENMENT BELIEF IN PROGRESS

The development of radically improved machinery (based on mechanized motive power) used in the new factory system of the late eighteenth century coincided with the formulation and diffusion of the modern Enlightenment idea of history as a record of progress. This conception became the fulcrum of the dominant American worldview. It assumes that history, or at least modern history, is driven by the steady, cumulative, and inevitable expansion of human knowledge of and power over nature. The new scientific knowledge and technological power was expected to make possible a comprehensive improvement in all the conditions of life—social, political, moral, and intellectual as well as material.

The modern idea of progress, as developed by its radical French, English, and American adherents, emerged in an era of political revolution. It was a revolutionary doctrine, bonded to the radical struggle for freedom from feudal forms of domination. To ardent republicans like the French philosopher Condorcet, the English chemist Priestley, and Benjamin Franklin, a necessary criterion of progress was the achievement of political and social liberation. They regarded the new sciences and technologies not as ends in themselves, but as instruments for carrying out a comprehensive transformation of society. The new knowledge and power would provide the basis for alternatives to the deeply entrenched authoritarian, hierarchical institutions of *l'ancien régime:* monarchical, aristocratic, and ecclesiastical. Thus in 1813 Thomas Jefferson wrote to John Adams describing the combined effect of the new science and the American Revolution on the minds of Europeans:

Science had liberated the ideas of those who read and reflect, and the American example had kindled feelings of right in the people. An insurrection has consequently begun, of science, talents, and courage, against rank and birth, which have fallen into contempt . . . Science is progressive.

Admittedly, the idea of history as endless progress did encourage extravagantly optimistic expectations, and in its most extreme form, it fostered some wildly improbable dreams of the "perfectibility of Man" and of humanity's absolute mastery of nature. Yet the political beliefs of the radical republicans of the eighteenth century, such as the principle of making the authority of government dependent upon the consent of the governed, often had the effect of limiting those aspirations to omnipotence.

The constraining effect of such ultimate, long-term political goals makes itself felt, for example, in Jefferson's initial reaction to the prospect of introducing the new manufacturing system to America. "Let our work-shops remain in Europe," he wrote in 1785.

Although a committed believer in the benefits of science and technology, Jefferson rejected the idea of developing an American factory system on the grounds that the emergence of an urban proletariat, which he then regarded as an inescapable consequence of the European factory system, would be too high a price to pay for any potential improvement in the American material standard of living. He regarded the existence of manufacturing cities and an industrial working class as incompatible with republican government and the happiness of the people. He argued that it was preferable, even if more costly in strictly economic terms, to ship raw materials to Europe and import manufactured goods. "The loss by the transportation of commodities across the Atlantic will be made up in happiness and permanence of government." In weighing political, moral, and aesthetic costs against economic benefits, he anticipated the viewpoint of the environmentalists and others of our time for whom the test of a technological innovation is its effect on the overall quality of life.

Another instance of the constraining effect of republican political ideals is Benjamin Franklin's refusal to exploit his inventions for private profit. Thus Franklin's reaction when the governor of Pennsylvania urged him to accept a patent for his successful design of the "Franklin stove":

Governor Thomas was so pleased with the construction of this stove as described in . . . [the pamphlet] that . . . he offered to give me a patent for the sole vending of them for a term of years; but I declined it from a principle which has ever weighed with me on such occasions, namely; viz., that as we enjoy great advantages from the inventions of others, we should be glad of an opportunity to serve others by any invention of ours, and this we should do freely and generously.

What makes the example of Franklin particularly interesting is the fact that he later came to be regarded as the archetypal self-made American and the embodiment of the Protestant work ethic. When Max Weber sought out of all the world *the* exemplar of that mentality for his seminal study, *The Protestant Ethic and the Spirit of Capitalism,* whom did he choose but our own Ben? But Franklin's was a principled and limited self-interest. In his *Autobiography,* he told the story of his rise in the world not to exemplify a merely personal success, but rather to illustrate the achievements of a "rising people." He belonged to that heroic revolutionary phase in the history of the bourgeoisie when that class saw itself as the vanguard of humanity and its principles as universal. He thought of his inventions as designed not for his private benefit but for the benefit of all.

THE TECHNOCRATIC CONCEPT OF PROGRESS

With the further development of industrial capitalism, a quite different conception of technological progress gradually came to the fore in the United States. Americans celebrated the advance of science and technology with increasing fervor, but they began to detach the idea from the goal of social and political liberation. Many regarded the eventual attainment of that goal as having been assured by the victorious American Revolution and the founding of the Republic.

The difference between this later view of progress and that of Jefferson's and Franklin's generation can be heard in the rhetoric of Daniel Webster. He and Edward Everett were perhaps the leading public communicators of this new version of the progressive ideology. When Webster decided to become a senator from Massachusetts instead of New Hampshire, the change was widely interpreted to mean that he had become the quasi-official spokesman for the new industrial manufacturing interests. Thus, Webster, who was generally considered the nation's foremost orator, was an obvious choice as the speaker at the dedication of new railroads. Here is a characteristic peroration of one such performance in 1847.

It is an extraordinary era in which we live. It is altogether new. The world has seen nothing like it before. I will not pretend, no one can pretend, to discern the end; but everybody knows that the age is remarkable for scientific research into the heavens, the earth, and what is beneath the earth; and perhaps more remarkable still for the application of this scientific research to the pursuits of life. . . . We see the ocean navigated and the solid land traversed by steam power, and intelligence communicated by electricity. Truly this is almost a miraculous era. What is before us no one can say, what is upon us no one can hardly realize. The progress of the age has almost outstripped human belief; the future is known only to Omniscience.

By the 1840s, as Webster's rhetoric suggests, the idea of progress was already being dissociated from the Enlightenment vision of political liberation. He invests the railroad with a quasi-religious inevitability that lends force to the characterization of his language as the rhetoric of the technological sublime. Elsewhere in the speech, to be sure, Webster makes the obligatory bow to the democratic influence of technological change, but it is clear that he is casting the new machine power as the prime exemplar of the overall progress of the age, quite apart from its political significance. Speaking for the business and industrial elite, Webster and Everett thus depict technological innovation as a sufficient cause, *in itself,* for the fact that history assumes the character of continuous, cumulative progress.

At the same time, discarding the radical political ideals of the Enlightenment allowed the idea of technological progress to blend with other grandiose national aspirations. Webster's version of the "rhetoric of the technological sublime" is of a piece with the soaring imperial ambitions embodied in the slogan "Manifest Destiny," and by such tacit military figurations of American development as the popular notion of the "conquest of nature" (including Native

Americans) by the increasingly technologized forces of advancing European-American "civilization." These future-oriented themes easily harmonized with the belief in the coming of the millennium that characterized evangelical Protestantism, the most popular American religion at the time. Webster indicates as much when, at the end of his tribute to the new railroad, he glibly brings in "Omniscience" as the ultimate locus of the meaning of progress.

The difference between the earlier Enlightenment conception of progress and that exemplified by Webster is largely attributable to the difference between the groups they represented. Franklin, Jefferson, and the heroic generation of founding revolutionists constituted a distinct, rather unusual social class in that for a short time the same men possessed authority and power in most of its important forms: economic, social, political, and intellectual. The industrial capitalists for whom Daniel Webster spoke were men of a very different stripe. They derived their status from a different kind of wealth and power, and their conception of progress, like their economic and social aspirations, was correspondingly different. The new technology and the immense profits it generated belonged to them, and since they had every reason to assume that they would retain their property and power, they had a vested interest in technological innovation. It is not surprising, under the circumstances, that as industrialization proceeded these men became true believers in technological improvement as the primary basis for—as virtually tantamount to—universal progress.

This dissociation of technological and material advancement from the larger political vision of progress was an intermediate stage in the eventual impoverishment of that radical eighteenth-century worldview. This subtle change prepared the way for the emergence, later in the century, of a thoroughly technocratic idea of progress. It was "technocratic" in that it valued improvements in power, efficiency, rationality as ends in themselves. Among those who bore witness to the widespread diffusion of this concept at the turn of the century were Henry Adams and Thorstein Veblen, who were critical of it, and Andrew Carnegie, Thomas Edison, and Frederick Winslow Taylor and his followers, who lent expression to it. Taylor's theory of scientific management embodies the quintessence of the technocratic mentality, "the idea," as historian Hugh Aitken describes it, "that human activity could be measured, analyzed, and controlled by techniques analogous to those that had proved so successful when applied to physical objects."

The technocratic idea of progress is a belief in the sufficiency of scientific and technological innovation as the basis for general progress. It says that if we can ensure the advance of science-based technologies, the rest will take care of itself. (The "rest" refers to nothing less than a corresponding degree of improvement in the social, political, and cultural conditions of life.) Turning the Jeffersonian ideal on its head, this view makes instrumental values fundamental to social progress, and relegates what formerly were considered primary, goal-setting values (justice, freedom, harmony, beauty, or self-fulfillment) to a secondary status.

In this century, the technocratic view of progress was enshrined in Fordism and an obsessive interest in economies of scale, standardization of process and product, and control of the workplace. This shift to mass production was accompanied by the more or less official commitment of the U.S. government to the growth of the nation's wealth, productivity, and global power, and to the most rapid possible rate of technological innovation as the essential criterion of social progress.

But the old republican vision of progress—the vision of advancing knowledge empowering human kind to establish a less hierarchical, more just and peaceful society—did not disappear. If it no longer inspired Webster and his associates, it lived on in the minds of many farmers, artisans, factory workers, shopkeepers, and small-business owners, as well as in the beliefs of the professionals, artists, intellectuals, and other members of the lower middle and middle classes. During the late nineteenth century, a number of disaffected intellectuals sought new forms for the old progressive faith. They translated it into such political idioms as utopian socialism, the single-tax movement, the populist revolt, Progressivism in cities, and Marxism and its native variants.

THE ROOTS OF OUR ADVERSARY CULTURE

Let me turn to a set of these late-eighteenth-century ideas that was to become the basis for a powerful critique of the culture of advanced industrial society. Usually described as the viewpoint of the "counter-Enlightenment" or the "romantic reaction," these ideas have formed the basis for a surprisingly long-lived adversarial culture.

According to conventional wisdom, this critical view originated in the intellectual backlash from the triumph of the natural sciences we associate with the great discoveries of Galileo, Kepler, Harvey, and Newton. Put differently, this tendency was a reaction against the extravagant claims for the universal, not to say exclusive, truth of "the Mechanical Philosophy." That term derived from the ubiquity of the machine metaphor in the work of Newton and other natural scientists ("celestial mechanics") and many of their philosophic allies, notably Descartes, all of whom tended to conceive of nature itself as a "great engine" and its subordinate parts (including the human body) as lesser machines.

By the late eighteenth century, a powerful set of critical, anti-mechanistic ideas was being developed by Kant, Fichte, and other German idealists, and by great English poets like Coleridge and Wordsworth. But in their time the image of the machine also was being invested with greater tangibility and social import. The Industrial Revolution was gaining momentum, and as power machinery was more widely diffused in Great Britain, Western Europe, and North America, the machine acquired much greater resonance: it came to represent both the new technologies based on mechanized motive power and the mechanistic mind-set of scientific rationalism. Thus the Scottish philosopher and historian Thomas Carlyle, who had been deeply influenced by the new German philosophy, announced in his seminal 1829 essay, "Signs of the Times," that the right name for the dawning era was the "Age of Machinery." It was to be the Age of Machinery, he warned, in every "inward" and "outward" sense of the word, meaning that it would be dominated by mechanical (utilitarian) thinking as well as by actual machines.

In his criticism of this new era, Carlyle took the view that neither kind of "machinery" was inherently dangerous. In his opinion, indeed, they represented *potential* progress as long as neither was allowed to become the exclusive or predominant mode in its respective realm.

In the United States a small, gifted, if disaffected minority of writers, artists, and intellectuals adopted this ideology. Their version of Carlyle's critical viewpoint was labeled "romantic" in reference to its European strains, or "transcendentalist" in its native use. In the work of writers like Emerson and Thoreau, Hawthorne and Melville, we encounter critical responses to the onset of industrialism that cannot be written off as mere nostalgia or primitivism. These writers did not hold up an idealized wilderness, a pre-industrial Eden, as preferable to the world they saw in the making. Nor did they dismiss the worth of material improvement as such. But they did regard the dominant view, often represented (as in Webster's speech) by the appearance of the new machine power in the American landscape, as dangerously shallow, materialistic, and one-sided. Fear of "mechanism," in the several senses of that word—especially the domination of the individual by impersonal systems—colored all of their thought. In their work, the image of the machine-in-the-landscape, far from being an occasion for exultation, often seems to arouse anxiety, dislocation, and foreboding. Henry Thoreau's detailed, carefully composed account of the intrusion of the railroad into the Concord woods is a good example; it bears out his delineation of the new inventions as "improved means to unimproved ends."

This critical view of the relationship between technological means and social ends did not merely appear in random images, phrases, and narrative episodes. Indeed, the whole of *Walden* may be read as a sustained attack on a culture that had allowed itself to become confused about the relationship of ends and means. Thoreau's countrymen are depicted as becoming "the tools of their tools." Much the same argument underlies Hawthorne's satire, "The Celestial Railroad," a modern replay of *Pilgrim's Progress* in which the hero, Christian, realizes too late that his comfortable railroad journey to salvation is taking him to hell, not heaven. Melville incorporates a similar insight into his characterization of Captain Ahab, who is the embodiment of the Faustian aspiration toward domination and total control given credence by the sudden emergence of exciting new technological capacities. Ahab exults in his power over the crew, and he explicitly identifies it with the power exhibited by the new railroad spanning the North American continent. In reflective moments, however, he also acknowledges the self-destructive nature of his own behavior: "Now in his heart, Ahab had some glimpse of this, namely, all my means are sane, my motive and my object mad."

Of course there was nothing new about the moral posture adopted by these American writers. Indeed, their attitude toward the exuberant national celebration of the railroad and other inventions is no doubt traceable to traditional moral and religious objections to such an exaggeration of human powers. In this view, the worshipful attitude of Americans toward these new instruments of power had to be recognized for what it was: idolatry like that attacked by Old Testament prophets in a disguised, new-fashioned form. This moral critique of the debased technocratic version of the progressive worldview has slowly gained adherents since the mid-nineteenth century, and by now it is one of the chief ideological supports of an adversary culture in the United States.

The ideas of writers like Hawthorne, Melville, and Thoreau were usually dismissed as excessively idealistic, nostalgic, or sentimental, hence impractical and unreliable. They were particularly vulnerable to that charge at a time when the rapid improvement in the material conditions of American life lent a compelling power to the idea that the meaning of history is universal progress. Only in the late twentieth century, with the growth of skepticism about scientific and technological progress, and with the emergence of a vigorous adversary culture in the 1960s, has the standpoint of that earlier eccentric minority been accorded a certain intellectual respect. To be sure, it is still chiefly the viewpoint of a relatively small minority, but there have been times, like the Vietnam upheaval of the 1960s, when that minority has won the temporary support of, or formed a tacit coalition with, a remarkably large number of other disaffected Americans. Much the same anti-technocratic viewpoint has made itself felt in various dissident movements and intellectual tendencies since the 1960s: the anti-nuclear movements (against both nuclear power and nuclear weaponry); some branches of the environmental and feminist movements; the "small is beautiful" and "stable-state" economic theories, as well as the quest for "soft energy paths" and "alternative (or appropriate) technologies."

TECHNOCRATIC VERSUS SOCIAL PROGRESS

Perhaps this historical summary will help explain the ambivalence toward the ideal of progress expressed by many Americans nowadays. Compared with prevailing attitudes in the U.S. in the 1840s, when the American situation was more like that of China today, the current mood in this country would have to be described as mildly disillusioned.

To appreciate the reasons for that disillusionment, let me repeat the distinction between the two views of progress on which this analysis rests. The initial Enlightenment belief in progress perceived science and technology to be in the service of liberation from political oppression. Over time that conception was transformed, or partly supplanted, by the now familiar view that innovations in science-based technologies are in themselves a sufficient and reliable basis for progress. The distinction, then, turns on the apparent loss of interest in, or willingness to name, the social ends for which the scientific and technological instruments of power are to be used. What we seem to have instead of a guiding political goal is a minimalist definition of civic obligation.

The distinction between two versions of the belief in progress helps sort out reactions to the many troubling issues raised by the diffusion of high technology. When, for example, the introduction of some new labor-saving technology is proposed, it is useful to ask what the purpose of this new technology is. Only by questioning the assumption that innovation represents progress can we begin to judge its worth. The aim may well be to reduce labor costs, yet in our society the personal costs to the displaced workers are likely to be ignored.

The same essential defect of the technocratic mind-set also becomes evident when the president of the United States calls upon those who devise nuclear weapons to provide an elaborate new system of weaponry, the Strategic Defense Initiative, as the only reliable means of avoiding nuclear war. Not only does he invite us to put all our hope in a "technological fix," but he rejects the ordinary but indispensable method of international negotiation and compromise. Here again, technology is thought to obviate the need for political ideas and practices.

One final word. I perhaps need to clarify the claim that it is the modern, technocratic worldview of Webster's intellectual heirs, not the Enlightenment view descended from the Jeffersonians, that encourages the more dangerous contemporary fantasies of domination and total control. The political and social aspirations of the generation of Benjamin Franklin and Thomas Jefferson *provided tacit limits to, as well as ends for, the progressive vision of the future.* But the technocratic version so popular today entails a belief in the worth of scientific and technological innovations as ends in themselves.

All of which is to say that we urgently need a set of political, social, and cultural goals comparable to those formulated at the beginning of the industrial era if we are to accurately assess the worth of new technologies. Only such goals can provide the criteria required to make rational and humane choices among alternative technologies and, more important, among alternative long-term policies.

Does improved technology mean progress? Yes, it certainly could mean just that. But only if we are willing and able to answer the next question: progress toward what? What is it that we want our new technologies to accomplish? What do we want beyond such immediate, limited goals as achieving efficiencies, decreasing financial costs, and eliminating the troubling human elements from our workplaces? In the absence of answers to these questions, technological improvements may very well turn out to be incompatible with genuine, that is to say social, progress.

MASS CONSUMPTION

By the end of the 19th century, the United States had surpassed England as an industrial nation. American output of steel, miles of railroad track, amount of production for export and home consumption passed all expectations. As mass production grew, industrial and household goods became more affordable, and Americans hungry for consumer goods responded to lower prices by buying. A vast range of items was available in the newly created department stores, in the growing catalog businesses of Sears Roebuck and Montgomery Ward, as well as the traditional general store. Consumers could buy cheap, mass-produced furniture, dishware, household machines, carriages, clothing, all of which had been produced in factories.

Along with mass production came the rise of mass consumption and advertising. Advertising became an important part of the new consumer culture; it introduced consumers to new products and to desires they didn't know they had. The first article in this section discusses the development of one amusing series of advertisements and the way advertisers exploited the mysterious science of electricity.

The cheaper consumer products served a democratizing function as they narrowed the gap between the working class and the middle class. One of the most important consumer goods was clothing, as the final selection suggests.

THE MESSAGE WAS ELECTRIC

Pamela W. Lurito

Images of electricity were first exploited to sell Victorian products; such advertising helped give electricity itself a high profile and promote technological progress.

Nobody sells electricity anymore. So taken for granted is it in our lives that it goes unmentioned and uncredited when electrical appliance manufacturers tout their wares. Even power companies now "sell" efficiency and goodwill—it is no longer considered appropriate to encourage the public to purchase electric power. Yet it has not always been this way. Indeed, electricity has been one of the most exciting and telling themes in American advertising.

Because electricity was a prime factor in technological developments from the mid-1800s, onward, popular images of it reflected very significant attitudes of the public toward progress in general. Advertisements of this critical era demonstrate the transition from the earliest perceptions of electricity as an awesome, quasi-magical panacea, to the 1930s view of it as a useful, convenient servant—remarkable, to be sure, but quite tame and predictable.

Both before and after the technological advances resulting in the practical, household availability of electricity, its powers attracted entrepreneurial attention. As a theme in advertising, electricity has promoted a host of products, events, and processes—some having nothing to do with electrical use—ranging from quack or specious implementations to modern appliances and power generation. Regardless of the potential for real benefit, all the advertisements shared a fundamental marketing appeal to popular hopes and shared ambitions for better health, welfare, and living standards through progress.

There were two major phases in the use of electricity as an advertising tool that are evident in advertisements from the mid-nineteenth century through the 1930s, each definable in terms of its target audience's attitude and understanding regarding electricity. The first audience was the general public before it had accumulated the education and experience necessary to assess electricity's realistic capabilities. The second audience evolved from the first as consumers of the early twentieth century learned to appreciate the true capabilities and limitations of electrical applications. The images of electricity in advertisements directed toward these two popular audiences dramatically reflect this growing sophistication.

Advertisements of the first phase were directed toward a nineteenth-century market where experiences with electricity were limited to hearsay, popular publications, theater lighting, occasional public utilities and transportation, the telegraph, and carnival-type demonstrations. To this audience, the powers of electricity were of a magical nature. Advertisers took advantage of this credulity by offering to bring the "magical spark" home to a willing and eager population. Although practical household applications of electricity were still well in the future for most people, the eagerness to make use of this highly publicized technological wonder was not overlooked by clever innovators and enterprising sales people. Whether promising miraculous cures or pointing out wonderful associations between the powers of lightning and electricity in general, the ads directed toward this market were startling, exciting, and dramatic.

There existed a profound social and cultural foundation for what seems to us now to have been unaccountable mass flights of fancy. The nineteenth century was characterized by its interest in and expectations of progress in all fields of science. William Ellery Channing wrote in 1841 that "Science has now left her retreats. . . . Through the press, discoveries and theories, since the monopolies of philosophers, have become the property of the multitudes." Public lectures and educational and self-improvement societies flourished throughout the nineteenth century and, together with the press and advertising promotions, stimulated the public imagination. Reinforcing the interest in science was a faith in progress that became the prevailing feature of American culture during the Victorian period—a confidence that real benefits would come to both individuals and society.

In this environment of hopefulness, the consumer advertisements of this era that used electricity as their theme either promised novel "electrical" means of solving old problems, or associated electricity and its wonders with standard and accepted products. Thus we find, on one hand, ads for every variety of patent-medicine electroquackery, as highlighted in *Spectrum* in November 1978. On the other, there were advertisements for tobacco, razors, and other existing products featuring the electricity theme. The promotions of the first phase ran the gamut from wild claims and potentially harmful devices to the innocuous "buzzword" association of electricity with otherwise unremarkable products.

Electroquackery included the application of the electrical theme to traditional patent medicines such as bitters and cough drops. Considerably more dramatic were the patent medicines and devices that promised to cure by the application of electricity or magnetism to the body. This concern was exploited for a variety of objects ranging from "Magnetic Hair Pins" and "Voltaic Electric Plasters" to so-called electric corsets, toothbrushes, belts, and assorted electric-shock devices. As Alfred P. Morgan, a student of the history of science, noted in *The Pageant of Electricity,* "when medicine was almost a total failure, it is not surprising that . . . anything, so supernatural as electricity and magnetism should have been hopefully examined. . . ."

During the Victorian period, the consuming public—and most likely promoters themselves—did not know precisely what electricity *could do,* and consequently it did not know what electricity could not do. Imagination, ambition, and hopefulness, supplemented by a generous portion of greed, permitted free rein in setting the limits of claims for electrical potency. Furthermore, as nineteenth-century Americans eagerly sought some benefit from the developments they saw springing up all about them, they were caught in a frustrating bind. In this transition era, people were well aware of technological advances in electricity, but they were impatient for practical domestic and health benefits for the ordinary citizen. Whatever else they did, all the products of this phase gave everyone something "electrical to take home as a share in progress."

A shocking Cupid: The anticipations and frustrations to which the Victorian electroquack advertising appealed could result in odd contradictions amidst the enthusiastic acclamations for the power of electricity. The German Electric Belt Agency of Brooklyn proclaimed "The Electric Era" in its extensive advertising. This was, in fact, the title of this 1891 pamphlet.

"The German Electro-Galvanic Belt" was claimed as a discovery "of more real benefit to the human race than all the others mentioned put together." Had this invention indeed cured all that pamphlet claimed, this might have been a credible boast. After 23 pages of testimonial and descriptions of the care and scientific expertise that combined to create the assorted types of belts, we are told that "Magnetism and Electricty are two entirely different things. A little horseshoe magnet you buy in the toy store will spin a compass all day but no one ever claimed it had the power to cure disease." Yet, continuing in the same tone of pontification, but with less veracity, "Electricity is a subtle fluid that is released by the decomposition of some metal, and it cannot be generated unless there is some form of battery used to produce the current." While Dr. Scott was not specifically named in the course of all this explanation, he was no doubt among the "bogus imitators" against whom the case was so firmly stated. One wonders if Dr. Scott was perturbed over this assessment of his promotional methods. Did the explanation and claims win over a clientele? We only know that the German Electric Belt Agency operated for over 20 years. But, then, so did Dr. Scott.

The booklet most eloquently illustrates the bind of the Victorian's transitional mentality as it juxtaposes mystical and realistic symbolism. On the front cover, a Venus-like figure reclines amidst ballooning light bulbs with a generator of sorts at her feet. Cupid, out of his usual element, carries a ticker tape to this goddess for her delight! Returning to reality, the back cover illustrates several electrical inventions. Even here, however, it seems that the collection of images was deemed incomplete without a final punctuation mark: one last bolt of lightning.

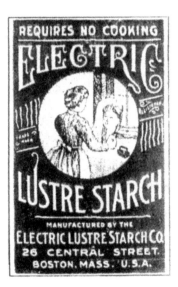

Inducing quality: Unlike the unadulterated quacks, many entrepreneurs elected merely to associate a common product with the theme of electrical progress. By virtue of the connotation alone, these advertisers sought a share of existing markets. The products illustrated here—"Electric Lustre Starch" and "Electric Brand" canned vegetables—are just the beginning of a long and diverse list. Others included "Electric Spices," "Young American Electric Sparklers," and "Electric Baking Soda." Lightning bolts or sparks on many packages and advertisements were de rigueur.

As comical and fantastic as some of the Victorian exploitations of the electricity theme seem to us today, they did serve a valuable function beyond that of momentarily allaying frustration. In aggregate, the advertisements developed popular awareness of electricity. While they contributed little to a critical understanding of what electricity would someday mean to American lifestyles, these advertisements did help bring the image of electricity to the public. They also fed the enthusiasm and anticipation that would contribute to the success of the twentieth-century power and appliance enterprises.

Public attitudes, aided by advertisements, made the transition from fantasy to practicality. A gradual shift in advertising saw campaigns designed to educate the public and to stir up its interest in genuinely practical applications of progress in electrical technology. This shift marked the beginning of the second phase of advertising that was directed to the "modern" twentieth-century consumer audience. Though a few promoters continued with the unrealistic and fanciful themes described above, such ads were rarely found in national media after World War I. As a rule, advertising campaigns directed toward the increasingly knowledgeable, post-Victorian audience all shared a distinguishing characteristic: an emphasis on respectability. This was in part a reaction against Victorian electroquackery and other overreaching speculations. While these new campaigns sometimes exaggerated the life-style benefits that might accrue from the use of their products, the ads were careful to exercise restraint on the claims that could be judged objectively. As they built up a new market with broad and long-range prospects, these advertisers were quite aware of the advantages of a technically responsible program that fostered public confidence.

Many features of this post-Victorian period of electricity advertising were due to the changed nature of the businesses doing the promoting. The multiplicity of small entrepreneurs typical of the nineteenth century was overshadowed by fewer but larger companies, usually engaged in power production or appliance manufacturing. Some of the power-generating companies such as Westinghouse and General Electric also manufactured appliances to help extend the use of electricity. Westinghouse went one step further in its promotions by starting up radio station KDKA in 1920. It was built and initially operated without commercial messages solely to give people a reason to buy and use radios. Most of the twentieth-century ventures required immensely greater capital investment and research programs than did the Victorian products exploiting the electricity theme. The competitive intensity and long-range goals of these larger companies were also incentives to responsible advertising.

The appliance and power-generating industries found it important to communicate the merits of respectable promotional strategies to middlemen dealing directly with the public. They directed many advertisements to the retailers through the influential trade journal, *Electrical Merchandising*. For example, in 1919, General Electric emphasized to retailers that Mazda (the trademark of Edison's light bulb and lighting appliances) was "not the name of a thing, but the mark of service." The Hoover Vacuum Co. squarely addressed the issue of dignified sales technique with the directive: "In selling Hoover there is no cleverness necessary. Just run your Hoover over."

In the early stages of this second phase there were also many advertisements for transition products that employed both electricity and either coal or gas. Most in this category publicized the advantages of adding electricity to an already well known product. These advertisements tended to be the most conservative of all, not challenging the old, but simply offering a new feature.

In early consumer advertising campaigns to develop markets for their products, the power and appliance companies had to keep in mind that the public was just learning to appreciate the benefits of electricity. There were a number of advertisements intended to educate as well as to tempt the consumer by illustrating and describing worthy applications of electricity. One innovation in attracting subscribers to the power companies was the "Wire-Your-Home League" first sponsored by the Philadelphia Electric Co. in 1916. This was a combination of public relations and advertising intended to "interest the housewife in electric service" through educational and economical appeals. This type of campaign was adopted by many other power companies around the nation by 1919.

During the first two decades of this century the evolution to modern ideas about electricity was far from complete. Indeed, there were still opulent displays of electricity's brilliance that far surpassed those of the Victorian years. The most exciting of these were in the 1910s, a transitional period in the growing public awareness of electricity's powers. Among the most spectacular of these events was "America's Electrical Week," Dec. 7–9, 1916. The events included parades, pamphlets distributed by the hundreds of thousands, media releases, politicians' praises, banquets, and special-price sales to the customer for electrical services. Climaxing the week's activities was an elaborate celebration for Woodrow Wilson's lighting of the Statue of Liberty, followed by an "electrical-vehicle parade."

The editors of *Electrical Merchandising* encouraged its readers to sponsor a campaign to "Brighten up for the Boys Return" at the close of World War I. These celebrations included huge flags made up of incandescent bulbs and every other conceivable way of giving the boys an "electrical welcome."

These twentieth-century displays and their nineteenth-century predecessors differed not only in extravagance, but also in that most of the modern displays were supported and often directly sponsored by enterprising power companies whose intentions were to sell more than just seats to the spectacles. A national organization, the Society for Electrical Development, inspired and coordinated many of these projects. And the cover of patriotism and community involvement gave an essential aura of propriety to the showmanship.

Relating to this were a variety of campaigns to appeal to the self-image of those members of society who could afford electrification before 1930. Many American advertisers upon entering the twentieth century frequently tried to don a much-needed air of respectability by replacing the charming, albeit naive, pictures in Victorian advertisements with more "sophisticated" works of fine art and highly stylized commercial art. This search for artistic prestige and esteem may have resulted from the Art Nouveau craze of the 1890s, and the continued application of high artistic standards and experimentation in many advertising designs lasted well into the Art Deco era of the 1920s and 1930s.

One of the leaders in this trend was General Electric with its Mazda campaigns. Throughout the 1920s and into the 1930s, Mazda ads and packaging designs featured popular commercial artists and art styles. In his early days, for instance, Norman Rockwell created many ads for Mazda, and Maxfield Parrish became noted for his uniquely toned Mazda posters.

Electricity advertising also used increasingly sophisticated psychological tools after World War I. These included deliberate appeals to personal fears and concerns for family safety. The anxieties generated by the suggestive advertisements were instantly allayed by assurances of the safety of electricity.

Frequently, electricity was compared to the pollution and dangerous alternatives for lighting and heat. For example, none too subtle was an advertisement from the early 1920s for Eveready Flashlights that reminded the farmer of the dangers of the lantern left in the barn. Though it was unlikely that a farmer would feel his way in the dark after leaving his lighted lantern behind in the straw, the point was legitimate.

Effective advertisements play on both objective and subjective concerns of their target markets. The Victorian quack and buzz-word advertising did both, combining lists of benefits with the drama of sparks, lightning bolts, and the allusions to progress that were so popular. This combination faded as electricity's true benefits began to infiltrate people's domestic lives at the turn of the century. For many years, the advertisements for consumers' electrical goods and services avoided emotionalism—the objective benefits they offered were remarkable enough. Furthermore, conservative appeals were appropriate when heavy-handed promises were under increasing criticism. A legitimate new technology had to avoid any tarnish on its respectable image. Therefore, between 1900 and the mid-1920s, the very real call to modernity was the prime appeal electrical companies made to popular needs.

In the meantime, the advertising industry of the 1920s was learning to use drama as it had never been used before. The appeal of modernity was no longer a helpful suggestion but became a command. Gradually, highly subjective needs and fears were targeted. One dramatic scene in a magazine advertisement of the 1920s illustrated the physical danger of doing without proper electrical equipment. Playing on fears related to an even newer technology—this electrical product gained in respectability. Thanks to the Conaphore headlights of the Corning Glass Co., the automobile and its passengers were saved from certain disaster at a railroad crossing. The appeal to popular concerns began in Victorian advertising, of course, but the technique was perfected in the 1920s with ads like this. That the advertisement itself had created or amplified the concerns did not lessen the promised capability of the products to assuage them. Ruth Schwartz Cowan and other contemporary historians have effectively documented many of the strategies used by advertisers of that era to draw emotional responses [see "To Probe Further" for references]. The new sources of anxiety included guilt, embarrassment, and the needs for approval and love. The electrical industries picked up on these sales-motivating factors with predictable results.

The second period of advertising electricity had to persuade homeworkers and builders to invest in wiring, appliances, and power-company subscriptions. The advertisements and promotions that did this were attractive and persuasive. Still, not even the sum total of these efforts seems sufficient to account for the rapid growth of electrification and the popular acceptance of its merits. In part, the explanation is in the objective advantages perceived by people as they witnessed electrification in public places and in the homes of others, and as public figures and journalists praised its benefits.

As the commercially motivated variable in the edification of the consumer, advertising reflected and affected the entire transition of popular attitudes toward electricity. The number of non-electrical products associated with electricity reached a peak in the 1880s and 1890s, at precisely the time when most people would have had the greatest awareness of electricity without having household use of it. After that point, advertising enlarged and motivated the public's access to the practical applications of electricity. The result was a shift in advertising emphasis from the Victorian drama of the captured spark to the personalized dramas calculated to promote electricity's realistic uses.

TO PROBE FURTHER

A History of Electricity by Edward Canby (New York: Hawthorn Books, 1963) and *The Pageant of Electricity* by Alfred P. Morgan (New York: Appleton-Century Co., 1939) are valuable background resources; both convey a sense of wonder about and respect for electricity.

Nothing recalls the excitement of the era more than the hard-to-find original materials. An exuberant German catalogue is *Die zweite industrielle Revolution: Frankfurt und das Elektrizität, 1800–1914* (Frankfurt: Historisches Museum Frankfurt, 1981). (Dr. Bayla Singer of the Franklin Institute recognized the four ladies pictured on the Electric Mixture Tobacco tin from the catalogue and alerted the author to it. It appears that the image was originally drawn from a ballet that celebrated the triumph of progress.)

Another category of sources focuses on the intellectual and cultural history of scientific ideas held by the nontechnologist. *The Growth of American Thought* by Merle Curti, third edition (New York: Harper and Books, 1964) is an excellent foundation, and Chapter 13 is especially helpful. Donald Zochert's "Science and the Common Man in Ante-Bellum America," *ISIS,* (December 1974) details the ways in which ordinary people became interested and involved in science before the advent of mass education and media.

A fine history of advertising itself is *The Story of Advertising* by James Playsted Wood (New York: Ronald Press Co., 1958).

Within the last decade, there has been excellent scholarship that ties together the histories of advertising and technology. A central work in this new field is "The 'Industrial Revolution' in the Home Household Technology and Social Change in the 20th Century" by Ruth Schwartz Cowan, *Technology and Culture,* Vol. XXIV, no. 2 (April 1983). The literature in this genre is exciting and growing fast.

Nothing is more intriguing, however, than the history of quack medicines and their promotion. With neither legal nor social restraints to inhibit them, hucksters probed the limits of human credulity. There are many entertaining accounts of the exploits of nostrum peddlers, but few approach the reliability of *The Toadstool Millionaires: A Social History of Patent Medicines in America* by James Harvey Young (Princeton: Princeton University Press, 1961). Devoted specifically to the electricity-related "cures" is the excellent article by Dennis Stillings and Nancy Roth, "When electroquackery thrived," *IEEE Spectrum,* Vol. XV, no. 11 (November 1978).

12

WE WERE WHAT WE WORE

Ink Mendelsohn

A Chicago judge ruled in 1908 that a nightgown was a luxury, not a necessity, and there-upon issued a restraining order forbidding an eighteen-year-old girl from buying one against her father's wishes. "The only possible use of a nightgown," the judge explained, "is to keep off flies and mosquitoes, and the bedclothes will do just as well." The father testified: "She never wore a nightgown in her life, and neither did her parents. She's been associating with nifty people, that's the trouble with her." Clearly, as recently as this century, all Americans did not enjoy freedom of dress.

By the 1920s, however, production and distribution of ready-to-wear clothing had reached a stage that enabled most men and women to dress stylishly at moderate cost. As a Midwestern businessman observed, "I used to be able to tell something about the back-ground of a girl applying for a job as a stenographer by her clothes, but today I often have to wait till she speaks, shows a gold tooth or otherwise gives me a second clew."

This egalitarian confusion of class distinctions would seem to reflect the ideals of the early Republic, but in fact, it had evolved only gradually. For much of our history, according to Claudia Kidwell, the head curator of the Smithsonian Institution's Costume Division, "Clothing's most pervading function has been to declare status." From the beginning Amer-icans have loved fine clothes. In 1676 Hannah Lyman and thirty-five other young women of Northampton, Massachusetts, were arrested for overdressing—specifically for wearing hoods. A defiant Hannah appeared in court in the offending garment and was censured and fined on the spot for "wearing silk in a flonting manner, in an offensive way. . . ." Along with their style of dress, the colonists had brought from England laws like the 1621 Virginia resolution to "supress excess in cloaths" and to prevent anyone but high government offi-cials from wearing "gold in their cloaths."

Declaring its "utter detestation and dislike" of men and women of "mean condition, education and calling" who would wear the "garb of gentlemen," the Massachusetts Gen-eral Court in 1639 particularly prohibited Puritans of low estate from wearing "immoder-ate great breeches, knots of riban, silk roses, double ruffles and capes." Women of low rank were forbidden silk hoods and scarves, as well as short sleeves "whereby the naked-ness of the arms may be discovered"—the daring new fashion popular among the upper classes.

Such legislation hardly seems to have been necessary for the somber Puritans of popular imagery. Yet rich, elegant, and stylish clothing was as important to New England merchants as it was to Virginia cavaliers or to the good dames of New Amsterdam. Although the Puritan Church did in fact preach simplicity of dress, it was widely ignored by a flock that counted fine clothing as an outward sign of God's favor. Eventually the laws attempting to dictate dress in the American colonies proved unenforceable and were abandoned.

This meant that for New Englanders of means, plain and dull-colored dress was not among the hardships of the New World. Bills and inventories record "pinck hose," "green sleeves," "a Scarlet petticoat with Silver Lace." One Massachusetts governor was noted for the gold-fringed gloves he wore, and another ordered several dozen scarlet coats to be sent to him from England.

Shipping lists, portraits, advertisements, court records, and tailors' bills give evidence of the fashion ties that bound prosperous American colonists to their counterparts overseas. Norwich garters—decorative ornaments worn by Sir Walter Raleigh—came over on the *Mayflower,* and a Madame Padishal of Plymouth, Massachusetts, posed for her portrait in a low-necked black velvet gown with a lace whisk to cover her bare neck, the latest court fashion in France.

Class distinctions had not been left on Old World shores, and fashion was clear evidence of social standing. Affluent American settlers eagerly sought news of style changes in Europe.

Margaret Winthrop, the wife of the governor of Massachusetts, insisted on "the civilest fashion now in use" when she ordered gowns from John Smith, the family tailor in London. But at that distance even personal tailoring could not guarantee good fit, as Smith made clear in a letter accompanying a coat for the governor: "Good Mr. Winthrop, I have, by Mr. Downing's directions sent you a coat. . . . For the fittness I am a little vncerteyne, but if it be too bigg or too little it is esie to amend, vnder the arme to take in or let out the lyning; the outside may be let out in the gathering or taken in also without any prejudice."

Not all clothing in colonial America, however, was made by a tailor. Elegantly dressed ladies or gentlemen in silks and brocades from London were outnumbered by craftsmen in leather aprons, female servants in simple petticoats and jackets and the men in livery, seamen and farmers coming to market in homespun trousers, and, in the South, slaves in hand-me-downs. A person's clothing indelibly marked an eighteenth-century man or woman.

Housewives made most of the clothing worn by average people. Using both imported and domestic fabrics, colonial women made their own clothes and their children's, and such simply constructed men's clothes as undergarments, shirts, and trousers. But a fashionably cut coat or smooth-fitting breeches were beyond their skills. By the second half of the eighteenth century, breeches were worn so skintight that—the story goes—in Alexandria, Virginia, they were hung on hooks and the wearer-to-be put them on by mounting three steps and letting himself into them from above. Small wonder, then, that the making of jacket, waistcoat, and breeches was left to the art of the tailor.

Preindustrial American clothing was mostly made to order. The well-to-do kept measurements on file with a London tailor, ordering, perhaps, as one gentleman did, "A Suit of Lemmon Collour Brocaded or flowered Lustering the best that can be had for Ten Shillings pr yard made Fashionable and Genteel to the Inclosed measures. . . ." And Americans—even after the Revolution—announced their stations in life sartorially. High-hatting went to a ridiculous extreme. Martha Washington may have worn a modest and democratic mob-cap, but hats worn by her contemporaries abounded with flowers, vegetables, windmills (that turned), shepherds with their sheep, and, in one case, a naval battle featuring a spun-glass French ship of war. Feathers as much as a yard and a half high topped turbans and other hats. At a New Year's Assembly in 1814, according to a news account of the day, Dol-ley Madison's "towering feathers above the excessive throng distinctly pointed out her sta-tion wherever she moved."

"Do not conceive that fine clothes make fine men any more than fine feathers make fine birds," George Washington advised his nephew Bushrod. But Washington himself loved fine clothes and believed that the dignity of a new nation depended to a degree on the outward appearance of its leaders. Records show that John Hancock owned a scarlet velvet suit. And on July 4, 1776, the Declaration of Independence wasn't even mentioned in Thomas Jeffer-son's daybook. He made only one entry that day: "For Seven pair of Womens Gloves, 20 shillings."

Not all Americans followed the latest fashions. Benjamin Franklin, a plain dresser him-self, urged his wife and daughter to eschew their feathers and silks for honest calico. And at Harvard College a dress code prohibited "Schollars" from wearing "strange, ruffian-like, or new-fangled fashions." But it is doubtful whether the "Schollars" abandoned their "lavish dress" any more than the Franklin women turned in their silks or the young Puritan Hannah Lyman gave up her hood.

By the end of the eighteenth century, class distinctions in dress were beginning to be threatened by new developments in technology. On December 20, 1791, Samuel Slater har-nessed the waterwheel at Carpenter's Clothier Mill in Pawtucket, Rhode Island, to the falls of the Blackstone River and thereby brought the Industrial Revolution to this country. Slater, a young English immigrant, combined waterpower and a superior system of cotton yarn manufacture to produce the first power-spun yarn in America. A few years later Eli Whitney's cotton gin pulled the fibers away from the cotton seeds—a technique that made the mass cultivation of cotton economically feasible. By 1814 the Boston businessman Fran-cis Cabot Lowell had collaborated with the machinist Paul Moody to perfect a power loom superior to the English models. At Lowell's Boston Manufacturing Company of Waltham, for the first time in history, every process of clothmaking was performed under one roof by power machinery.

An ample supply of fabric encouraged an emerging ready-to-wear industry. Early in the nineteenth century clothing manufacture also began to move to the factory, where, as the century progressed, steadily improved machinery was to make much shorter work of what hands alone could do.

One of the earliest clothing manufactories was the United States Army Clothing Estab-lishment, begun in Philadelphia at the start of the War of 1812 to meet the need for enlisted men's uniforms. It organized production into several key operations. The uniform was cut from a standardized pattern; the pieces were packaged with buttons, padding, lining, facing cloth, and thread and then sent out for sewing to "widows and other meritorious females," who could by "close application . . . make twelve shirts per week and the same number of pants." Civilian manufacturers followed the model of inside and outside labor division pro-vided by this "immense Government Tailor's Shop."

Military organization may have been precise, but the fit of the uniforms was not. The real hero of the ready-to-wear revolution was the custom tailor. This specialist, who had once sewn only for those able to afford his individualized services, rescued ready-made clothing from the realm of "slops"—cheap, coarse, and ill-fitting garments that marked their wearers as second-class citizens. Early in the nineteenth century custom tailors began to modify their techniques in order to manufacture ready-made clothing that was cheaper than custom, yet fashionable and reasonably well fitting. The tailor had a new weapon: the tape measure. "Scientific principles" helped tailors establish standardized rules for measurement that meant they could make not only styles for individuals but apparel for everybody. By 1832 most tailors carried a large stock of ready-made clothing.

"Clothing is created out of motivation," says Claudia Kidwell. "The wealthy wanted to maintain distinctions. Everyone else wanted to close the gap. When the working man took off his apron, he wanted to be part of the gentry. He wore frockcoat, vest and trousers to work, then took off his coat and rolled up his sleeves."

By mid-century the editor Horace Greeley could write, "No distinction of clothing between gentlemen and otherwise can be seen in the United States." Men—but not women—could purchase in a range of prices a great variety of garments manufactured in Baltimore, Newark, Albany, Rochester, Philadelphia, and New York.

Representative of the Eastern manufactories was the New York retail clothing shop founded in 1818 by Henry Sands Brooks as a "gentlemen's store run by gentlemen" and by 1850 known as Brooks Bros. Before the widespread use of the sewing machine in clothing manufacture, cloth was inspected and cut, and trimmings for garments provided, by a small number of people in the shop. A pool of more than a thousand seamstresses on the outside sewed the pieces together by hand and added the finishing touches. Returned and found satisfactory, the garments then went to the sales department. In 1859 Brooks Bros. advertised a "large and complete assortment of Ready-Made Clothing and Furnishings/Goods of superior style and make."

Thanks to ready-made clothes, a common style of dressing found favor across the land. Clothes made on the Eastern seaboard were available across the country. In Philadelphia the Clothing Palace offered "the most extensive assortment and the finest quality of READY-MADE GARMENTS for the lowest cash price in plain figures." Alfred Munroe of New Orleans challenged anyone to match his twenty-three hundred coats, nineteen hundred pantaloons, fifteen hundred vests, and eight thousand shirts. San Francisco's Keyes & Co. advertised "$100,000 stock in the very latest styles."

For promotional vigor, however, it was hard to top Boston's George Simmons who described his store, Oak Hall, as a "Spacious Magnificent & Inviting TEMPLE, the Centre of Trade, the Wonder of an Admiring World." In pursuit of "large sales, small profits and quick returns," Simmons sent up balloons announcing bargains and threw free overcoats from his roof. Simmons boasted of the "largest and best assortment of Ready-Made Clothing and Furnishing Goods to be found in the United States." Here "the Man of Fashion, the Professional, Gentlemen Clerks with moderate salaries, Merchants, Mechanics and Farmers, Military and Naval Officers" could find "any article from a pair of Gloves to a superfine Dress or Frock coat." In short, Oak Hall and its counterparts had something for everybody—as long as everybody was male. Women would have to wait several decades to participate in the democracy of dress.

Ready-made clothing for women at mid-century consisted of the one-size-fits-all cloak, worn since the seventeenth century, and the corset. Blouses, skirts, and dresses that were complexly constructed, individually fitted, and subject to changes in style were still too formidable a challenge for clothing manufacturers before the Civil War. Women depended on their own sewing skills or on dressmakers, who were numerous and charged little, for the better part of their wardrobes.

"A Victorian lady stayed at home and stuck to her needlework," according to Pamela Puryear, the author of *Dressing Victorian* (1987). Puryear became interested in historical clothing when she moved into her great-grandparents' home in Navasota, Texas, and found her great-grandmother's 1873 wedding dress. A cousin then gave her twenty-two trunks of clothes belonging to his grandparents and great-grandparents. Puryear discovered that in Texas Victorian women in a reasonably comfortable economic position dressed the same way as women in Boston or New York. "Clothing revealed a Victorian woman's station in life," Puryear writes. "Women wearing a tight corset, at least four petticoats, dresses with tight elbows and gloves *inside* the house, didn't do the cleaning and the washing. What you wore was you."

Hallie Gudger of Old Washington, Texas, wore for her portrait a dress with a satin bodice, double ruffled organdy at the neck, satin rosettes on the skirt and on the sleeves, a draped overskirt, an underskirt, and a bustle. Mary Frances Wickes of Houston was photographed in the late 1850s in a dress of "black silk with gathers in the bodice and triangular black gimp edging. The sleeves were sewn with a geometric interlace of a lighter-colored braid," probably done with the new sewing machine.

Between 1842 and 1895 the United States issued more than seven thousand patents for sewing machines and their accessories. Elias Howe and Isaac Singer fought for the right to be called the machine's inventor. But it was Allen B. Wilson who created the machine first adopted by the clothing manufacturers. A shirt that had taken fourteen hours and twenty-six minutes to sew by hand could be sewn on the "Wheeler and Wilson" in one hour and sixteen minutes. In the 1860s Brooks Bros. reported that a good overcoat, which had once required six days of sewing, could be done in half that time by machine.

Mechanization revolutionized the garment industry in the late nineteenth century. Powerful machines that were able to slice through a hundred layers of cloth at a time brought the speed of cutting clothes in line with the sewing operation. Completely automatic looms meant one weaver could produce four hundred yards of fabric an hour. Improved cylinder presses had the capability of printing from two to twelve colors simultaneously. As calico florals rolled off the cylinders, one of the most expensive fabrics of the eighteenth century became one of the cheapest of the nineteenth.

Almost all the processes of clothing manufacture had moved into the machine age. Only pressing was still done by hand. The heavy tailor's iron held its own until the early twentieth century, when Adon J. Hoffman of Syracuse dislocated his shoulder and invented a steam pressing machine operated by a foot pedal.

Foot power and hand power were needed in ever-greater quantity as production in the garment industry accelerated. New Americans, by and large, did the job. In the 1840s Irish tailors, cutters, and seamstresses came to America in unprecedented numbers. Later in the decade German tailors arrived and with their wives and children produced clothing at home. But it was the great migration from eastern and southern Europe—Poland, Russia, and

Italy—beginning in 1880 that provided the garment industry with the cheap labor that permitted mass production in this country. Beryl Fried, a founder of the Cloakmaker's Union, described working conditions as he knew them in 1885 and as they continued to be until immigrant clothing workers formed their own union in 1914: "Eighteen men and women were crowded into a small dark room: operators, pressers and finishers. During the season there was no time limit. We started working at dawn and stopped at ten or eleven at night. If a worker happened to be an hour late he was met by the others with ridicule, 'Here comes the doctor.' In their conception only a doctor could permit himself the luxury of sleeping so late."

In a crazy quilt of inside and outside shops, factory and home production, contracting and subcontracting, the men, women, and children of the garment industry worked long hours for low wages in overcrowded, unsanitary, and unsafe conditions. By their toil they gave a new word to the English language—sweatshop—and they gave to this country an immense variety of clothes that the majority of Americans could afford.

During the late 1890s the Sears, Roebuck catalog listed men's suits costing from ninety-eight cents to twenty dollars, and on a single day Sears sold nine thousand of them. The "trusty blue serge suit" was worn by store clerks, office workers, professionals, and businessmen, so that Giuseppe Giacosa, an Italian who visited in 1908, was struck by the fact that "no European would be able to pick out by eye who there represents the infinite variety of professions, trades, states, fortune, culture, education that may be encountered among the whole people . . . the shape and texture of the clothing in all shows the same care, the same cut, and almost the same easy circumstances." While visiting Chicago's slaughter-houses, he saw the workers at day's end change their bloody clothes and emerge "a lordly collection of gentlemen" in "handsome ties and plaid jackets."

Even the shirt, that once reliable indicator of social status, dividing white collar from blue, no longer divided men—at least from a distance. Shirts with detachable collars and cuffs, as advertised by the Arrow Collar man, meant that every man could without excessive laundry costs wear what appeared to be a clean white shirt every day. Working men's blue shirts turned up as sportswear along with shirts in a kaleidoscopic array of colors and patterns. Some sense of proportion was retained, however. Boston's Jordan Marsh department store in 1883 announced selections that included "mostly neat designs, such as stripes, figures, spots etc. Large figures, stripes, pug dogs, armchairs etc. have been avoided."

Clothes even for occasions too formal for the trusty blue serge were available off the rack and were adapted to the American love of comfort. Thanks to Griswold Lorillard, who in 1886 appeared in a tailless evening coat at the Tuxedo Park Club's formal autumn ball, the tuxedo became part of America's sartorial style.

In the years before World War I, sports and leisure activities swept across America. One of the nation's largest manufacturers of clothing, Browning King, proclaimed, "In these days of almost universal wheeling no man's or boy's wardrobe is complete without a bicycle suit." There were bathing suits, tennis suits, yachting suits, and golf clothes. But there were no blue jeans. Levi's waist pantaloons or overalls—in blue denim or brown duck—were still strictly work clothes.

Working clothes began to be important for women, too, after the Civil War. Many women came into the business world as "typewriters" to operate that clacking invention, and as retail establishments proliferated, there was a need for shopgirls. Thousands of immigrant women worked in factories. With no time to sew or suffer endless fittings at a dressmaker's, women needed ready-to-wear clothing. A women's garment industry emerged and grew, until by 1919 it exceeded the men's clothing industry in number of establishments and value of production.

Carson Pirie Scott & Co. of Chicago explained that its women's suits were "what the name was meant to imply—strictly man-tailored." But when the woman-on-the-go removed the jacket of her tailored suit, she stood revealed in shirtwaist and skirt, the American girl immortalized by the illustrator Charles Dana Gibson. For the first time in America, women had the equivalent of the trusty blue suit—a uniform that blurred social and economic distinctions. Once the basic investment in the suit had been made, the look could be changed for a mere dollar—the price of a blouse pleated at the shoulders "giving the pronounced Gibson effect."

Now there was a new pastime in America: shopping. "Consumer palaces" began to appear in America's cities in response to the large assortment of factory-made goods that were being produced. A typical department store early in the twentieth century was reported to have six miles of sales counters. In one window display, Jordan Marsh re-created the hall of Henri II's palace at Fontainebleau out of "ladies', misses', and children's silk, lisle, and cotton hose." Another store urged everybody to come in: "We want you to feel perfectly at home and free to inspect the goods and ask for information, regardless of whether you wish to buy or not."

"Before department stores," Kidwell points out, "if you wanted to see luxury goods, you had to be deemed a suitable client at a small specialty store." The department stores went out of their way to suit everyone. Wanamaker's held white sales; R. H. Macy & Co. gave away fans with its picture on them; and Jordan Marsh & Co. sent out free catalogs for mail-order service.

By 1872 small-town residents and farmers could also see all manner of goods simply by looking in a catalog. Aaron Montgomery Ward's first "catalog" was a one-page price list. But by 1875 it had grown to 152 pages listing 3,899 items including: #1399—striped velvet vests for $2.50 each; #1406—Black Union Cassimere suit for $12.00; and #1456—2 pairs of Blue Denim Overalls for $1.25. Sears, Roebuck and Co., proudly calling itself the "Cheapest Supply House on Earth," had a 1,120-page catalog in 1898. Mail-order catalogs were the first outlets for women's ready-to-wear clothing, and by the early twentieth century some ten million Americans shopped by mail.

By 1920 almost any American was able to acquire any article of apparel he or she was able to afford. The nation's garment industry had successfully achieved mass production of clothing at low-to-moderate prices. Now that the national closet could easily be filled, the question became, What would Americans choose to hang there?

Whatever they chose, it would soon go out of style. In the past, styles had changed slowly. Now, with almost unlimited capacity for production, there had to be a reason for buying new clothes, even if the closet was full. Fashions began to change with every season.

To report the rapidly changing styles, fashion communication itself became an industry. In the twenties Paris fashions were reported by newspapers all over the country. Papers ran fashion ads and featured fashion columns. There were fashion magazines for every audience. *Vogue* wanted to help the women of "more than average wealth and refinement with their clothes and social life." Magazines like *Woman's Home Companion* were content to offer advice to the millions of women with average wealth—the housewives of America. *Glamour of Hollywood,* later simply *Glamour,* was subtitled "For the Girl with a Job." And the males of America had *Esquire,* which, when begun in 1933, set as its goal "the establishment of elegance."

Before long the fashions these magazines were reporting came not from Paris but from Hollywood. When Clark Gable took off his shirt in *It Happened One Night* (1934) and revealed a bare chest, undershirt sales in America plummeted. And when Joan Crawford wore an Adrian-designed dress with multiruffled, puffed sleeves in *Letty Lynton* (1932), the story of a "girl who loved too often and too well," American women everywhere bought dresses with multiruffled, puffed sleeves. Who needed Paris when for $18.74 Macy's had a copy of the very gown Rita Hayworth wore to marry Aly Khan?

In the 1930s not only Hollywood but the rest of California, with its mild climate and casual way of life, began to influence what other Americans wore. California companies made an American contribution to international clothing history—sportswear. Even the French were impressed.

Levi Strauss, one of California's first clothing manufacturers, had gotten together with a tailor, Jacob Davis, in 1873 to give the world blue jeans. But not until the 1930s, when Western movies became popular and Easterners began visiting dude ranches in the West, did America decide that jeans were romantic. Soon young Americans made these guaranteed-to-shrink-and-fade blue denim pants the ultimate sartorial symbol of social equality.

Teen-agers all across the country began to wear blue jeans. In Los Angeles, in the 1940s, high schoolers walked around with one hand permanently protecting the right buttock. The little red Levi's tab, the first external manufacturer's brand, was a lure to razor-wielding classmates who collected them. In the mid-fifties, James Dean, in the movie *Rebel without a Cause,* and Marlon Brando, in *The Wild Ones,* turned T-shirts and blue jeans into the emblems of youthful rebellion. In the sixties and seventies T-shirts and blue jeans became the universal uniform of social protest. "Blue jeans were adopted by the 'enemy'—adults," says the Smithsonian Institution's twentieth-century clothing specialist, Barbara Dickstein. Today Levi's—the all American pants—are sold in at least seventy countries, including the U.S.S.R.

"Contemporary clothing blurs generational and social distinctions," Dickstein comments. The avant-garde designer Rudi Gernreich once explained it this way: "Clothes are just not that important. They're not status symbols any longer. They're for fun." Ultimately, the late designer decided that fashion for both sexes was "a kind of flaunting of one's personality."

Three hundred years earlier, in 1676, Hannah Lyman had "flonted" her personality with a silk hood and become one of the first Americans to fight for equality in dress. By the mid-nineteenth century the democratization of clothing that we enjoy today was well under way. In Philadelphia the Great Central Clothing Depot was flourishing at Seventh and Market streets selling such "Fashionable Ready-made Clothing" as cloaks, dress and frock coats, and trousers.

Fittingly, in this very building, in 1776, one of America's earliest wearers of trousers, Thomas Jefferson, had created the pattern for a new nation's democracy—the Declaration of Independence.

TWENTIETH CENTURY

13

FREDERICK WINSLOW TAYLOR
THE MESSIAH OF TIME AND MOTION

Spencer Klaw

INTRODUCTION

As the unionization movement took hold among unskilled workers toward the end of the nineteenth century, industrialists looked for ways to restore managerial control over their factories. Frederick W. Taylor (1856–1915) provided part of the answer with his ideas for structuring work and workers to maximize efficiency. The keys were absolute authority over the workplace by management and strict adherence to basic principles established by observation and experiment. Time-motion studies determining the speed at which basic tasks could be accomplished and detailed instruction sheets specifying the sequence of those tasks were the foundation of what became known as Scientific Management. Taylor's "principal tool" was the stop watch, which became the much-hated symbol of Scientific Management to many workers.

Scientific Management promised efficiency in the workplace and profits for those companies that embraced its principles. Taylor became a hero among Progressive reformers, who valued efficiency and saw his ideas as a means of promoting social harmony. But efficiency came at a price. Factory owners had to turn decision-making over to a new class of management consultants, and workers had to submit to a backbreaking pace dictated by machines and seemingly arbitrary "laws" governing each component of their jobs. Diminution of individual responsibility, loss of identity, regimentation, and decreased pride in work have been attributed directly or indirectly to Taylorism. Ironically, the quest for efficiency in the workplace early in the twentieth century may have planted the seeds for a decline in American competitiveness in the 1970s. Some analysts blame management for shortsighted corporate "group think" and see a lack of worker autonomy as major reasons why United States manufacturing firms fell behind foreign companies in productivity and profits. In the 1980s and 1990s, new ways of thinking, involving more worker independence and involvement, have finally led American companies to compete on more even terms in the global economy.

Toward the end of the last century an idea took form in the mind of a Philadelphia factory engineer that was destined to change, in profound and troubling ways, the nature of work in the modern world. The engineer was Frederick Winslow Taylor, a brash and eccentric young man whose most notable prior accomplishment had been the invention of a crook-handled tennis racquet, shaped like a giant teaspoon, with which he had taken the measure of a number of the leading players of the day. The idea that came to Taylor was that just as there was a science of metals (metallurgy) and a science of machines (mechanics), there must be a science and technology of work, whose laws could be discovered by observation and experiment. He was soon convinced—and he was to spend the rest of his life trying to convince others—that only by requiring workers to submit to the authority of those laws, and thereby to surrender all claims to autonomy or discretion in their work, could the full potential of the industrial revolution at last be realized.

The key element in Taylor's new technology of work, to which he later gave the name of "scientific management," was the time-and-motion study. This was, and is, a technique for determining how fast a job can reasonably be performed, and for identifying, and eliminating, inefficient and time-wasting practices. Its symbol and principal tool is the stop watch, and its end product is an instruction sheet specifying the exact sequence of operations to be followed in doing a given job, and the exact time, to the second, in which each operation is to be completed. Workers, Taylor wrote, "must do what they are told promptly and without asking questions or making suggestions. . . . It is absolutely necessary for every man in an organization to become one of a train of gear wheels."

In factories where Taylor's ideas were put into effect, output doubled or even tripled, and profits soared. Wages went up too, for it was a fixed principle with Taylor that workmen meeting the new production standards were entitled to bonuses of 30 to 60 percent or more. Such striking demonstrations of what scientific management could do eventually caught the public fancy, and in the last years of Taylor's life—he died in 1915—magazines and newspapers competed in praising him. The popular journalist Will Irwin, writing in *The Century,* observed, for example, that efficiency was "a kind of religion" for Taylor and his disciples. Their object, he added, "is not only the increase of production, but the ultimate happiness of the world—satisfied stomachs, shod feet, light hearts, untroubled souls." Taylor's admirers included a number of the leading reformers of the day, among them Louis D. Brandeis and Herbert Croly, the founder of the *New Republic,* who saw scientific management as a magical device for enriching labor without impoverishing capital.

Capital and labor, however, were slower than the general public and the reformers to embrace Taylor's ideas. For many years, factory managers, with a few notable exceptions, refused to make the sweeping changes in the way they ran their plants that Taylor insisted were just as important as time-and-motion studies if the full benefits of scientific management were to be reaped. Union leaders, for their part, denounced Taylorism as a new form of the speed-up, and as a scheme for turning men into machines.

But the principles of factory management laid down by Taylor—principles whose most spectacular application was the modern assembly line, with its meticulously planned flow of parts and materials, and its complete subordination of man to machine—were too potent to be resisted very long. Within a few years of Taylor's death, the unions largely had ceased to oppose his ideas—who could oppose efficiency?—demanding only that they be given say in determining what was to constitute a fair day's work. A new generation of managers, many of whom had been trained, like Taylor, as engineers, impatiently rooted out the wasteful practices and the permissive attitudes toward work that Taylor had deplored, and took pride in transforming their factories into huge, intricately articulated production machines. Scientific management soon took root in other countries besides the United States, notably in France, where, in 1918, Premier Georges Clemenceau ordered all factories under control of the Ministry of War to begin at once to put Taylor's ideas into operation. In the same year Lenin took note of "the refined brutality of bourgeois exploitation" that he said was a mark of scientific management, but went on to say that Russians must nevertheless "systematically try it out and adapt it to our own ends." By the 1930s Taylor's ideas were regarded by practical men everywhere as revealed truth.

Recently, to be sure, those ideas have come under increasing attack. The attackers include, for example, the Marxist writer Harry Braverman, whose influential *Labor and Monopoly Capital,* subtitled *The Degradation of Work in the Twentieth Century,* is taken up largely with a bitter critique of the Taylorian gospel. Scientific management is also out of favor with many business school professors. Some corporate executives have even become disenchanted to the point of supporting heretical experiments in the organization of work on non-Taylorian lines. In the United States and Europe, notably in Norway and Sweden, workers have been grouped into teams whose members are freed from the tyranny of time-and-motion studies and are permitted to arrange among themselves how best, for example, to put together an automatic transmission.

But most factory managers and industrial engineers in Russia and the socialist countries of Eastern Europe as well as in the noncommunist world are inclined to look on such experiments as soft-headed do-goodism. By and large, Taylor's truth is still mighty and prevails. Indeed, as Peter Drucker, a leading student of business management, has suggested, scientific management "may well be the most powerful as well as the most lasting contribution America has made to Western thought since the Federalist Papers."

Frederick Taylor was born in Germantown, on the outskirts of Philadelphia, in 1856, and very early in life displayed two closely related traits that were strongly to mark his career. According to his admiring biographer, Frank Barkley Copley, these were "a passion for improving and reforming things," and "a divine discontent with anything short of the *one best way.*" "Even a game of croquet was a source of study and careful analysis with Fred," a boyhood friend recalled years later, adding that, on cross-country tramps, Taylor "was constantly experimenting with his legs" to discover the most efficient method of walking.

Taylor grew up in easy circumstances, his father having come into enough money as a young man so that he could give up the practice of law and devote himself to reading poetry and the classics, and performing good works. In his teens young Fred Taylor traveled in Europe with his family for three years, during which he briefly attended schools in Germany and France. Later he went to Exeter, where he captained the baseball team and, in his senior year, ranked first in his class. He had planned to go to Harvard and, eventually, to become a lawyer. Instead, for reasons that are obscure—Taylor himself used to speak unconvincingly of a need to rest his eyes after too much night study at Exeter—he went to work as an apprentice pattern-maker and machinist in a small Philadelphia pump factory. He stayed there four years, leading a double life as a machine-shop hand by day and a proper Philadelphian by night. He belonged to the Young America Cricket Club, sang in a choral society, acted in amateur theatricals—he was particularly admired for his skill in impersonating young women—and went to dances where he discharged his debt to Philadelphia society by choosing half (but no more) of his partners from a group of wallflowers whose names he had listed for himself in advance.

In 1878, having completed his apprenticeship, he took a job with another Philadelphia firm, the Midvale Steel Company, where he rose, over the next six years, from lathe-hand to machineshop foreman, master mechanic, and chief works engineer. He had not been at Midvale long before he was seized with an urge to improve and reform things there. To fit himself better for the task he persuaded Stevens Institute, in Hoboken, New Jersey, to let him take its regular course in mechanical engineering on a home-study basis. Since he was working six and sometimes seven days a week at Midvale, he had to do most of his studying at night or early in the morning. For a while he got up at 2 A.M., studied until 5, and then napped for half an hour to freshen himself for his day at Midvale, which began at six-thirty. But for most of the astonishingly short time that it took him to earn his engineering degree—he got it in two and a half years—he studied each evening from nine until midnight, and then cooled himself off mentally by taking a half hour's run through the streets of Germantown. "Sometimes," Copley writes, "he would be seen stopping under a street lamp to consult a paper or a blank-book; apparently even he who runs may study."

Taylor got his degree from Stevens in 1883, and it was around this time that he began timing jobs with a stop watch. His aim was to get a fair day's work out of the men in Midvale's machine shop, who he was convinced could easily double or triple their daily output but chose instead to "soldier" on the job—thereby, in Taylor's view, sinning not only against their bosses, but against themselves and society at large. Taylor recognized, however, that it was not easy to persuade men to produce more when experience had taught them that, if they did, the piece rates governing the amount of their wages would sooner or later be cut, and they would end up doing more work for the same pay.

The first requirement, Taylor decided, was to end the wrangling over what constituted a fair day's work by determining how each job could be done most efficiently, and by establishing daily output standards from which there would be no appeal because they would be, as he saw it, completely scientific. But as he went about analyzing how the machinists did their jobs, he was impressed by the amount of time wasted because of improper (or improperly sharpened) tools, or because spare parts or materials were not at hand and had to be hunted up. He concluded that if Midvale were to get the most out of its machinists, there would have to be changes in the way the shop was run. Work would have to be planned, for instance, so that the right tools and materials would be available when and where they were needed. In short, management as well as labor would have to learn to go about its work in a scientific way. The problem remained of persuading the machinists to accept the new order. His solution was to offer them a big raise, along with assurances that since the new arrangement was "scientific," and since it was profitable to employer as well as to employees, there would be no reason for management ever to alter it.

Taylor's fellow managers viewed his stop-watch experiments as symptoms of mild insanity. He was permitted to carry them out, his biographer suggests, mainly because Midvale's owners were ready to indulge the whims of a man who had been able to get more work out of the company's machineshop hands even without a stop watch and who, moreover, was contributing to Midvale's profits by his talents as an inventor of new and more efficient metal-working machinery. But gradually Taylor was able to show that his work with the stop watch was paying off. "Eventually," Copley writes, "they all had to concede that in the madness of a man who gets two forgings turned where only one had been turned before, there must be a gleam of method, and that it might be a good thing for the works in general to go crazy to this extent."

Word of what Taylor had accomplished at Midvale had begun to get around by 1893, and he decided to set himself up as a new kind of consulting engineer, offering to install his management system in any plant whose owners were prepared to pay him thirty-five dollars a day and to do exactly as he told them. Among the clients who agreed to this arrangement was Bethlehem Steel, which retained Taylor at the urging of Joseph Wharton, the Philadelphia financier and philanthropist, who was one of the company's major stockholders. Taylor spent three years in Bethlehem, Pennsylvania, where he rode a bicycle to work and was known as "Speedy."

Bethlehem's huge plant was the scene of two feats of scientific management of which Taylor was particularly proud. One was his success in boosting, in some instances by 300 percent, the tonnage handled each day by the laborers whom the company employed to load pig iron onto railroad cars. He also saved Bethlehem large sums of money by introducing science into shoveling. In 1898, when Taylor went to work for Bethlehem, some five hundred men were employed by the company to shovel coal, iron ore, coke, and other materials. With a view to increasing their efficiency, Taylor set out to discover, by experiment, exactly how much a shoveler should pick up each time he stuck his shovel into a pile of iron ore or coal. It turned out that the shovelers worked most efficiently, moving the greatest amount of material in the course of a day, when each shovel-load weighed no more and no less than twenty-one and a half pounds. To make sure that a shoveler picked up exactly twenty-one and a half pounds, no matter what he happened to be shoveling, Taylor had the company lay in various sizes and shapes of shovels, ranging from a very small flat shovel for shoveling ore, to an immense scoop for lightweight rice coal. He also worked out rules for shoveling. Shovelers were shown, for instance, exactly how to use their body weight, instead of just their arm muscles, when pushing a shovel into a pile of iron ore, and they were required to develop, and stick to, the proper shoveling form.

At the end of three years one hundred and forty shovelers were doing the work formerly done by five hundred. Even after taking into account a 60 percent pay increase for the shovelers, and a sharp rise in overhead costs—the payroll now included shoveling instructors, as well as work planners whose jobs included seeing to it that the right shovels were on hand at the right places—Taylor had succeeded in reducing by 50 percent Bethlehem's cost of handling materials.

Despite such achievements, Taylor was far from popular at Bethlehem. Some resistance to his ideas was to be expected, since he was bent not only on shaking up comfortable old routines, but on transferring authority from old-line department heads and foremen to a new hierarchy of production planners, specification writers, and other technical specialists. But Taylor made things much harder for himself by the tongue-lashings he administered to anyone at Bethlehem who had the gall to question his orders. A visitor to his office later recalled the terms in which Taylor, at the time of his arrival, was bawling out a hapless works manager. "Now look here," Taylor told his victim, "I don't want to hear anything more from you. You haven't got any brains, you haven't got any ability—you don't know anything. You owe your position to your family pull, and you know it. Go on and work your pull if you want to, but keep out of my way, that's all." Taylor made little effort to hide his scorn for Bethlehem's president, Robert Linderman. Once when he was scheduled to meet with Linderman and other company officials he allegedly showed up half an hour late, swinging a golf club, and insisted on talking about golf. Linderman, for his part, complained to Taylor's patron, Joseph Wharton, that Taylor's bullheadedness was disrupting operations. Eventually Wharton gave in. One day in April, 1901, Taylor found a note on his desk, signed by Linderman, which read, in full: "I beg to advise you that your services will not be required by this Company after May 1st, 1901."

Over the years Taylor had made money in successful business deals as well as from his inventions, and he had invested his money shrewdly. As a result, by the time he was fired by Bethlehem he was in a position to support himself, his wife, and three young adopted children in a more than comfortable style even if he never earned another dollar. He therefore decided, at the age of forty-five, to get out of the consulting business and to spend the rest of his life as an unpaid proselytizer for scientific management, ready to offer free counsel to anyone genuinely interested in his ideas. The task of putting those ideas into effect, for which Taylor must now have recognized that he was temperamentally unsuited, was to be left to disciples who had worked with him at Bethlehem and other companies.

This decision enabled Taylor to end the peripatetic life he and his wife had been leading, and to move back to Philadelphia to stay. Buying an eleven-acre estate in Chestnut Hill, to which he gave the name "Boxly" after the century-old box hedges that were one of its most striking features, he flung himself into the job of improving his new property. Large sections of the hedgerows were relocated by means of a gigantic transplanting machine of Taylor's devising, and a hill was leveled to improve the view from the newly built Southern Colonial mansion into which the Taylors moved in 1904. Taylor took personal charge of the leveling, applying his customary methods not only to the twenty-odd laborers employed on the job, but to the horses that pulled the excavating scoops. "We found out," he used to tell visitors, "just what a horse will endure, what percentage of the day he must haul with such a load, how much he can pull, and how much he should rest." The house itself contained special features designed by Taylor. The circular conservatory, for example, was equipped with a moving platform that ran on a high circular track, so that the man charged with caring for the flowers could stand above them and pull himself around the room.

After settling at Boxly, Taylor had more time for golf, which he had taken up as therapy but had come to love. He played the game well—he once shot an impressive seventy-six on the championship Ekwanok course in Manchester, Vermont—but in a thoroughly unorthodox fashion, using clubs of his own design. When teeing off he customarily employed a driver nearly a foot longer than other people's, and started his swing with his back turned to the ball. His boldest innovation was a two-handled putter, which he swung between his legs, like a croquet mallet, and which he used with excellent results until it was outlawed by the U.S. Golf Association. Taylor was as dissatisfied with conventional putting greens as he was with conventional putters, and at Boxly he conducted elaborate, and ultimately successful, experiments aimed at shortening by years the time needed to produce a first-class putting surface.

But Taylor permitted neither hedgemoving nor golf to interfere seriously with his missionary work for scientific management. In 1903 he presented to the American Society of Mechanical Engineers a paper called *Shop Management,* later published as a monograph, in which he set forth systematically the ideas he had been working out for twenty years. It gradually gained him a number of converts, and elicited a stream of letters from manufacturers, military officers, government officials, and others eager to learn more about his theories and their application. Many of these inquiries drew from Taylor an invitation to visit him in Chestnut Hill. Singly and in groups those so favored would be shown into the great living room at Boxly, with its two huge Taylor-designed picture windows, where Taylor would lecture them for two hours. Interruptions were frowned on, visitors being provided with scratch-pads on which to jot down, for later asking, questions that might occur to them along the way. Later the visitors were sent off to tour two Philadelphia factories that had been Taylorized under the watchful eye of the master. Taylor's ideas also began to attract attention at universities. Dean Edwin F. Gay of Harvard's new Graduate School of Business Administration, who had been a visitor to Boxly, decided to make scientific management the keystone of the first-year curriculum, and invited Taylor to give a series of lectures at the school. Yet despite such recognition Taylor remained a rather obscure figure, unknown to the general public and thought of by most manufacturers, if they had heard of him and bothered to think of him at all, as just the sort of crank one would expect to find lecturing at Harvard.

Then, quite suddenly, he became a national hero. The agent of his transformation was Louis D. Brandeis. The railroads of the eastern half of the country had asked the Interstate Commerce Commission for permission to raise their freight rates, and Brandeis had agreed to represent, without charge, a group of shippers who were protesting the increase. It occurred to Brandeis that it might impress the ICC if he could show that the railroad owners would not need higher rates if they would only manage their properties more efficiently. He had read *Shop Management,* and he now went to Boxly, where Taylor gave him the standard two-hour lecture, holding up a warning finger whenever Brandeis tried to break in with a question. "I quickly recognized," Brandeis said later, "that in Mr. Taylor I had met a great man—great not only in mental capacity, but in character."

After further meetings with Taylor, and talks with several of his followers, Brandeis was convinced that he had found the right weapon with which to batter down the railroads' defenses. The ICC had begun hearings on the proposed increases, and in November 1910 Brandeis fired his first salvo. He announced that he had witnesses who would prove that scientific management could save American railroads at least a million dollars a day. This statement, and the testimony of the engineers and industrialists whom Brandeis put on the stand, were prominently featured in the newspapers and—the railroads' sour demurrals notwithstanding—warmly hailed by editorial writers. Although Taylor did not himself testify before the ICC (which eventually ruled against the railroads), most of Brandeis's witnesses generously acknowledged him as their guide and teacher.

Soon pilgrims were showing up at Boxly in bands of twenty-five or more, and the press was filled with accounts of Taylor and his work. The *Philadelphia North American,* swelling with local pride, printed an appreciation, headed "A Great Philadelphian." In it, Taylor was praised as "the economic . . . revolutionist whose gospel may prove to be the hitherto undiscovered means of remedying all the industrial wrongs against which socialism is a protest." The *Outlook,* more restrained, allowed that he had organized "a new and important force in American industrial and social life." The March 1911 issue of *The American Magazine* carried an editorial titled "The Gospel of Efficiency," followed by a laudatory sketch of Taylor written by the one-time muckraker Ray Stannard Baker. The sketch was followed by the first installment of a book by Taylor, *The Principles of Scientific Management,* which he had been working on for years, and which turned out to be perhaps the most influential work on management ever published.

Public fascination with scientific management was heightened by its association with a new religion of efficiency. While Taylor himself was concerned almost exclusively with efficiency in industry, bookstores were soon filled with books explaining how to apply the principles of scientific management to one's personal life. Some of these inspirational works were written by ex-ministers, and some by established producers of success literature, like Elbert Hubbard and Orison Swett Marden, who knew a good thing in the success line when they saw it. Churchmen spoke of making worship more efficient. "People," one minister explained, "like to be tied up to progressive, wide awake, and going concerns." A proposal was made to introduce efficiency into higher education by encouraging professors to establish central banks of standardized lecture notes. Books appeared with titles like *The New Housekeeping* and *Household Engineering: Scientific Management in the Home.* One writer suggested setting up a chain of housekeeping experiment stations to develop and test "principles of domestic engineering."

Meanwhile, demand was rising for the services of engineers trained by Taylor. By 1914, scientific management, while it could not be described as widespread, was being practiced to some degree in eighty industries, including naval construction, printing, and mining, and the manufacture of typewriters, locomotives, clothing, glass, shoes, soap, and textiles. To Taylor's gratification, moreover, his belief that scientific management was as good for the workers as it was for their bosses was shared by many progressives like Brandeis and the young socialist writer Walter Lippmann. In their eyes, scientific management beautifully exemplified the kind of benevolent expertise with which they hoped to bring about social harmony and material progress without overthrowing the capitalist order.

Yet for all the attention his ideas were finally receiving, Taylor's last years were not happy ones. More and more often he fell prey to the conviction that he was being martyred on the altar of ingratitude and greed. The perpetrators of his martyrdom, as he saw it, included false prophets of scientific management—"a crowd of industrial patent medicine men," as they were described by Professor Robert F. Hoxie of the University of Chicago— who promised instant salvation to manufacturers afflicted by low output and low profits.

Taylor was less hurt, however, by the corruption of his ideas, and by the eagerness with which business men were buying worthless nostrums instead of the genuine article, than he was by the hostility of organized labor. Addressing his fellow workers in 1911 on the evils of scientific management, President Samuel Gompers of the American Federation of Labor wrote sarcastically, "So there you are, wageworkers in general, mere machines. . . . Hence, why should you not be standardized and your motion-power brought up to the highest possible perfection in all respects, including speed? Not only your length, breadth, and thickness as a machine, but your grade of hardness, malleability, tractability . . . can be ascertained, registered, and then employed as desirable. Science would thus get the most out of you before you are sent to the junkpile."

Taylor publicly denounced Gompers as one of the country's "most blatant demagogues." But he could not so scornfully dismiss objections of intelligent workmen like A. J. Portenar, a union printer (and the author of a book about labor) who had visited Boxly, and who thoughtfully set forth his criticism of scientific management in a letter to Taylor that he composed directly on a linotype. In reply, Taylor noted plaintively that the time and money he had devoted to the cause had been spent "entirely with the idea of getting better wages for the workmen—of developing the workmen coming under our system to make them all higher class men—to better educate them—to help them live better lives, and, above all, to be more happy and contented."

Such protestations of good intentions did not disarm Taylor's labor critics. They not only shared Gompers's revulsion at the prospect of men being turned into robots by the Circe's wand of Taylorism, but attacked scientific management on other grounds as well. They scoffed at the claim that work standards derived from stop-watch studies were scientific. In practice, they argued, such standards reflected the time-study man's entirely subjective estimate—or his boss's estimate—of how hard a man should be expected to work. Time-and-motion studies could thus be used as justification for driving workers to exhaustion, and there was little comfort to be had from Taylor's protests that any manager who improperly speeded up his workers was a traitor to scientific management. Skilled workers, who made up the bulk of union members at the time, were further alarmed by the prospect that, as jobs became Taylorized—that is, split up among several workers, each performing a relatively simple and rigidly specified task—traditional skills would lose their market value. Taylor himself conceded the truth of this argument. No machine-shop boss should be satisfied, he wrote, "until almost all of the machines in the shop are run by men who are of smaller calibre and attainments, and who are therefore cheaper than those required under the old system."

Union men also derided Taylor's assertion that the bonuses offered to workers for meeting the new goals set by their scientific managers were scientifically determined. The only fixed rule governing the size of such bonuses, they suggested, was that however much a worker might benefit from scientific management, his employer should benefit even more. This point was neatly made by the socialist Upton Sinclair in a letter to *The American Magazine,* which had carried Taylor's account of the prodigies performed under his tutelage by Bethlehem's pig-iron handlers. "[Taylor] tells how workingmen were loading twelve and a half tons . . . and he induced them to load forty-seven tons instead," Sinclair wrote. "They had formerly been getting $1.15; he paid them $1.85. . . . I shall not soon forget the picture which he gave us of the poor old laborer who was trying to build his pitiful little home after hours, and who was induced to give 362 [sic] percent more service for 61 percent more pay." Taylor was provoked into answering in words that betrayed—indeed, proclaimed—the condescension, often tinged with contempt, that underlay his attitude toward workingmen. Citing "a long series of experiments," about which he gave no details, he wrote that it had been established that when men of the caliber of pig-iron loaders were given much more than a 60 percent bonus "many of them will work irregularly and tend to become more or less shiftless, extravagant and dissipated. Our experiments showed, in other words, that for their own best interest it does not do for most men to get rich too fast."

In 1912 Taylor testified at length before a congressional committee looking into scientific management. The investigation had been authorized after a group of molders employed at the army's arsenal at Watertown, Massachusetts, had walked off the job rather than submit to the "humiliating" and "un-American" ordeal of being timed with a stop watch. The committee chairman, a former miners' union official, allowed union representatives to question all witnesses, and when it came Taylor's turn to face them, he blew up. "At the close of his testimony," his biographer, Copley, writes, "he was deliberately baited by his labor-leader opponents. Two of them went at him at the same time with insults and sneers. Insofar as the plan was to make him lose his temper, to destroy his self-control, it was a success. With flushed face, he hurled denunciations at his opponents and made accusations which in the nature of things he could not prove. For a time it appeared as if blows would be struck." Exactly what was said is unknown, since the interchange was stricken from the record. According to Copley's account, "Taylor's friends who were there present viewed the scene with emotions such as one might experience upon seeing a magnificent stag worried and brought low by a pack of wolves."

Over the next three years Taylor's friends had more and more reason to worry about his state of mind. "While he gave many signs of a mellowing nature," Copley writes, "there at the same time were symptoms of increasing nervous instability. Men who had business relations with him could not be sure in what mood they would find him. He who all along had been an inspiration now sometimes depressed people, giving them a sense of fearful strain." For comfort Taylor turned repeatedly to an uplifting essay called "The Dreamers," by a writer named Herbert Kaufman, which read, in part, "They are the architects of greatness. . . . They are the chosen few—the Blazers of the Way—who never wear Doubt's bandage on their eyes—who starve and chill and hurt, but hold to courage and to hope."

In the late winter of 1915 Taylor caught pneumonia, and on March 21, one day after his fifty-ninth birthday, he died. He was buried on a hill overlooking the Schuylkill River, and his grave was marked with a stone inscribed "Frederick W. Taylor, Father of Scientific Management."

In one way time has vindicated Taylor. His ideas are now taken as much for granted, by most planners and organizers of factory and office work, as the idea of the division of labor that so powerfully influenced the Industrial Revolution. If Taylor had not invented scientific management, it would have been invented by someone else. The engineering principles that had been applied with such success to the design of industrial machines were certain to be applied, sooner or later, to the men who operated them.

But Taylor's vision of an era in which managers and the managed would work together in harmony and mutual respect was not to be fulfilled. Nor could it have been fulfilled, since Taylor, for all his obviously genuine protestations of concern for the workingman, looked at the world of work through the eyes of the employer. As Braverman argues convincingly in *Labor and Monopoly Capital,* Taylor did not develop a science of work, but something quite different: a science of management that would enable employers to get the most possible work out of their employees.

It is true that factory workers, partly through the power of the unions that Taylor so hated and mistrusted, have secured a share of the fruits of their increased productivity. But there have been unmistakable signs—absenteeism, carelessness, sabotage, wildcat strikes—of a mounting conviction that the price exacted from them for their relative prosperity has been much too steep. The recent experiments in job enlargement, offering workers more variety and autonomy on the job, mark a recognition that applying Taylorism in its undiluted form may not, after all, be the best way to maximize profits.

But such palliatives seem inadequate to restore significantly the reliance on individual knowledge and skill that Taylor taught employers to regard as an impediment to higher profits. That these profits were to be achieved by condemning industrial workers to a spiritual and psychological hell was clear to, among others, Taylor's printer correspondent, A. J. Portenar. "It depresses me horribly," Portenar wrote after reading Taylor's *Shop Management.* "The whole thing looms up vaguely before me as an inhuman inexorable machine, gliding smoothly on its way, but crushing not only all in its way, but sapping the vitality of all connected with it." The years have confirmed the validity of Portenar's fears, and exposed the naiveté of the 1912 progressives who so warmly embraced Taylor and Taylorism. For today it is hard to take seriously any general scheme for human betterment that does not seek to revive the pride in craftsmanship, and the sense of control over one's work, that Taylor was at such pains to do away with in the name of progress.

14

MASS PRODUCTION

Ford Motor Company

INTRODUCTION

At once hero, villain, and icon, Henry Ford symbolized the dynamism of America in the early twentieth century. In 1913, at his Highland Park, Michigan, factory, Ford introduced the moving assembly line to the manufacture of Model T automobiles. The result was mass production. Ford said that the inspiration for the moving assembly line came from "disassembly lines" that he had seen in the Chicago meat-packing industry that were used for the processing of animal carcasses. In reality, he borrowed the idea from Westinghouse Air Brake Company, where an overhead conveyor had been used in the foundry since 1890. Regardless of where the idea came from, the moving assembly line made possible mass production, permitting the manufacture of quality goods at low cost and making those goods available to the masses of American people.

This selection, from the 1926 *Encyclopedia Britannica,* appeared over Ford's name, and in it the term mass production was used for the first time. Ford did not write the piece; rather it was written and submitted by a spokesman at the Ford Motor Company. But it represents Ford's thinking about what constitutes mass production—especially how it is distinct from quantity production and production using automatic machine tools. Not all agree about the originality of Ford's concept of mass production. Regardless, the moving assembly line and mass production forever changed the way products were manufactured, how the workplace was organized, and how workers themselves went about their jobs. Possibly no twentieth-century technology had more far-reaching implications and consequences.

MASS PRODUCTION

The term mass production is used to describe the modern method by which great quantities of a single standardized commodity are manufactured. As commonly employed it is made to refer to the quantity produced, but its primary reference is to method. In several particulars the term is unsatisfactory. Mass production is not merely quantity production, for this may be had with none of the requisites of mass production. Nor is it merely machine production, which also may exist without any resemblance to mass production. Mass production is focusing upon a manufacturing project of the principles of power, accuracy, economy, system, continuity and speed. The interpretation of these principles, through studies of operation and machine development and their coordination, is the conspicuous task of management. And the normal result is a productive organization that delivers in quantities a useful commodity of standard materials, workmanship and design at minimum cost. The necessary, precedent condition of mass production is a capacity, latent or developed, of *mass consumption,* the ability to absorb large production. The two go together, and in the latter may be traced the reasons for the former.

I. THE ORIGINS OF MASS PRODUCTION

In origin mass production is American and recent; its earliest notable appearance falls within the first decade of the 20th century. The mere massing of men and materials is a procedure as old as the pyramids. Basic industries, like weaving, domestic baking, house construction and wooden ship building, are carried on, with only superficial changes, much as they were in ancient Egypt. Cottage manufactures and handicrafts moulded the practices of industry until the invention of the steam engine. With the coming of power machines, the seat of industry was removed from the homes of the people and a new work centre, the factory, was established. Much harsh criticism has been uttered against "the factory system," but it is perhaps fair to say that its first effect was to emancipate the home from being a mere adjunct to the loom or bench, and its later effect was to provide the home with means to develop the dignified status which it has now attained.

The Factory System Giving Way

The early factory system was uneconomical. Its beginning brought greater risk and loss of capital than had been known before, lower wages and more precarious outlook for the workers, and a decrease in quality of goods. More hours, more workers, more machines did not improve conditions; all every increase did was enlarge the scale of fallacies built into business. Mere massing of men and tools was not enough; the profit motive, which dominated enterprise, was not enough. There remained the scientific motive which grew eventually into what is called mass production.

The new method came after the failure of the mercantile and financial emphasis in manufacture. The advent and progress of financial control of industry were marked by two developments, the corporation and the labour revolt. Artificial combination of industrial plants into vast corporations for financial purposes was the first movement toward *mass* in industry. It proceeded on the theory that complete financial control would automatically bring complete profit advantage. The theory ignored many vital principles of business and its fallacy became apparent, but not before serious social hostility had been incurred.

However, it was out of the social strife thus engendered that the idea began to emerge that possibly the difficulty lay in the neglect of scientific manufacturing principles. Industry was conceded to be necessary and useful. The service it rendered was regarded as of sufficient value to afford fair compensation for all engaged in it; it was therefore urged that the attention of management should be more directly focused on the actual labour processes that were employed. This led to what was known early in the 20th century as the "efficiency movement" with its accompaniments of time-study and similar methods, although its roots were laid in the experiences of sound industrial observers as early as 1878. It cannot be said, however, that the efficiency experts did more than direct attention to the problem, by showing, in selected instances, how the then current methods were wasteful of men's earning power, and how their correction and improvement could lead to greater production, hence higher wages, and therefore a general betterment of labour relations. They emphasized a more intelligent management of methods than was then in use; they did not see that a wholly new method was possible which would simply abolish the problems of which the old method, under most intelligent management, was inevitably prolific. For example they dealt with methods which enabled laborers whose task was to load 12-1/2 tons of pig-iron a day, to load 47-1/2 long tons a day for an increase in the day's pay from $1.15 to $1.85. They did not see that another and better method might be devised which would make it unnecessary for a working-man to carry 106,400 lb. of pig-iron to earn $1.85. Mass production was not in their view, but only the alleviation of the worst errors of competitive factory practice.

The Motor Industry Leads the Way

To the motor industry is given the credit of bringing mass production to experimental success, and by general consent the Ford Motor Company is regarded as having pioneered in the largest development of the method under a single management and for a single purpose. It may, therefore, simplify the history of mass production and the description of its principles if the experience of this company is taken as a basis. It has been already suggested that mass production is possible only through the ability of the public to absorb large quantities of the commodity thus produced. These commodities are necessarily limited to necessities and conveniences. The greatest development of mass production methods has occurred in the production of conveniences. The motor vehicle represents a basic and continuous convenience-transportation.

Mass production begins, then, in the conception of the public need of which the public may not as yet be conscious and proceeds on the principle that use-convenience must be matched by price-convenience. Under this principle the element of service remains uppermost; profit and expansion are trusted to emerge as consequences. As to which precedes the other, consumption or production, experiences will differ. But granted that the vision of the public need is correct, and the commodity adapted to meet it, the impulse to increased production may come in anticipation of demand, or in response to demand, but the resulting consumption is always utilized to obtain such increase of quality, or such decrease of cost, or both, as shall secure still greater use-convenience and price-convenience. As these increase, consumption increases, making possible still greater production advantages, and so on to a fulfillment that is not yet in view.

The commodities that conduce to civilized living are thus far enjoyed by only a small fraction of the world's inhabitants. The experience of the Ford Motor Company has been that mass production precedes mass consumption and makes it possible, by reducing costs and thus permeating both greater use-convenience and price-convenience. If the production is increased, costs can be reduced. If production is increased 500%, costs may be cut 50% and this decrease in cost, with its accompanying decrease in selling price, will probably multiply by 10 the number of people who can conveniently buy the product.

II. THE PRINCIPLES OF MASS PRODUCTION

As to shop detail, the keyword to mass production is simplicity. Three plain principles underlie it: (a) the planned orderly progression of the commodity through the shop; (b) the delivery of work instead of leaving it to the workman's initiative to find it; (c) an analysis of operations into their constituent parts. These are distinct but not separate steps; all are involved in the first one. To plan the progress of material from the initial manufacturing operation until its emergence as a finished product involves shop planning on a large scale and the manufacture and delivery of material, tools, and parts at various points along the line. To do this successfully with a progressing piece of work means a careful breaking up of the work into its "operations" in sequence. All three fundamentals are involved in the original act of planning a moving line of production.

This system is practiced, not only on the final assembly line, but also throughout the various arts and trades involved in the completed project. The motor car assembly line offers an impressive spectacle of hundreds of parts being quickly put together into a going vehicle, but flowing into that are other assembly lines on which each of the hundreds of parts have been fashioned. It may be far down the final assembly line that the springs, for example, appear, and they may seem to be a negligible part of the whole operation. Formerly one artisan would cut, harden, bend, and build a spring. In 1928 the making of one leaf of a spring is an operation of apparent complexity yet is really the ultimate reduction to simplicity of operation.

A Typical Operation Described

For its illustrative value let us trace the course of a spring leaf after it has progressed from iron ore through ingot, bloom, and billet stages, and is rolled into strips. (1) Beginning as a strip of steel prepared by the steel mill, it is placed in a punch press for cutting and piercing. The workman puts the strip into press until it hits a stop, then trips the press. The cut-off and pierced piece falls on a belt conveyor which runs along the loading end of a series of heat-treating ovens. (2) A second workman takes the pieces from the belt conveyor and places them on a conveyor which passes through the furnace (in which temperature is automatically controlled); thence they are deposited at a certain temperature by this conveyor at the unloading end of the furnace. (3) The heated piece is lifted with tongs by a third operator and placed in a bending machine which gives the leaf its proper curve and plunges it in oil, the temperature of which is maintained at a definite degree by apparatus beyond the operator's control. (4) As the bending machine emerges from the oil bath, the same operator takes out the leaf and sets it aside to air-cool. (5) The leaf is then drawn by a fourth operator through molten nitrate kept at a regulated temperature. (6) A fifth workman inspects it.

As a set of springs on the Ford car requires on an average 17 leaves, and 25,000 springs are an average day's output, this operation must be visualized as employing a great battery of lines similar to the one briefly described. As all the leaves in a spring are of different length and curve, from the bottom or master leaf to the top leaf, this operation must be visualized as one of the many carried on simultaneously by different batteries of machines, each battery working on its own special size. All of these lines, with their various machines and operations, are converging on the point where the leaves are assembled into springs. The leaf whose progress has been described is the simplest one.

The operation proceeds as follows: (7) A sixth workman removes the leaf from the conveyor which carries it from the molten nitrate, and inserts a bolt and tightens it. (9) An eighth workman puts on the right and left hand clips and grinds off the burns. (10) A ninth workman inspects it. (11) He hangs the spring on a conveyor. (12) The spring passes the tenth workman, who sprays it with paint, and the conveyor carries the spring above the ovens where it was originally heated, and the radiated heat "force dries" the paint. (13) The conveyor continues to the loading dock, where the eleventh workman removes it.

One workman under the old system could attend the leaf through all these phases, or even make a complete spring, but his production would be limited. Where large quantities of the same article are to be made, the simplest operation may involve the whole time of one man. A one-minute operation may involve the whole time of one man. A one-minute operation will require one man a full day of eight hours to accomplish it on 480 pieces. Now this simple part, a spring leaf, must be identical in strength, finish, and curve with millions of others designed to fulfill the same purpose, and this becomes a complicated and delicate procedure requiring automatic machinery, the most accurate of measuring devices, pyrometer controls, "go" and "no go" gauges—in fact, the best facilities that can be provided by modern management. The leaf described, which is a minor matter when compared with the whole great process, becomes a major matter when considered by itself; it must have its own supply of material delivered in sufficient quantities at indicated places—for example, steel at 1; heat at 2; power and oil at 3; molten nitrate at 5; bolts at 7; nuts at 8; clips at 9; paint at 12. In this process the secrets of many arts and trades are employed.

The story of this minor part illustrates what is meant by orderly progression of the article through the shop. It goes to meet other parts of the motor-car which have come from other parts of the plant by similar processes. The story illustrates also what is meant by delivering the work to the workman: every workman's task is prepared for him by some other workman and delivered to his hand. The third principle also is illustrated—the analysis of a single job into its constituent operations. The simplicity of the part here described should not be permitted to exclude from view the multitude of other operations, ranging from the heaviest forgings to the lightest manipulations in bench assembly of delicate electrical instruments. Some gauge inspections involve measurements to the ten-millionth part of an inch.

The economies arising from this method are obvious. The machinery is constantly in use. It would be economically impossible to maintain all this equipment for the service of men occupied in the entire operation of making springs. Presses, furnaces, bending machines, oil baths would be idle while the workman progressed from operation to operation. Use–convenience in the commodity would be lessened, while price–convenience would be destroyed. Economy in machine hours is, however, only one element; there is also economy in time and material and labour. Mass production justifies itself only by an economy whose benefits may be transmitted to the purchaser.

III. THE EFFECTS OF MASS PRODUCTION

But it is not the history and principle of mass production which provoke the widest discussions; the *effects* of it have been placed under scrutiny. What have been the effects of mass production on society?

(1) Beginning with management, where unquestionably mass production methods take their rise, there is a notable increase in industrial control, as distinguished from financial control. The engineer's point of view has gained the ascendancy and this trend will undoubtedly continue until finance becomes the handmaid instead of the mistress of productive industry. Industrial control has been marked by a continuous refinement of standardization which means the instant adoption of the better method to the exclusion of the old, in the interests of production. Financial control was not, in its heyday, marked by a tendency to make costly changes in the interests of the product. The economy of scrapping the old equipment immediately upon the invention of the better equipment was not so well understood. It was engineering control, entrenched in mass production methods, that brought in this new readiness to advance. In this way, management has been kept close to the shop and has reduced the office to a clearinghouse for the shop. Managers and men have been brought into closer contact and understanding. Manufacturing has been reduced to greater singleness of purpose.

(2) The effect of mass production of the product has been to give it the highest standard of quality ever attained in output of great quantities. Conditions of mass production require material of the best quality to pass successfully through the operations. The utmost accuracy must control all these operations. Every part must be produced to fit at once into the design for which it is made. In mass production there are no fitters. The presence of fitters indicates that the parts have been produced unfit for immediate placement in the design. In works of art and luxury this accuracy is achieved at the cost of careful handiwork. To introduce hand methods of obtaining accuracy into mass production would render mass production impossible with any reference to price-convenience. The standard quality of the product is guaranteed by the fact that machines are so constructed that a piece of work cannot go through them unless it exactly accords with specifications. If the work goes through the tools, it must be right. It will thus be seen that the burden of creation is in management in designing and selecting the material which is to be produced by the multiple processes utilized in mass production.

(3) The effect of mass production on mechanical science has been to create a wide variety of single purpose machines which not only group similar operations and perform them in quantity, but also reproduce skill of hand to a marvelous degree. It is not so much the discovery of new principles as the new combination and application of old ones that mark this development. Under mass production, the industry of machine making has increased out of all comparison with its previous history, and the constant designing of new machines is a part of the productive work of every great manufacturing institution.

(4) The effect of mass production on employees has been variously appraised. Whether the modern corporation is the destruction or salvation of arts and crafts, whether it narrows or broadens opportunity, whether it assists or retards the personal development of the worker, must be determined by observable facts. A cardinal principle of mass production is that hard work, in the old physical sense of laborious burden-bearing, is wasteful. The physical load is lifted off men and placed on machines. The recurrent mental load is shifted from men in production to men in designing. As to the contention that machines thus become the masters of men, it may be said the machines have increased men's mastery of their environment, and that a generation which is ceaselessly scrapping its machines exhibits few indications of mechanical subjection.

The need for skilled artisans and creative genius is greater under mass production than without it. In entering the shops of the Ford Motor Company, for example, one passes through great departments of skilled mechanics who are not engaged in production, but in the construction and maintenance of the machinery of production. Details of from 5,000 to 10,000 highly skilled artisans at strategic points throughout the shops were not commonly witnessed in the days preceding mass production. It has been debated whether there is less or more skill as a consequence of mass production. The present writer's opinion is that there is more. The common work of the world has always been done by unskilled labour, but the common work of the world in modern times is not as common as it was formerly. In almost every field of labour more knowledge and responsibility are required than a generation or two ago.

Some Criticisms Answered

Mass production has also been studied with reference to what has been called the monotony of repetitive work. This monotony does not exist as much in the shops as in the minds of theorists and bookish reformers. There is no form of work without its hardness; but needless hardship has no place in the modern industrial scheme. Mass production lightens work but increases its repetitive quality. In this it is the opposite of the mediaeval ideal of craftsmanship where the artisan performed every operation, from the preparation of the material to its final form. It is doubtful, however, if the mass of mediaeval toil was as devoid of monotony as has sometimes been pictured, but it is absolutely certain that it was less satisfactory in its results to the worker. In well managed modern factories the tendency to monotony is combated by frequent changes of task.

The criticism of mass production as a means of reducing employment has long since been out of court. The experience of the Ford Motor Company is that wherever the number of men has been reduced on manufacturing operations, more jobs have been created. A continuous programme of labour reduction has been paralleled by a continuous increase in employment. As to the effect of mass production on wages and the relations between managers and men, there is little need to speak. It is perhaps the most widely understood fact about mass production that it has resulted in higher wages than any other method of industry. The reason is at hand. The methods of mass production enable the worker to earn more and thus to have more. Moreover, the methods of mass production have thrown so much responsibility on the craftsmanship of management, that the old method of financial adjustment by reduction of wages has been abandoned by scientific manufacturers. A business that must finance by drafts out of the wage envelopes of its employees is not scientifically based. It is the problem of management to organize production that it will pay the public, the workmen and the concern itself. Management that fails in any of this is poor management. Disturbed labour conditions, poor wages, uncertain profits indicate lapses in management. The craftsmanship of management absorbs the energies of many thousands of men who, without mass production methods, would have no creative opportunity. Here the modern method broadens instead of narrows individual opportunity.

(5) As to the effects of mass production on society, the increasing supply of human needs and the development of new standards of living are the elements to be estimated. The enlargement of leisure, the increase of human contacts, the extension of individual range, are all the result of mass production.

WHY INTERNAL COMBUSTION?

Rudi Volti

INTRODUCTION

The ubiquitousness of the internal combustion engine in today's motor vehicles masks some of its inherent technological deficiencies. We tend to forget that the internal combustion engine works well only within a narrow torque band, or range of rotational speeds. This means that there must be some way of disengaging the engine from the drive wheels when the vehicle is at rest and fitting a transmission to permit a variety of road speeds within the engine's torque restrictions. Moreover, the internal combustion engine must be started each time it is used, necessitating a small auxiliary electric motor and associated wiring and power source. At the turn of the century, it was by no means clear that the internal combustion engine was better than its steam and electric competitors.

In this selection, Rudi Volti points out that the internal combustion engine won out over its rivals as a result of the concurrent development of complementary technologies—the transmission and electric starter—and because of the changing role of the automobile in American society. As long as the automobile was a toy for the rich, no one minded putting up with its shortcomings; but when it became a means of personal mass transportation, those deficiencies were no longer tolerable. By the 1920s, the internal combustion engine proved to be more practical for everyday use than steam or electric power.

In sum, it was not inevitable that the internal combustion engine would prove superior to the alternatives for powering motor vehicles. There was nothing inherent in the technology of 1900 pointing to the superiority of the internal combustion engine. Rather, external, nontechnical factors—chiefly changes in the perception of how the automobile fit into American transportation needs—were the principal reasons why the internal combustion engine succeeded and other technologies failed.

From 1899 to 1901 the largest-selling car in America by far was the steam-powered Loco-mobile. Sixteen hundred of them were produced in 1900 alone, an impressive feat of mass production by the standards of the time. Other companies produced a small handful of steamers as well, plus 1,575 electric cars and just 936 powered by internal combustion.

Electric cars were the main competition for steam; in 1895 an electric was cited at America's first automobile race, in Chicago, "for the best showing made on official test for safety, ease of control, absence of noise, vibration, heat or odor, cleanliness and general excellence." That triumph had helped build a market for several electric-car makers.

By contrast the internal-combustion engine seemed to many to have a bleak automotive future. Col. Albert A. Pope, the largest manufacturer of automobiles before the turn of the century, concentrated initially on electric cars because "you can't get people to sit over an explosion." A turn-of-the-century critic voiced the sentiments of many when he derided the internal combustion engine as "noisy, unreliable, and elephantine, it vibrates so violently as to loosen one's dentures," and added, "The automobile industry will surely burgeon . . . but this motor will not be a factor."

Less than two decades later the internal-combustion engine had become the undisputed power plant of choice for the vast majority of car manufacturers. By 1917 approximately 3.5 million automobiles were registered in the United States, and fewer than 50,000 were electrics. Steam had virtually vanished; the last major manufacturer, the famous Stanley Motor Carriage Company, produced in that year a grand total of 730 steamers, substantially fewer cars than Ford turned out before lunch on an average day.

What happened? Why were steamers and electrics unable to maintain the dominance they had enjoyed at the beginning of the century? The easy answer, of course, is that the internal-combustion engine was technically superior. It was, but that does not adequately explain anything, for no consumer buys anything on the basis of abstract technical virtues. Technological superiority is relevant only when it addresses specific needs, and needs and expectations change over time. Moreover, technologies, superior or otherwise, are not self-sufficient; they often depend on the availability of complementary technologies.

That was especially true for the internal-combustion engine. Unlike a steam engine or electric motor, it operates effectively only within a relatively narrow range of rotational speeds, so it needs a transmission device that allows the engine to produce sufficient power irrespective of the speed of the car's driving wheels. At first this purpose was served by the sliding-gear transmission, invented by Emile Levassor in 1891. Levassor's famous assessment of his device—*"brutal mais ça marche"* (brutal, but it works)—was accurate. But without the clunky mechanism and its successors, gasoline-powered automobiles would have been impossible.

A steam engine, on the other hand, required nothing so elaborate as the internal-combustion engine's accompanying clutch and gearbox, although it could benefit from a two-speed transmission for hill climbing. Yet the complementary technology the steam engine did need was never satisfactorily developed. The engine could be a model of simplicity, compactness, and power, but it was no better than the boiler that supplied it with steam. This proved to be a weak link in the system. The problem was the small size of the boilers that could be installed in passenger automobiles. A car's boiler simply could not maintain an adequate reserve of steam unless the whole process was carefully monitored and regulated by the driver.

In the beginning this was not a drawback; it could even be seen as an advantage. When automobiles were first manufactured, in the 1890s, they were primarily viewed as playthings for the well-heeled and adventurous. Nobody bought a car to commute or run errands. So a high degree of operator involvement could actually be an enjoyable challenge, making the steam car a superior technology for its clientele.

Cars with internal-combustion engines required a fair degree of attention too; the manipulation of clutches and gearboxes called for considerable skill, and the maintenance of carburetors and ignition systems presented many snares for the unwary. As one early account had it, "to diagnose its ailments from the indirect tokens of sound and feeling, as must often be done, calls for a higher order of intelligence." The basic mechanism of a steam auto was more easily comprehended, but its operation could be daunting. One 1900 account noted that "the steam vehicle is one of the simplest of self-propelled vehicles, but . . . of all vehicles it requires the most intelligent care to keep it in good condition." As one British writer observed, "the early steam cars required a very sensitive ear and touch for their proper manipulation, and these are qualities in which the ordinary driver of a motor-car has hitherto been conspicuously lacking."

While cars powered by internal combustion made rapid strides in what we would today call user friendliness, operating a steamer remained difficult and complicated. Abner Doble, who mounted the last serious effort to make a popular steam car, admitted in 1917 that the existing steamers were all "too complicated to operate, requiring intelligent and unfailing attention."

The Stanley brothers, Francis E. and Freelan O., who after 1910 were the only remaining major manufacturers of steamers, made few concessions to the drivers of their cars. For women the arrangement of the Stanley's controls must have been particularly annoying, for reasons described in a Stanley owner's later recollections: "Directly under the driver's seat and placed horizontally are two more valve wheels. . . . The awkwardness of their position indicates that they are for occasional use only, for the driver must reach between his legs to get at them. No automobile intended for female drivers would be designed like this." The dashboard of a Stanley was festooned with gauges that required regular attention: boiler water level, steam pressure, main-tank fuel pressure, pilot-tank fuel pressure, oil sight glass, and tank water level. Just to start the car required the manipulation of thirteen valves, levers, handles, and pumps.

Starting up was a chore that bedeviled the drivers of both steam and internal-combustion automobiles. Cranking the latter could be an adventure. If the operator forgot to retard the spark first, the engine's kickback could easily break his or her arm. A steamer was much more reliable to start, at least during the first decade of the century, but it required a time-consuming series of operations and a wait of up to twenty minutes. One steam enthusiast explained the advantage: "I much prefer to wait than to spend time in repeated cranking on a hot day." His views put him in the minority; most drivers preferred cranking. Even so, starting an internal-combustion engine was a real struggle until Charles F. Kettering devised the first effective electric starter for the 1912 Cadillac—another example of a complementary technology that was necessary for the gasoline engine's ultimate success.

Early steamers also suffered from a short operating range. Since they discharged their spent steam into the atmosphere, they required as much water as fuel, and a trip of more than a hundred miles or so required a stop by a stream or watering trough to replenish the tank. One proponent of steamers argued that "the motorist who cannot afford to stop for a few moments after a hundred-mile run, and smoke a cigarette while an ostler throws in a few buckets of water, had better take the railway train."

The automobile's role changed dramatically in less than two decades, from that of a toy for the sporting rich to that of a conveyance for the masses. In 1908 there were still fewer than two hundred thousand cars on the nation's roads; by 1917 there were three and a half million. The steamer's shortcomings became serious liabilities under these circumstances. One industry analyst noted sadly in 1916 that "a little extra care was all that was required to run a steam car, but the hurrying, intense American public would not give that extra touch."

If the internal-combustion and steam car both required a lot of their operators, the electric was quite the opposite. It had no clutch or transmission and no difficult starting procedure. Also, it was quiet and odorless and reliable. Its drawbacks were limited speed and range. The batteries that powered it were heavy, amounting to 40 percent of the weight of the vehicle, and they provided little energy for all that weight. (Even today, charged electric batteries typically produce ten watt-hours per pound, while gasoline produces six thousand watt-hours per pound.) Two of the greatest electrical inventors of all time, Charles Steinmetz and Thomas Edison, tried unsuccessfully to develop an improved car battery, leading an exasperated journalist to write in 1908 that "Mr. Edison's bunk has come to be somewhat of a joke—a real joke." The battery remained an inefficient source of energy.

Nonetheless, the electric car's shortcomings must be seen in context. Its battery's limitations were important only if the car was expected to perform as a long-distance conveyance. In the first years of the century, 98 percent of all car trips covered fewer than sixty miles, and speeds averaged twenty to twenty-five miles per hour. For short-range driving, the electric car was often the best available. Its capabilities were well illustrated in 1908, when a woman who owned a Studebaker electric (top speed: seventeen mph) challenged the owner of a forty-horsepower gasoline-powered touring car to a race through Philadelphia. The rules of the contest stipulated that each driver had to make twenty-five stops over ten miles, to simulate a normal round of shopping and social calls. City congestion offset the gasoline car's speed advantage, and the need to crank it after every stop hampered it further. The electric won by ten minutes.

The practicality of electric cars could have been considerably increased by the development of a network of battery-charging stations. Curbside chargers were installed in some cities, but never extensively. Battery-exchange stations could even have been set up to make electrics useful for long-distance travel. Instead of being filled with a tankful of gas, the cars would have picked up fresh batteries in exchange for spent ones. The technical and economic problems were difficult but hardly insurmountable.

That, of course, never happened. Electric-car manufacturers never produced more than six thousand cars in a year, and their product slowly vanished. As with steam cars, the technical limitations are usually blamed, but the electric's failure has also to do with the nature of the car's customers and manufacturers. In fact, because of the users that it attracted, the electric's very virtues became part of its undoing. Its reliability, silence, cleanliness, and ease of operation endeared it particularly to women drivers, who were also less likely than men to be put off by its limitations. A 1915 magazine article extolled the electric's appeal to a woman: "She knows that it fulfills all of the demands of her daily routine of calling, shopping, and pleasure seeking. She knows that she likes to run it because there is a certain charm in its simplicity of operation and control—a sort of mild fascination. She knows, too, that she can step into its beautifully cushioned and brocaded interior, enjoy every minute of her ride and arrive at her destination as fresh and spotless as when she started."

As long as women were the primary clientele for electric cars, men weren't likely to buy many, a matter noted by one automobile journal: "The fact that anything, from a car to a color, is the delight of the ladies is enough to change his interest to mere amused tolerance. . . . Having imagined effeminacy into the electric, he dismisses it from his mind and buys a gas car without a struggle." One manufacturer, hoping to win male buyers, introduced in 1915 a low-slung, fast-looking electric roadster. It changed few minds.

Electric cars suffered also from their image as a luxury for the wealthy. They were usually cheaper to operate and maintain than gasoline cars, but they were extremely expensive to buy. In 1913 the average electric cost twenty-eight hundred dollars—the equivalent of roughly thirty-five thousand dollars today—while a Model T could be had for a little more than six hundred dollars. And the price of electrics was actually rising while that of gasoline cars fell.

The rising price tag resulted partly from the adoption of better batteries, but the main reason was the attitudes of the manufacturers. They saw their electric cars, as one journalist put it, "as a thing to be marketed only in comparatively small quantities to a leisure class." One industry analyst complained that "we advertise and teach our dealers and their salesmen to talk luxurious appointments, upholstery to match gowns and liveries, coach work and finish beyond compare. . . . Why create the impression one must be a millionaire to own an electric?"

Catering to a small and stable market, the makers of electric cars were little inclined to pursue lower prices. Indeed, while Ford showed the world the profitability of mass production, one description of an electric-auto factory boasted that "there is little place for the uneducated laborer in the plant." One industry analyst complained that "the high price of electrics is caused mostly by extravagant methods which require a large margin to provide for the waste."

If the manufacturers of electric autos failed to help themselves, another industry also served them less well than might have been expected. Electric-utility companies might have found in electric cars at least a partial solution to a perennial problem of power generation—making optimal use of installed capacity in the face of widely fluctuating demand over the twenty-four hours of each day. Thomas Edison suggested that power stations go into the garage business to stimulate the demand for electric vehicles; his advice went unheeded. Meanwhile, oil companies aggressively set up outlets to fuel internal-combustion cars.

The small size of the electric-car market was partly to blame for this. Electric-company officials sometimes argued that they would get more involved only when the manufacturers reduced the price of the cars. So a vicious circle was drawn. The small market kept the power companies from building more charging facilities, and the lack of charging facilities helped keep the market small. And there was little promise of economic benefit for the power companies anyway; one power-station manager estimated that keeping the batteries of one electric truck charged would produce no more revenue over a year than powering eighteen electric irons.

Compelling as they were, these cost considerations were ultimately of secondary importance. The limited speed and acceleration of electric cars doomed them for most motorists. Even if electric cars were perfectly sufficient for most transportation needs, automobiles have never been viewed solely in that light. The automobile was maturing into a practical transportation tool, but it never ceased to be an instrument of fun and excitement. The electrical engineer Charles Steinmetz was way off the mark when he claimed in 1914 that "the two characteristics which gave the gasoline car the dominance—high speed and high mileage—ceased to be of importance when the automobile dropped from a sporting appliance to a business commodity." Steinmetz predicted that within ten years a million electric cars would be on the nation's roads. No such thing could happen as long as very many automobile buyers were attracted by the sportiness of internal-combustion cars.

By 1917 both steam and electric cars were heading for extinction. The market for automobiles had been changing; the changes had brought different technical demands, and the shortcomings of the electric car and the steamer had grown more evident as the internal-combustion automobile had rapidly improved. The production of six- and eight-cylinder engines and better-balanced crankshafts had greatly reduced the gasoline car's vibration, destroying one of the chief competitive advantages of the steam auto. And the introduction of the gasoline car's electric starter co-opted one of the main selling points of the electric car.

Undoubtedly, some of the choices that resulted in the triumph of the internal-combustion engine were made on the basis of production economies and profit maximization, as well as unthinking technical conservatism and plain sloth. But it may be fairly asserted that if steam, electric, or some other power source had met the needs of a significant group of automobile buyers, the technology would not have been completely eclipsed by internal combustion. The automotive industry was much more fragmented in the first decades of the century than now, with dozens of manufacturers competing for sales at any given time. Intense competition stimulated innovation, and manufacturers produced automobiles with abundant new features.

Since 1917 or so, many incremental improvements have made the internal-combustion engine vastly more powerful, reliable, and economical, but there have been few serious efforts to replace it with anything radically different. Chrysler made a few sallies into the gas-turbine field in the 1950s and 1960s; General Motors came close to mass-producing cars with Wankel engines in the 1970s and is now working on a marketable electric car. A significant number of cars are powered by diesel engines, but the standard car power plant is still the four-stroke spark-ignition internal-combustion engine, of the type first built by Nikolaus Otto in 1876.

There is no saying that this will never change. Before the 1960s the control of exhaust-borne pollutants was never considered a major issue. As early as 1896 an electrical engineer complained that "all the gasoline motors we have seen belch forth from their exhaust pipe a continuous stream of partially unconsumed hydrocarbons in the form of a thick smoke with a highly noxious odor," but although the problem was recognized, there was little reason to attempt to design a low-emission engine. There was no market for one because no motorist could realize an advantage by buying it; the market would exist only if everyone were required to buy one. Over the last two decades such a market has, of course, been created by government edict, and as this has occurred, the technical requirements have once again changed. In addition to the virtues modern drivers already expected from their cars' engines, they now must expect to meet pollution standards. As the standards grow increasingly strict, the need may conceivably arise to replace the internal-combustion engine with something else. It would be a fine irony if the new power plants were descendants of the steamers and electrics that were shouldered aside by internal combustion so many decades ago. The changing requirements of motorists and society led to changed power-plant technologies in the past. Who knows whether it could happen again?

THE WHEELS—AND WINGS—OF PROGRESS

Richard Overy

INTRODUCTION

To most Americans and Europeans, the first decade of the twentieth century appeared to herald a new age of peace and prosperity, brought about at least in part by the boundless potential of new technologies. The automobile and the airplane, in particular, promised to free people from the dual tyranny of time and distance. Perhaps more than anything else at the time, these exciting new machines evinced the direct correlation between technological advance and social progress.

But, as Richard Overy shows in this selection, there was also considerable ambivalence about new technologies and the belief that they would lead to a better world. In Britain, for example, people worried that the automobile would bring about a hectic new pace to life and possibly even lead to the demise of a class system that was so much a part of the fabric of society. With the airplane came fears as early as 1910 of aerial attack and mass destruction from the sky. To Britishers accustomed to the protection of the North Sea and the English Channel the airplane represented as much threat as promise.

Even before the cataclysm of World War I, people began to recognize the paradoxical nature of modern technology. What could be liberating could also be confining, even deadly. Henceforth, many thoughtful individuals began to express doubts that technology was an unmitigated good and counseled that it might be wise to slow what had previously been the unquestioned pursuit of progress.

On August 9th, 1896, the German engineer, Otto Lilienthal, crashed to his death in a small experimental glider. He and his brother Gustav had spent years trying to adapt the lessons of bird flight so that man could fly. On this particular day Otto had gone to the experimental field, a group of sandhills at Stöllen near Magdeburg, to try one more flight before packing all the apparatus up. A gust of wind upturned the glider. Otto had failed to fit the shock absorber that would have saved his life.

A few years before his death Otto published the book that made him famous, *Birdflight as the Basis for Aviation* (1891). His was a lifelong obsession, first expressed as a young boy in the 1860s, with the idea that one day man would be able to fly. "He longs to soar upward and to glide, free as the bird, over smiling fields, leafy woods and mirror-like lakes," wrote Otto in 1891. His study of birdflight convinced him that it was only a matter of time before science produced the artificial equivalent necessary to "free our foot from mother earth." A decade later science obliged. In 1905 the first true flights using a small petrol-driven engine were made by the Wright brothers in the United States; the first flight without any kind of launching apparatus was made in France three years later. Lilienthal's contribution to aero-dynamic theory played a vital part in the early development of powered flight.

Two years before Otto Lilienthal's death, in July 1894, there occurred in France an event that marked a turning point in the development of modern technology. The owners of *Le Petit Journal* organised a contest for horseless carriages, a seventy-eight mile road trial between Paris and Rouen. The object was to demonstrate the competing virtues of cars powered by steam, electricity, or petrol. Of 102 entries only twenty-one actually made it to the start; fourteen petrol-driven cars and seven steam carriages. All of the petrol cars reached Rouen, but only three of the steam-driven ones, one of which recorded the fastest average speeds. In terms of speed, economy and reliability the petrol-powered vehicles were judged the most successful and the first prize was divided between Panhard & Levassor and Peugeot. Although steam and electric cars continued to be developed for another decade, the Paris trials showed their limitations. On the road as in the air, it was the petrol engine that provided the real breakthrough. Without the development of light and efficient engines, powered by a readily available and convenient fuel, the great technological leap at the turn of the century would barely have been possible.

The initial development of the engine was a slow process, dating back to experiments in France and Germany in the 1860s. It was in 1860 that Etienne Lenoir produced a small gas-fired engine which was applied unsuccessfully to a road vehicle several years later. In 1862 the Frenchman, Beau de Rochas, invented the four-stroke engine, followed three years later by the development of the Otto and Langen four-stroke gas engine in Germany, the direct forerunner of the internal combustion engine. For the following two decades scientists worked away at the problem of finding an effective fuel for the new engine.

Two German engineers, Karl Benz and Gottlieb Daimler, produced the breakthrough in the 1880s. Benz produced first a workable engine that could vaporise petrol effectively, then, in 1885, a working vehicle, a small three-wheeler capable of no more than a few miles an hour. Daimler, who produced an internal combustion engine in 1884 which was the model for all future development, built a motorcycle in 1886, then a small car and in 1888 applied his engine to a small airship. After a further six years Daimler had produced a modified and reliable petrol-driven engine which was rapidly patented world-wide. From then on development was swift. The modern carburetor was invented by Daimler's collaborator, Wilhelm Maybach, in 1893. In 1897 Rudolf Diesel perfected the heavy-oil engine which still bears his name.

The 1890s were a watershed in the development of modern technology. Success came at the end of a long period of frustrated research and invention. The serious pursuit of powered flight and of mechanical transport went back a century. In Britain in the 1820s and 1830s efforts to apply the steam engine to road transport reached a peak. The hostility of horse-carriage owners, high toll charges, and mechanical weaknesses brought the effort to a halt by the 1840s. Instead steam traction was found to be much more effective on fixed rails.

The railway boom met the need for faster and more flexible transport. Some early aeronautical pioneers tried to apply the steam engine to powered flight. Others used gas engines or giant rubber bands. Though none of these developments promised much, they helped to seek a clear agenda for the engineering community. The final breakthrough in the last fifteen years of the century depended, as most technical developments do, on the patient, painstaking work of experiment and invention from the previous generation for whom the unlimited technical possibilities released by industrialisation were a matter of faith.

Once the critical threshold was reached in the 1890s the pace of change accelerated rapidly. Only a decade separated the clumsy motorised tricycle from the elegant motor carriages of the turn of the century. The new invention was taken up first by the wealthy and titled, who enjoyed its novelty and excitement, and the very obvious statement of status and prestige car ownership represented. The first head of state to buy one was the Sultan of Morocco, who bought a small Daimler car at the Paris World Fair in 1889. The German Kaiser, Wilhelm II, was fascinated by motor cars. By the First World War he had twenty-five, kept in the royal stables, next to the horses. Emperor Franz-Joseph of Austria was an avid collector—he encouraged the development of electric cars, one of which was built by Ferdinand Porsche who, thirty years later, designed the Volkswagen. Tsar Nicholas II shared this motoring enthusiasm. In 1914 he had two Rolls-Royce cars delivered to St. Petersburg which were later confiscated by the Bolshevik government and used as Lenin's state cars.

But very quickly motor transport ceased to be the monopoly of the well-to-do. Motor taxis appeared in all major cities. Tractors were developed for use in agriculture. After 1900 lorry transport began to usurp the horse for short delivery jobs. Well before the coming of mass motoring, producers embraced the vision of a new age of cheap, easy mass travel. When Henry Ford set up his own car company in 1903 it was with the deliberate intention of catering to the small townsman and small farmer of the Midwest who needed greater mobility than the horse or railway could provide. The British car-maker, William Morris, set out shortly before the First World War to produce cheaper, standardised cars for mass consumption. "From the first," he later wrote, "I set out to cater for the man in the street." Renault in France aimed his small two-cylinder cars at French peasants who lived too far from the rail network; Porsche produced high-quality racing cars, but dreamed of producing "a small economic car of good performance" to "popularise motoring." The late nineteenth century "bicycle craze" gave a foretaste of the democratisation of consumption, and it is no accident that many of the pioneers of mass motoring began their careers producing bicycles—Ford, Morris, Opel were the most famous. By the 1920s mass motoring was a reality. The Ford "Model T" sold over 15 million. In 1905 there were probably no more than 200,000 cars and lorries worldwide. By 1930 there were 26 million in the United States alone, 1.5 million in Britain and in France, 500,000 in Germany.

It would be wrong to see this process as an entirely smooth one. Though it proved impossible to reverse the triumph of technology expressed by the motor-car and the aeroplane, they were not universally welcomed. To the enthusiastic pioneers of the 1890s they represented the fulfilment of a promise. Modern science and technology could free man from the physical limitations that kept him rooted to the earth and largely dependent on the horse. The new technology could potentially emancipate people from very real limitations of mobility and communication. Yet the new technology could also be perceived as a threat, either to establish vested interests or a more general, unpredictable threat to the secure, self-confident, ordered world of late nineteenth century Europe. The new technology was one component of an aggressive, exhilarating destabilising modernity which had its counterpart in art, in literature, in music.

Some of the objections to the motorcar were mundane. The new form of transport threatened the livelihood of the horse businesses which had remained after the advent of the railway—mainly short-distance delivery work, or cab companies in cities. Although it was to be some time before horses disappeared from city streets, the motor-vehicle from the start threatened to eclipse horse-transport (the number of horses in the USA dropped by almost half between 1913 and 1930). Horse companies lobbied for controls on motor transport, forging a strange alliance with indignant upperclass riders who resented the new status symbol, or with town populations resentful of the danger and inconvenience of the early motor vehicles. In Britain motor cars were at first controlled by the Locomotive Act of 1878 which restricted all mechanical road vehicles to a speed of four miles an hour on open road, and two miles an hour in towns. In addition three people had to accompany each vehicle, one of whom had to walk twenty yards in front carrying a red flag.

A lively debate emerged in Britain in the mid-1890s over the repeal of this act. The motorists' lobby, led by Sir David Salomons, who organised the first public motor show in Britain in 1895, argued for the freedom of the highways, partly on the grounds that a lively motor-car trade would boost employment and should be encouraged. The issue was taken to Parliament where it provoked angry denunciation of the motor car. Finally a new bill, the Locomotives on Highways Act, was passed in November 1896. Under its terms motor vehicles were restricted to 14 miles per hour, were compelled to carry warning lights and a warning bell, and to pay an annual duty of two to three guineas. Some form of taxation was imposed on cars in all countries. It was, the Liberal Prime Minister Henry Asquith remarked in 1907, "almost an ideal tax, because it is a tax on a luxury which is apt to degenerate into a nuisance. . . ."

Wherever the motor vehicle was introduced, central and local government placed it under restriction, limited its speed, controlled its use, and imposed taxes and duties, both on the vehicle and its fuel. This was partly a response to public pressure against what was perceived by many to be a public nuisance. It was also partly out of concern for the motorists themselves and the high rate of accidents suffered in the early days of motoring. Taxation was felt to be necessary as a contribution to the upkeep of roads, most of which in the 1890s were unsuitable for motor traffic. Since the arrival of the railway, roads had fallen into disuse. Long distance horse transport was expensive and inefficient by the standard of rail transport. The coming of motor vehicles forced local authorities to begin a programme of roadbuilding and maintenance which culminated in the interwar years in great state-sponsored building projects, Mussolini's *Autostrade* or Hitler's *Autobahnen*. In the United States in 1905 there were only 150 miles of brick or tarmac road; by 1925 there were 1.2 million miles.

The advent of modern motor technology eventually transformed the industrial economy and the landscape. At the turn of the century little of this material impact was yet evident. What the coming of the motor-vehicle did do was to create a powerful sense of the end of one age and the dawn of another. The new technology promised alarmingly to speed up the pace of things. "Are we moving too fast—not merely in the making of automobiles, but in life generally?" asked Henry Ford. His answer was an emphatic "no." Others saw things differently. In November 1896 the home secretary received a complaint from the Duke of Teck not about cars, but about bicycles in Richmond Park, ridden "not as if guided by sensible thoughtful People, but by Maniacs, Persons in a state of madness. They went about in a pace like Lightning, looking neither right nor left. . . ." Kenneth Graham in his *fin de siècle* fable, *The Wind in the Willows,* published in 1908, bemoaned the coming of the motor-car. Toad of Toad Hall became behind the wheel "the terror, the traffic-queller, before whom all must give way or be smitten into nothingness. . . ." There was in all this some sense of class uneasiness. Motorcars were identified with social *arrivistes,* with the newly rich. The poor Duke of Teck found the bicycles being ridden by "Groups of Roughs."

Above all motor transport was identified, wrongly in fact, with America and Americanisation. Genteel Europeans could bemoan the invasion of vulgar materialism, mass consumerism, as an overseas invention. When Henry Ford began to mass-produce motor cars at very low cost he did so by introducing entirely new factory methods—time and motion studies, conveyor belt production, "scientific management"—which transformed attitudes to industrial production. Very soon "Fordism" became widely imitated. It provoked strong hostility from labour organisations which saw it as yet another way to exploit the worker, through the coercion of the moving production line. But it also aroused the hostility of conservatives in Europe who regretted the passing of older traditions of skill and craftsmanship, and the restless, mechanical age which threatened to subordinate everything to the pace and needs of the machine. Ford himself was very aware of this confrontation between the old age and the new:

> Certainly we are moving faster than before. But is twenty minutes in a motor car easier or harder than four hours' solid trudging down a dirt road? . . . And soon we shall be making in an hour by air what were days' journeys by motor. Shall we then be nervous wrecks? The men at the top, the men who are changing all these things, will tell you the same. They are not breaking down. They are marching the way progress is going and find it easier to go along with progress than to try to hold things back.

Ford's vision of the future was one for the common man, "the labourer in the streetcar." This was the same aim for those other builders of a new age, Lenin and Hitler. The Soviet authorities embraced Fordism and motorisation after 1917 as symbols of a new age of scientific, socialist production, distinct from the indulgent, plutocratic world it had replaced. Hitler's love of fast cars is well known. He remained fascinated with the new technology all his life, but he was particularly attracted to Ford's ideas about mass motoring and the emancipatory effects of modern technology. Hitler personally authorised the search for what became the Volkswagen, ordering a "small four-seater car . . . a sort of low-priced family car in which one could go for weekend trips . . . a car for the people." The German car industry opposed the idea. One of its spokesmen later claimed that it was unheard of that "the common man should be driving a car . . . we were thinking more of a sort of covered up motorcycle." But Hitler was thinking of just such a thing, harnessing German technology to the construction of a New Order in Germany, in which workers, like the well-to-do, could own a car. By the 1930s mass motoring and mass, populist, politics were both components of the new age.

The disquiet created by the motorcar was matched by a very real ambivalence over the future of aviation. Unlike motor vehicles, aviation was immediately perceived to have a very real military application. Indeed science fiction, well before the Wright brothers' historic flights, had already anticipated the likely effects of dropping explosive devices from the air, either from balloons, airships or aircraft. Fictional accounts assumed that the terror effect of attack from the air, even with limited forces, would be sufficient to achieve a military objective. With the coming of successful powered flight, the military application was obvious. In 1908 Count Zeppelin successfully flew the airship which was to bear his name. The strategic implications were immense. For the British, used for so long to the immunity to invasion provided by geography and a strong navy, it was a shock to discover that Britain was "no longer an island." The threat to the existing order was clear. In 1913 Herbert Strang, author of popular air fiction, wrote in the introduction to one of his books that "the fate of Empires will in future, be decided neither on land nor sea but in the air. . . ."

The British seem to have been particularly susceptible to exaggerated and alarmist views of the future of air power. This was partly a reflection of the fact that aviation made very slow ground in Britain compared with continental Europe and the United States, and was more of an unknown quantity. Partly it was a product of the traumatic realisation that, as one British air enthusiast put it in 1916, "every inland town lies on the coast of the ocean of the air, liable to instant and violent attack." For the British population this fact required the same kind of psychological readjustment Americans faced in the 1950s when they realised that Soviet intercontinental missiles could reach U.S. cities. The fear of air bombardment of devastating effect haunted the British ruling classes down to the Second World War, and goes a long way towards explaining the British option in the 1930s for a strategic bombing force capable of deterring an enemy or, if necessary, retaliating in kind.

The threat of the aeroplane ushered in a new strategic age which culminated in Hiroshima and the post-war superpower confrontation. Some profound sense of how air power threatened to undermine or even obliterate the existing order was supplied in another book from 1908, H. G. Wells's *The War in the Air*. In this novel of the new age of technology, Wells contrasts the opulent, progressive Europe in which he lived with the barren consequences of mass bombing and military madness. For Wells, industrial society was at a crossroads, capable through technology, which his contemporaries regarded as the hallmark of progress, of creating the very forces that could utterly annihilate it. This is a paradox that the modern age has yet to resolve, the illusion of irrepressible progress and the reality of apocalyptic menace:

And now the whole fabric of civilisation was bending and giving, and dropping to pieces and melting in the furnace of war . . . Up to the very eve of the War in the Air one sees a spacious spectacle of incessant advance, a worldwide security, enormous areas with highly-organised industry and settled populations, gigantic cities spreading gigantically, the seas and oceans dotted with shipping, the land netted with rails and open ways. Then suddenly the German air-fleets sweep across the scene, and we are in the beginning of the end.

SEX AND THE AUTOMOBILE IN THE JAZZ AGE

Peter Ling

INTRODUCTION

There is a dynamic, interactive relationship between technology and social change. The automobile, perhaps more than any other technology in this century, has dramatically altered the way we go about our day-to-day lives. Most of us get to work in an automobile, drive to the mall to shop or see a movie, take a car to visit friends across town (or sometimes just around the corner), or think nothing of piling the family into the car for a cross-country trip to visit the in-laws. Directly or indirectly, automobile manufacturing, parts and materials supply, road design and construction, and a host of auto-related service industries have become a vital part of the American economy.

During the 1920s, the automobile became part of the new youth culture of the "Jazz Age." Many blamed the automobile for a decline in morality and a rise in premarital and teenage sex. The closed-body automobile offered unprecedented mobility, privacy, and freedom. Fast cars and "fast women" seemed to go together in a way that portended the imminent collapse of respectable society.

Yet, as Peter Ling shows in this article, the relationship between the automobile and changing sexual patterns was much more complex. Well before the automobile achieved widespread use, courtship practices had shifted away from "calling" to "dating," particularly among lower and middle-class Americans. Rather than causing these changes, the automobile indirectly contributed to their extension or continuation. Although it was an important factor in changing sexual mores, the automobile did not determine those changes. The root causes lay elsewhere—in society, demographics, economics, politics, and psychology.

Thanks to the richness of the new recording media of film, phonograph, and glossy magazine, the imagery of the 1920s remains deeply etched on the popular memory. Like the 1960s, the 1920s are remembered as "teenage" years in which an older generation said: "Thou shalt not" and youth replied: "I will!" Youth itself was one essential element in the iconography of the decade. When not dancing or kissing, the carefree flapper and her boyfriend were commonly depicted seated in an automobile, for the motor car was another key symbol of the so-called "Jazz Age."

Some contemporaries saw "fast cars" and "fast" conduct as inextricably mixed. But did the automobile really deserve to be called "the Devil's wagon" or "a brothel on wheels?" One chronicler of courtship was the popular press. The August 1924 edition of *Harper's* magazine carried an article entitled: "Is the Young Person Coming Back?" which recounted the experience of a young man who asked a city girl if he might call on her. The nub of this humorous piece was that when the young man came to "call," he found to his astonishment that "she had her hat on." To older Americans, this could signify only one thing: she expected to go out. This was not what the unsophisticated youth had anticipated at all. To him, coming to call meant being received in the family parlour, making light conversation with the girl and her mother. On subsequent occasions, it might involve taking tea with them and listening politely while the young woman displayed her skills as a pianist. But this was not what the woman had in mind. She was expecting "a date"; to be taken out and "treated," and the young man ended up spending four weeks' savings in an effort to meet her expectations.

A generation later, dating had become so accepted that social scientists felt that Americans had to be reminded that there had been no "dates" before around 1900. Moreover, these scholars linked dating directly to the introduction of the automobile, which was more widely owned by Americans in 1927 than by the citizens of any other nation. There was a car for every five Americans in 1927 whereas in Great Britain there was one for every forty-four people. It would be the swinging sixties before car ownership here reached the American level of the roaring twenties. By combining mobility and privacy, the automobile offered young Americans in the 1920s a "getaway" vehicle from parental supervision. Consequently, students of American courtship attributed the rise of dating to the automobile's arrival. Dr. Evelyn Duvall in a 1956 textbook for teenagers, for instance, declared simply that the car had changed courtship.

To understand the automobile's contribution to this change, however, one should first clarify the nature of earlier courtship practices. The convention of calling was not universal practice in late nineteenth-century America. It was a bourgeois custom based on the concerns and capabilities of the middle classes. As a courtship ritual, calling involved three of the pillars of bourgeois life: the family, respectability, and in particular, privacy. The focal point of calling was gaining admittance into the private family sphere of the home which was the central expression of bourgeois status. Although privacy itself had only become a realistic possibility in the eighteenth century, thereafter it had rapidly established itself as a necessity for the affluent and an aspiration for the poor. A badge of respectability, privacy was profoundly important to the nineteenth-century bourgeois family whose individual members each pined for rooms of their own. Only affluence afforded such spaciousness and so the separate parlour in which callers applied for admission into the bosom of the family was itself a status symbol. As guardians of the home, women were the chief arbiters of who could call and who would never be invited. Daughters could invite male suitors to call but there remained a parental veto on who would be received. In this way, family honour and essential privacy could be preserved. However, parental oversight always threatened to infringe the maturing offspring's right to privacy. To uphold their own notions of honour and ethics, Peter Gay points out, parents went to extraordinary lengths. They would "open their children's letters, oversee their reading, chaperone their visitors, (even) inspect their underwear." To the dismay of the younger generation, bourgeois parents failed to respect the principle of privacy they preached.

For the mass of working-class Americans, such privacy was very remote from the daily reality of overcrowding. Cramped lodging houses made the social niceties of "calling" ludicrously impractical. Of course, a large proportion of the American working class was either immigrant or the children of immigrants and so tried to continue in the New World their traditional practices of chaperonage and female seclusion. However, as social workers like Jane Addams noted, the need for everyone to earn money in impoverished working-class households made such customs hard to maintain, while crowded living conditions simultaneously prevented the adoption of bourgeois habits. The working classes consequently pioneered dating as an expedient born of the opportunities offered and the comforts denied to them. Forced out onto the streets, Addams warned, working-class youth was highly susceptible to the enticements of commercialised entertainment. Recognising the need for relaxation after a harsh working day, Addams worried nonetheless about the vulgarity of available leisure facilities. She told her middle-class readers of pathetic instances when her work took her into one of Chicago's many saloons and she would be stopped by naive youths who asked her to introduce them to a "nice" girl. Addams clearly believed that none would be found in such a place.

If poverty pushed the lower orders onto the streets, wealth enabled the upper classes to explore every avenue of city life. Money gave access to theatres, restaurants, galleries, and clubs. By 1900, the traditional events of the season, such as the opera, began to be deemed *passé* by a growing number of privileged youths. These "bohemians" began to perceive the possibility of a new freedom arising from the anonymity of crowded city streets. Paradoxically, the public places of the metropolis could be profoundly private, provided one avoided the stamping ground of one's own social class. Thus, affluent youth figuratively "crossed the tracks" to enjoy a surer privacy amidst working-class crowds than they experienced in their parents' homes. A revolution in etiquette had begun.

Women who regularly read the *Ladies Home Journal,* who could recall being warned in 1907 that it was scandalous to be seen dining alone with a man, even a relative, learnt from a debutante of 1914 that it was "now considered smart to go to the low order of dance halls, and not only be a looker-on, but also to dance among all sorts and conditions of men and women . . . ." Thus leisure-class and working-class youth began to date and sometimes to frequent the same venues. Given the existence of dating among working-class Americans prior to 1900 and its adoption by the leisure class of the so-called "mauve" decade, dating was an established urban practice before motoring was. By 1912, no more than 4.2 percent of American households had automobiles. A far larger proportion, one suspects, saw their daughters leave the house to sample city delights by carriage, trolley-car, or on foot. Courtship was changing, therefore, even before the motor-car drew up to the average American's door.

If dating pre-dated motoring, public anxiety over sex preceded both. However, there were particular reasons why the turn of the century saw an increase in this concern. In the 1890s, just as courtship was made respectable by being confined to the front parlour, so the sexual subject itself was supposedly made safe by being excluded from public life. The taboo even extended to medical societies who were reluctant to discuss sexual practices and their associated health hazards. However, this "conspiracy of silence," as its critics termed it, was challenged because of a growing professional recognition of the spread of venereal diseases and of the serious health implications. Ostensibly respectable men, it was known, were contracting syphilis from prostitutes and then transmitting the disease to their wives and unborn children. Horror at this "syphilis of the innocent" was intensified by alarmist forecasts of the spread of such infections via the numerous shared facilities of the late nineteenth-century city, such as the omni-present drinking cup and, of course, communal toilets. Such fears of contagion were politically useful to all groups seeking to curtail casual social contact. Racial segregation, for example, was advocated on the grounds of the high incidence of contagious diseases among Negroes. When female workers in the Treasury Department in Washington urged racial segregation in federal offices, they reported specifically their fears of infection from shared toilet facilities. Similarly, nativists, calling for immigration restriction, urged tougher health standards and inspection procedures at immigration entry points. Thus at the start of this century the VD threat seemed graver and more pervasive than anyone had previously imagined. Moreover, in a world of contagion, improved transport undermined attempts to quarantine the dangerous classes.

Physicians concerned with the health hazards of VD eventually formed the American Social Hygiene Association (ASHA) in 1905. Despite its euphemistic name, the organisation differed from earlier purity campaigners in its belief that the taboo on public discussion of sex must be ended. As these doctors knew, ignorance injured the pure as well as the profane. For the general welfare, therefore, American youth should be given sex education in order to dispel harmful myths, notably the deeply ingrained belief that the male sex need was so great that sexual continence was physically harmful for a man. Hundreds of thousands of pamphlets were distributed to warn young Americans of the perils of sexual promiscuity. In addition, the mass-circulation magazines of this "muck-raking" age eagerly seized on a sensational topic and published exposés of the so-called "white slave trade" and prostitution. Like earlier moral campaigners, however, the ASHA regarded prostitutes as the vital source of venereal infection. Consequently, municipal and state authorities were pressed to eradicate "red-light" districts, while at the federal level, Congress passed the Mann Act of 1911, which made it a criminal offence to transport a woman across state lines for sexual purposes.

This last measure reflected the public outcry provoked by the press campaign against the alleged trafficking of women for brothels: the "white slave trade." It was not primarily a response to the ability of motorists to escape legal restrictions on sexual conduct by crossing state lines. National governmental concern over the health dangers of prostitution peaked with America's mobilisation for war in 1917. Fearing that the armed forces would be decimated by VD before they reached the Western Front, the Wilson administration appointed ASHA lawyer Bascom Johnson to oversee the suppression of red-light districts near military bases. It was Johnson who first pointed to the automobile as an obstacle in the fight against vice. "The automobile prostitute," he wrote, "is the bane of law enforcement officials." In January 1919, Johnson urged federal legislation to combat this new phenomenon. However, as the concurrent moral crusade of Prohibition demonstrated, such legislation would be hard to enforce. Government at all levels had neither the officers nor the newly purchased motor vehicles to patrol city streets and country highways.

The fixed abode of ill repute, however, was vulnerable to the anti-vice campaign. Robert and Helen Lynd noticed the impact of one such "clean-up" campaign in Muncie, Indiana. During the local oil and natural gas boom of the 1890s, Muncie had had twenty to twenty-five brothels. However, the anti-vice campaign of the First World War period had been so vigorous that by the early 1920s the city had at most "three fly-by-night furtively conducted houses of prostitution catering exclusively to the working class." The Lynds also reported, however, a statement by Muncie's juvenile court judge that "the automobile has become a house of prostitution on wheels." This echoed the concurrent observation of the U.S. Public Health Service Director, Dr. O. C. Wenger, that, with the suppression of red-light districts, "the entire situation has changed. The automobile has replaced the room of the prostitute." Thus, the social hygiene campaign had eradicated neither the myth of an overpowering male sexual need nor prostitution, but by suppressing brothels, it had forced the "ladies of the night" to take their show (and its attendant health hazards) on the road.

The Lynds also cite a Cleveland hospital survey which reported that a large number of male venereal patients claimed to have been infected not by full-time prostitutes but by working women whose low pay pushed them into accepting "treats" in exchange for sex. If these so-called "amateurs" comprised a large proportion of prostitutes, then their poverty helped to define its location. At the turn of the century 80–90 percent of female wage-earners lived at home because their incomes were too low for them to live alone. The minority who rented lodgings were objects of moral suspicion as they struggled to eke out their meagre incomes. Unable to afford suitable accommodation for their dishonourable secondary profession and no longer housed in communally accepted red-light districts, prostitutes found an economical expedient in the form of their client's car. This may explain in part why three brothels for the working class remained in Muncie since the latter's car ownership and use was less extensive than that found among higher income groups. Car ownership was, however, incredibly high. Only 10 percent of Muncie's families had incomes above the U.S. Census Bureau's subsistence level of $1,921 at a time when motor trade authorities reckoned that owning a cheap car required an annual income of $2,800. Nonetheless, two out of every three families in Muncie owned cars.

If more citizens of Muncie had cars than could apparently afford them, then equally, more residents had sex than the guardians of public morality would have preferred. Of the thirty girls charged with "sex crimes" before the juvenile court in the year prior to September 1st, 1924, nineteen committed the offence in an automobile, while the remaining eleven declined to say. The juveniles' judge seems to have had grounds for describing the car in lurid terms. However, prostitution was not intrinsically a juvenile offence nor was it the only sex crime under Indiana law, so we cannot assume that the thirty women were charged with prostitution. Another category of sex crime was having sex with a minor (that is, under the age of consent, which varied from state to state). Given that the accused appeared before a juvenile court, it seems likely that at least some were guilty of sexual precocity rather than prostitution. The judge's blanket condemnation reflected his adherence to a moral code which regarded all extra-marital sex as debased and therefore classed all females who participated in it as "fallen women."

With hindsight, his outburst may seem to us unjust. Presumably, therefore, one should welcome the arrival of back-seat sex in the 1920s as a harbinger of sexual liberation. Now freed from the oppressive scrutiny of their guardians, young people were able to respond to their "natural" desires. The automobile aided this process, especially when car manufacturers shifted from open-top to closed-body models, improved interior upholstery, and included a heater as a standard feature. Increased public spending on highway improvement helped, too, by making secluded beauty spots more accessible to couples in search of inspiration and opportunity. However, just as the current drug problem in America has encouraged a sympathetic scholarly reappraisal of Prohibition, so the AIDS pandemic obliges us to reassess our attitudes to the social hygienists. Some doctors in the 1920s recognised that the easy mobility provided by private passenger cars and improved roads had serious implications for the containment of contagious diseases in the same way as medical authorities in our own time acknowledge the contribution of a network of air routes to the global spread of AIDS.

However, this is not the principal reason why the concern expressed in the 1920s about the incidence of sex in cars should be treated with understanding rather than smug derision. The move from calling to dating was not simply a move away from prudish parental oversight but also a transition from a courtship conducted in a place defined culturally as female, the home, to a sphere defined as male, public life. While many of the Victorian conventions surrounding the notion of separate spheres were undoubtedly oppressive, the calling ritual by virtue of its location in the home gave bourgeois women (mothers and daughters) a measure of control that should not be forgotten. The emergence of dating entailed the loss of this control for women.

The different conventions governing invitations under the two patterns of courtship indicate this shift of power. Under the calling system, the woman asked the man and could refuse to receive him, even when he called. Under the dating system, however, it was left to the man to issue invitations since he would bear the expense. Moreover, whatever the disadvantages of courtship conducted within the parental home, it did provide a comparatively safe environment in which to meet a man about whom a woman might know relatively little. To those who argue that this is a defence of the kind of double standard that imprisoned women for years (men can go out; women cannot), my response must be that since the social hygienists did not break the belief in an overpowering male sexual need, women in the twentieth century continued to face men largely conditioned to the idea that they must not readily take "no" for an answer. Getting out into a sexist public world was not automatically liberating.

Moreover, the practicalities of dating made courtship manifestly a process governed by cash and thereby accentuated the treatment of women as a commodity. The low wages of female workers ensured that many working women had to scrimp on essentials to have money for leisure. The willingness of a man to bear the cost of an evening-out became vitally important under such circumstances. Economic inequality thus ratified male power. Dating became an exercise in the machismo of capitalism; the man with money could afford to ask girls out; he had a car to take them out in; he drove, he paid, and she had to be "good company" in return. In this sense, prostitution became a paradigm of sexual relations in general and the automobile truly became a brothel on wheels. Social reformer Mary Simkovitch observed acidly in 1910: "The young men of the big cities today are not gallantly paying the way of these girls for nothing."

However, nothing was what they might get, despite the persistence of sexual inequality throughout the century. When an American teens' magazine of the 1950s asked: "Does a girl have to pet to be popular?," one boy responded: "When a boy takes a girl out and spends $1.20 on her (like I did the other night) he expects a little petting in return (which I didn't get)." While this incident, like the earlier account of a youth spending the equivalent of four weeks' savings on his date, indicates that dating was not automatically male-controlled, male car ownership did not help women in this power struggle. The automobile was part of the male-owned wealth that gave an implied right to command, a right made manifest by the driver's choice of homeward route. Women had to bargain and the sexual practice of "petting" emerged as an integral part of this process. A wide variety of sexual practices short of intercourse constituted petting. The overwhelming majority of teenagers interviewed by the

Lynds in the mid-1920s said they had been to petting parties and the automobile was the commonest place to pet. Of course, neither the desire for nor the pleasure from petting was always confined to the male. Moreover, it was grudgingly accepted that the woman should have a brake on the pace of progression through the various phases of petting, even though the man was expected to try to get as far as he could.

Each of the phases of petting came to be associated with a corresponding emotional stage in a couple's relationship. Kissing, while not automatic, was all right if the two merely liked each other; "deep" or "French" kissing indicated romantic attachment; breast touching through the clothing heralded that things were becoming serious, and continued under the bra, if the feelings intensified; finally, explorations "below the waist" were reserved only for couples who considered themselves truly in love. The culmination of this logic was intercourse with one's fiancé. The first large-scale surveys of American sexual practices conducted during the 1950s suggested that this had been the experience of young women in the 1920s. Alfred Kinsey reported that women who reached sexual maturity in the 1920s were far less likely to be virgins at marriage than were those who matured before the First World War. Nonetheless, a majority of women under thirty years old during the 1920s did not experience premarital sex, and half of those that did had sex only with their fiancés. As a prelude to matrimony rather than a wholly unrelated activity, such sex may be regarded as less revolutionary than it might otherwise appear, and correspondingly the automobile which facilitated such sexual encounters may be deemed less subversive than some contemporaries feared.

Americans did have sex in automobiles in the 1920s. However, the contribution of the motor car to the much-vaunted wantonness of the twenties was an indirect one. Even before the automobile was available young Americans of the leisure class were seeking anonymous places where they could ignore the bounds of propriety. Working-class youth had even earlier resorted to the streets in search of companionship and pleasure. What the automobile produced was a diffusion and intensification of this incipient pattern of dating. Other factors were also important to this trend. Successful campaigns against child labour and in favour of prolonged compulsory schooling both reflected and reinforced changing notions of youth itself. Increasingly, adolescence in particular was seen as a time of experimentation, a somewhat separate, and some believed therapeutic, prelude to adult life. Thus we should not accept uncritically the idea that customs and institutions simply react belatedly to technological change. American society in the 1920s was struggling to accommodate social as well as technological innovations.

At the same time the inertia and shortsightedness of institutions must not be overlooked. One simple reason why motoring was so deeply implicated in the youth practices of the 1920s was the absence of any effective restriction on the right to drive. In Muncie, young teenagers could drive, provided they could persuade their parents to lend them the car. The Lynds remark that such requests were a major cause of family arguments in Muncie, and the outcome of these domestic disputes hinged on parental attitudes to youth as well as mass car ownership. While legislative inaction and parental trust enabled apparently sex-hungry teenagers to take to America's roads in the 1920s, the active state suppression of red-light districts pushed prostitutes too, into cars in secluded parking spots. Just as the moralists feared, the automobile had become a brothel on wheels. Yet the deplorable thing was not that so much had changed, but that sexism remained the same. Dating was hazardous not because of automobility but because of male attitudes to sex. For, as most women came to appreciate, they were most in danger when the car was parked.

LESS WORK FOR MOTHER?

Ruth Schwartz Cowan

INTRODUCTION

The conventional wisdom holds that advanced, labor-saving technologies result in more leisure time and generally lead to a higher quality of life. This notion is consistent with turn-of-the-century ideas of progress and the necessary relationship between technological advance and social improvement. Yet, as we have seen with other technologies, the reality is quite different. New technologies can be deceptive. They often complicate our lives rather than simplifying them, and they can lead to totally unanticipated social and economic problems.

Ruth Schwartz Cowan focuses on three technologies—the portable vacuum cleaner, the electric washing machine, and the automobile—to see how they have affected the amount of time the typical homemaker spends on household chores. Surprisingly, she finds that as a result of the introduction of these machines, women actually had to spend more time than did their mothers or grandmothers on routine household tasks. There are many reasons for this phenomenon, not least of which was that most of the new household technologies set higher standards of cleanliness and imposed on women jobs previously done by servants or chauffeurs, but Cowan's study raises a deeper question of technological determinism. Did these new technologies cause women's work to change? Or did they underscore or accelerate shifts in women's roles and work that were already underway? Either way, a complex variety of new household technologies, ranging from sewing machines to electric can openers to microwave ovens, has had little effect on the amount of effort a woman puts into housework, which remains, as it was at the turn of the century, a lonely, full-time job for which there is little appreciation or compensation.

Things are seldom what they seem. Skim milk masquerades as cream. And labor-saving household appliances often do not save labor. This is the surprising conclusion reached by a small army of historians, sociologists, and home economists who have undertaken, in recent years, to study the one form of work that has turned out to be most resistant to inquiry and analysis—namely, housework.

During the first half of the twentieth century, the average American household was transformed by the introduction of a group of machines that profoundly altered the daily lives of housewives; the forty years between 1920 and 1960 witnessed what might be aptly called the "industrial revolution in the home." Where once there had been a wood- or coal-burning stove there now was a gas or electric range. Clothes that had once been scrubbed on a metal washboard were now tossed into a tub and cleansed by an electrically driven agitator. The dryer replaced the clothesline; the vacuum cleaner replaced the broom; the refrigerator replaced the icebox and the root cellar; an automatic pump, some piping, and a tap replaced the hand pump, the bucket, and the well. No one had to chop and haul wood any more. No one had to shovel out ashes or beat rugs or carry water; no one even had to toss egg whites with a fork for an hour to make an angel food cake.

And yet American housewives in 1960, 1970, and even 1980 continued to log about the same number of hours at their work as their grandmothers and mothers had in 1910, 1920, and 1930. The earliest time studies of housewives date from the very same period in which time studies of other workers were becoming popular—the first three decades of the twentieth century. The sample sizes of these studies were usually quite small, and they did not always define housework in precisely the same way (some counted an hour spent taking children to the playground as "work," while others called it "leisure"), but their results were more or less consistent: whether rural or urban, the average American housewife performed fifty to sixty hours of unpaid work in her home every week, and the only variable that significantly altered this was the number of small children.

A half-century later not much had changed. Survey research had become much more sophisticated, and sample sizes had grown considerably, but the results of the time studies remained surprisingly consistent. The average American housewife, now armed with dozens of motors and thousands of electronic chips, still spends fifty to sixty hours a week doing housework. The only variable that significantly altered the size of that number was full-time employment in the labor force; "working" housewives cut down the average number of hours that they spend cooking and cleaning, shopping and chauffeuring, to a not insignificant thirty-five—virtually the equivalent of another full-time job.

How can this be true? Surely even the most sophisticated advertising copywriter of all times could not fool almost the entire American population over the course of at least three generations. Laborsaving devices must be saving something, or Americans would not continue, year after year, to plunk down their hard-earned dollars for them.

And if laborsaving devices have not saved labor in the home, then what is it that has suddenly made it possible for more than 70 percent of the wives and mothers in the American population to enter the work force and stay there? A brief glance at the histories of some of the technologies that have transformed housework during the twentieth century will help us answer some of these questions.

The portable vacuum cleaner was one of the earliest electric appliances to make its appearance in American homes, and reasonably priced models appeared on the retail market as early as 1910. For decades prior to the turn of the century, inventors had been trying to create a carpet-cleaning system that would improve on the carpet sweeper with adjustable rotary brushes (patented by Melville Bissell in 1876), or the semiannual ritual of hauling rugs outside and beating them, or the practice of regularly sweeping the dirt out of a rug that had been covered with dampened, torn newspapers. Early efforts to solve the problem had focused on the use of large steam, gasoline, or electric motors attached to piston-type pumps and lots of hoses. Many of these "stationary" vacuum-cleaning systems were installed in apartment houses or hotels, but some were hauled around the streets in horsedrawn carriages by entrepreneurs hoping to establish themselves as "professional housecleaners."

In the first decade of the twentieth century, when fractional-horsepower electric motors became widely—and inexpensively—available, the portable vacuum cleaner intended for use in an individual household was born. One early model—invented by a woman, Corrine Dufour—consisted of a rotary brush, an electrically driven fan, and a wet sponge for absorbing the dust and dirt. Another, patented by David E. Kenney in 1907, had a twelve-inch nozzle attached to a metal tube attached to a flexible hose that led to a vacuum pump and separating devices. The Hoover, which was based on a brush, a fan, and a collecting bag, was on the market by 1908. The Electrolux, the first of the canister types of cleaner, which could vacuum something above the level of the floor, was brought over from Sweden in 1924 and met with immediate success.

These early vacuum cleaners were hardly a breeze to operate. All were heavy, and most were extremely cumbersome to boot. One early home economist mounted a basal metabolism machine on the back of one of her hapless students and proceeded to determine that more energy was expended in the effort to clean a sample carpet with a vacuum cleaner than when the same carpet was attacked with a hand broom. The difference, of course, was that the vacuum cleaner did a better job, at least on carpets, because a good deal of what the broom stirred up simply resettled a foot or two away from where it had first been lodged.

Whatever the liabilities of early vacuum cleaners may have been, Americans nonetheless appreciated their virtues; according to a market survey taken in Zanesville, Ohio, in 1926, slightly more than half the households owned one. Later improvements in design made these devices easier to operate. By 1960 vacuum cleaners were found in 70 percent of the nation's homes.

When the vacuum cleaner is viewed in a historical context, however, it is easy to see why it did not save housewifely labor. Its introduction coincided almost precisely with the disappearance of the domestic servant. The number of persons engaged in household service dropped from 1,851,000 in 1910 to 1,411,000 in 1920, while the number of households enumerated in the census rose from 20.3 million to 24.4 million. Moreover, between 1900 and 1920 the number of household servants per thousand persons dropped from 98.9 to 58.0, while during the 1920s the decline was even more precipitous as the restrictive immigration acts dried up what had once been the single most abundant source of domestic labor.

For the most economically comfortable segment of the population, this meant just one thing: the adult female head of the household was doing more housework than she had ever done before. What Maggie had once done with a broom, Mrs. Smith was now doing with a vacuum cleaner. Knowing that this was happening, several early copywriters for vacuum cleaner advertisements focused on its implications. The vacuum cleaner, General Electric announced in 1918, is better than a maid: it doesn't quit, get drunk, or demand higher wages. The switch from Maggie to Mrs. Smith shows up, in time-study statistics, as an increase in the time that Mrs. Smith is spending at her work.

For those—and they were the vast majority of the population—who were not economically comfortable, the vacuum cleaner implied something else again: not an increase in the time spent in housework but an increase in the standard of living. In many households across the country, acquisition of a vacuum cleaner was connected to an expansion of living space, the move from a small apartment to a small house, the purchase of wall-to-wall carpeting. If this did not happen during the difficult 1930s, it became more possible during the expansive 1950s. As living quarters grew larger, standards for their upkeep increased; rugs had to be vacuumed every week, in some households every day, rather than semiannually, as had been customary. The net result, of course, was that when armed with a vacuum cleaner, housewives whose parents had been poor could keep more space cleaner than their mothers and grandmothers would have ever believed possible. We might put this everyday phenomenon in language that economists can understand: the introduction of the vacuum cleaner led to improvements in productivity but not to any significant decrease in the amount of time expended by each worker.

The history of the washing machine illustrates a similar phenomenon. "Blue Monday" had traditionally been, as its name implies, the bane of a housewife's existence—especially when Monday turned out to be "Monday . . . and Tuesday to do the ironing." Thousands of patents for "new and improved" washers were issued during the nineteenth century in an effort to cash in on the housewife's despair. Most of these early washing machines were wooden or metal tubs combined with some kind of hand-cranked mechanism that would rub or push or twirl laundry when the tub was filled with water and soap. At the end of the century, the Sears catalog offered four such washing machines, ranging in price from $2.50 to $4.25, all sold in combination with hand-cranked wringers.

These early machines may have saved time in the laundering process (four shirts could be washed at once instead of each having to be rubbed separately against a washboard), but they probably didn't save much energy. Lacking taps and drains, the tubs still had to be filled and emptied by hand, and each piece still had to be run through a wringer and hung up to dry.

Not long after the appearance of fractional-horsepower motors, several enterprising manufacturers had the idea of hooking them up to the crank mechanisms of washers and wringers—and the electric washer was born. By the 1920s, when mass production of such machines began, both the general structure of the machine (a central-shaft agitator rotating within a cylindrical tub, hooked up to the household water supply) and the general structure of the industry (oligopolistic—with a very few firms holding most of the patents and controlling most of the market) had achieved their final form. By 1926 just over a quarter of the families in Zanesville had an electric washer, but by 1941 fully 52 percent of all American households either owned or had interior access (which means that they could use coin-operated models installed in the basements of apartment houses) to such a machine. The automatic washer, which consisted of a vertically rotating washer cylinder that could also act as a centrifugal extractor, was introduced by the Bendix Home Appliance Corporation in 1938, but it remained expensive, and therefore inaccessible, until after World War II. This machine contained timing devices that allowed it to proceed through its various cycles automatically; by spinning the clothes around in the extractor phase of its cycle, it also eliminated the wringer. Although the Bendix subsequently disappeared from the retail market (versions of this sturdy machine may still be found in Laundromats), its design principles are replicated in the agitator washers that currently chug away in millions of American homes.

Both the early wringer washers and their more recent automatic cousins have released American women from the burden of drudgery. No one who has ever tried to launder a sheet by hand, and without the benefits of hot running water, would want to return to the days of the scrub board and tub. But "labor" is composed of both "energy expenditure" and "time expenditure," and the history of laundry work demonstrates that the one may be conserved while the other is not.

The reason for this is, as with the vacuum cleaner, twofold. In the early decades of the century, many households employed laundresses to do their wash; this was true, surprisingly enough, even for some very poor households when wives and mothers were disabled or employed full-time in field or factory. Other households—rich and poor—used commercial laundry services. Large, mechanized "steam" laundries were first constructed in this country in the 1860s, and by the 1920s they could be found in virtually every urban neighborhood and many rural ones as well.

But the advent of the electric home washer spelled doom both for the laundress and for the commercial laundry; since the housewife's labor was unpaid, and since the washer took so much of the drudgery out of washday, the onetime expenditure for a machine seemed, in many families, a more sensible arrangement than continuous expenditure for domestic services. In the process, of course, the time spent on laundry work by the individual housewife, who had previously employed either a laundress or a service, was bound to increase.

For those who had not previously enjoyed the benefits of relief from washday drudgery, the electric washer meant something quite different but equally significant: an upgrading of household cleanliness. Men stopped wearing removable collars and cuffs, which meant that the whole of their shirts had to be washed and then ironed. Housewives began changing two sheets every week, instead of moving the top sheet to the bottom and adding only one that was fresh. Teenagers began changing their underwear every day instead of every weekend. In the early 1960s, when synthetic no-iron fabrics were introduced, the size of the household laundry load increased again; shirts and skirts, sheets and blouses that had once been sent out to the dry cleaner or the corner laundry were now being tossed into the household wash basket. By the 1980s the average American housewife, armed now with an automatic washing machine and an automatic dryer, was processing roughly ten times (by weight) the amount of laundry that her mother had been accustomed to. Drudgery had disappeared, but the laundry hadn't. The average time spent on this chore in 1925 had been 5.8 hours per week; in 1964 it was 6.2.

And then there is the automobile. We do not usually think of our cars as household appliances, but that is precisely what they are, since housework, as currently understood, could not possibly be performed without them. The average American housewife is today more likely to be found behind a steering wheel than in front of a stove. While writing this article I interrupted myself five times: once to take a child to field-hockey practice; then a second time, to bring her back when practice was finished; once to pick up some groceries at the supermarket; once to retrieve my husband, who was stranded at the train station; once for a trip to a doctor's office. Each time I was doing housework, and each time I had to use my car.

Like the washing machine and the vacuum cleaner, the automobile started to transform the nature of housework in the 1920s. Until the introduction of the Model T in 1908, automobiles had been playthings for the idle rich, and although many wealthy women learned to drive early in the century (and several participated in well-publicized auto races), they were hardly the women who were likely to be using their cars to haul groceries.

But by 1920, and certainly by 1930, all this had changed. Helen and Robert Lynd, who conducted an intensive study of Muncie, Indiana, between 1923 and 1925 (reported in their famous book *Middletown*), estimated that in Muncie in the 1890s only 125 families, all members of the "elite," owned a horse and buggy, but by 1923 there were 6,222 passenger cars in the city, "roughly one for every 7.1 persons, or two for every three families." By 1930, according to national statistics, there were roughly 30 million households in the United States—and 26 million registered automobiles.

What did the automobile mean for the housewife? Unlike public transportation systems, it was convenient. Located right at her doorstep, it could deposit her at the doorstep that she wanted or needed to visit. And unlike the bicycle or her own two feet, the automobile could carry bulky packages as well as several additional people. Acquisition of an automobile therefore meant that a housewife, once she had learned how to drive, could become her own door-to-door delivery service. And as more housewives acquired automobiles, more businessmen discovered the joys of dispensing with delivery services—particularly during the Depression.

To make a long story short, the iceman does not cometh anymore. Neither does the milkman, the bakery truck, the butcher, the grocer, the knife sharpener, the seamstress, or the doctor. Like many other businessmen, doctors discovered that their earnings increased when they stayed in their offices and transferred the responsibility for transportation to their ambulatory patients.

And so a new category was added to the housewife's traditional job description: chauffeur. The suburban station wagon is now "Mom's Taxi." Children who once walked to school now have to be transported by their mothers; husbands who once walked home from work now have to be picked up by their wives; groceries that once were dispensed from pushcarts or horse-drawn wagons now have to be packed into paper bags and hauled home in family cars. "Contemporary women," one time-study expert reported in 1974, "spend about one full working day per week on the road and in stores compared with less than two hours per week for women in the 1920s." If everything we needed to maintain our homes and sustain our families were delivered right to our doorsteps—and every member of the family had independent means for getting where she or he wanted to go—the hours spent in housework by American housewives would decrease dramatically.

The histories of the vacuum cleaner, the washing machine, and the automobile illustrate the varied reasons why the time spent in housework has not markedly decreased in the United States during the last half-century despite the introduction of so many ostensibly laborsaving appliances. But these histories do not help us understand what has made it possible for so many American wives and mothers to enter the labor force fulltime during those same years. Until recently, one of the explanations most often offered for the startling increase in the participation of married women in the work force (up from 24.8 percent in 1950 to 50.1 percent in 1980) was household technology. What with microwave ovens and frozen foods, washer and dryer combinations and paper diapers, the reasoning goes, housework can now be done in no time at all, and women have so much time on their hands that they find they must go out and look for a job for fear of going stark, raving mad.

As every "working" housewife knows, this pattern of reasoning is itself stark, raving mad. Most adult women are in the work force today quite simply because they need the money. Indeed, most "working" housewives today hold down not one but two jobs; they put in what has come to be called a "double day." Secretaries, lab technicians, janitors, sewing machine operators, teachers, nurses, or physicians for eight (or nine or ten) hours, they race home to become chief cook and bottle washer for another five, leaving the cleaning and the marketing for Saturday and Sunday. Housework, as we have seen, still takes a lot of time, modern technology notwithstanding.

Yet household technologies have played a major role in facilitating (as opposed to causing) what some observers believe to be the most significant social revolution of our time. They do it in two ways, the first of which we have already noted. By relieving housework of the drudgery that it once entailed, washing machines, vacuum cleaners, dishwashers, and water pumps have made it feasible for a woman to put in a double day without destroying her health, to work full-time and still sustain herself and her family at a reasonably comfortable level.

The second relationship between household technology and the participation of married women in the work force is considerably more subtle. It involves the history of some technologies that we rarely think of as technologies at all—and certainly not as household appliances. Instead of being sheathed in stainless steel or porcelain, these devices appear in our kitchens in little brown bottles and bags of flour; instead of using switches and buttons to turn them on, we use hypodermic needles and sugar cubes. They are various forms of medication, the products not only of modern medicine but also of modern industrial chemistry: polio vaccines and vitamin pills; tetanus toxins and ampicillin; enriched breads and tuberculin tests.

Before any of these technologies had made their appearance, nursing may well have been the most time-consuming and most essential aspect of housework. During the eighteenth and nineteenth centuries and even during the first five decades of the twentieth century, it was the woman of the house who was expected (and who had been trained, usually by *her* mother) to sit up all night cooling and calming a feverish child, to change bandages on suppurating wounds, to clean bed linens stained with excrement, to prepare easily digestible broths, to cradle colicky infants on her lap for hours on end, to prepare bodies for burial. An attack of the measles might mean the care of a bedridden child for a month. Pneumonia might require six months of bed rest. A small knife cut could become infected and produce a fever that would rage for days. Every summer brought the fear of polio epidemics, and every polio epidemic left some group of mothers with the perpetual problem of tending to the needs of a handicapped child.

Cholera, diphtheria, typhoid fever—if they weren't fatal—could mean weeks of sleepless nights and hard-pressed days. "Just as soon as the person is attacked," one experienced mother wrote to her worried daughter during a cholera epidemic in Oklahoma in 1885, "be it ever so slightly, he or she ought to go to bed immediately and stay there; put a mustard [plaster] over the bowels and if vomiting over the stomach. See that the feet are kept warm, either by warm iron or brick, or bottles of hot water. If the disease progresses the limbs will begin to cramp, which must be prevented by applying cloths wrung out of hot water and wrapping round them. When one is vomiting so terribly, of course, it is next to impossible to keep medicine down, but in cholera it must be done."

These were the routines to which American women were once accustomed, routines regarded as matters of life and death. To gain some sense of the way in which modern medicines have altered not only the routines of housework but also the emotional commitment that often accompanies such work, we need only read out a list of the diseases for which most American children are unlikely to succumb today, remembering how many of them once were fatal or terribly disabling: diphtheria, whooping cough, tetanus, pellagra, rickets, measles, mumps, tuberculosis, smallpox, cholera, malaria, and polio.

And many of today's ordinary childhood complaints, curable within a few days of the ingestion of antibiotics, once might have entailed weeks, or even months, of full-time attention: bronchitis; strep throat; scarlet fever; bacterial pneumonia; infections of the skin, or the eyes, or the ears, or the airways. In the days before the introduction of modern vaccines, antibiotics, and vitamin supplements, a mother who was employed full-time was a serious, sometimes life-endangering threat to the health of her family. This is part of the reason why life expectancy was always low and infant mortality high among the poorest segment of the population—those most likely to be dependent upon a mother's wages.

Thus modern technology, especially modern medical technology, has made it possible for married women to enter the work force by releasing housewives not just from drudgery but also from the dreaded emotional equation of female employment with poverty and disease. She may be exhausted at the end of her double day, but the modern "working" housewife can at least fall into bed knowing that her efforts have made it possible to sustain her family at a level of health and comfort that not so long ago was reserved only for those who were very rich.

WHY WILBUR AND ORVILLE?

Peter L. Jakab

INTRODUCTION

On a cold December morning in 1903, two brothers from Ohio, Orville and Wilbur Wright, realized the dream of centuries when, from an isolated beach at Kitty Hawk, North Carolina, they made the world's first powered flight.

From the beginning, much about this remarkable success has been difficult to explain. After all, how could a couple of unknown bicycle builders from Dayton, without college educations, succeed where so many others had failed? What did they have going for them that all the others did not? From where did their special genius come? What were the secrets of their success?

The conventional answer that aviation historians have given to these questions usually revolves around the fact that the Wrights had the good sense to learn to fly and control their airplane in glider form before they put power into it. They learned a great deal about the use of aerodynamic surfaces to control the airplane in a satisfactory manner, and together with the experience they had acquired as pilots, they were able to fly their plane without difficulty when they did put power into it.

Without disagreeing with this conventional answer, Peter Jakab, a curator at the National Air and Space Museum, has recently isolated another factor for analysis. In his 1990 study, *Visions of a Flying Machine: The Wright Brothers and the Process of Invention*, Jakab draws attention to the importance of visual thinking, and what is sometimes called "the mind's eye," in the Wrights' invention of the airplane. As Jakab explains, many of the best engineers "see" things in their minds before engaging in the empirical process leading to the actual invention. The machine has to "look right," both in an aesthetic and a practical sense, before the inventors are convinced they are on the right track. The Wrights, as Jakab demonstrates, were masters at thinking visually and translating abstractions into hardware.

While reading the excerpt, identify three or four instances of the Wright brothers' thinking in this visual sense. Also, consider the following: if they had not thought visually, could their airplane still have been successful? Is there a reliable process of invention that does not involve visual thinking?

WHY WILBUR AND ORVILLE?

The inventive method that undergirded the Wright brothers' aeronautical research and experimentation was comprised of many elements. Some were techniques readily adopted from common engineering practice, others were innate abilities of a less tangible nature. The blending of these standard approaches to technical investigation and the Wrights' own unique talents resulted in the impressive flow of creativity that produced the world's first airplane.

In general, the Wright brothers' approach to mechanical flight reflected a strict engineering perspective. They did not develop their aircraft using uninformed trial-and-error methods like so many of their contemporaries, nor did they tackle the problem as theoretical scientists. The distinctions are important to understanding the Wrights' inventive process. Wilbur and Orville did not set out to discover the theoretical principles of flight in the same sense that Newton or Einstein sought to explain physical phenomena in nature. The Wrights' work focused explicitly on determining the design features required to make an airplane fly. Among their considerations, for example, were the shape of the airfoil; the size and layout of the wing planform; and the type and the location of stabilizing surfaces, structural design, materials, and control mechanisms. While they certainly took advantage of established scientific tenets and formulas pertaining to the forces involved in heavier-than-air flight, they did not develop any that were fundamentally new. They investigated the relationships between such things as lift and drag, flight loads and structure, and stability and control in order to find the best combination of design features for the size and form of aircraft they believed would fly. The goal was less to understand *why* in principle these forces behaved as they did than to learn *how* in actual practice they acted with respect to one another, and in turn to use this information to construct a successful flying machine. This was engineering in its most basic form and the supporting foundation for all other aspects of the Wrights' inventive method.

The keen engineering technique that characterized their work was not the product of professional training in engineering. In fact, neither Wilbur nor Orville received their high school diplomas. Because of a sudden family move back to Dayton, Ohio, in June of 1884, Wilbur was unable to complete all the final requirements of his senior year curriculum at an Indiana high school. Despite being nearly finished, Wilbur never bothered to complete his formal course of study. Orville chose not to follow the prescribed curriculum in his junior year, opting for a series of advanced college preparatory courses instead. As a result, he was not going to qualify for his high school degree at the end of his senior year and decided to forego attending school at all for that term. Like his brother, Orville evinced little concern over missing out on his degree.

Despite their lack of interest in formal credentials, the Wrights were committed to broad learning and were excellent students. They made good use of the extensive family library and supplemented their formal schooling with a great deal of private study. They excelled in mathematics and science, and were both well read in the humanities and fine writers. Years later, Orville reflected upon the environment he and his siblings grew up in:

> We were lucky enough to grow up in an environment where there was always much encouragement to children to pursue intellectual interests; to investigate whatever aroused curiosity. In a different kind of environment, our curiosity might have been nipped long before it could have borne fruit.

The Wrights are often described as high school dropouts. While this is true, such a characterization belies their extensive self-education and their strong intellect.

An important beginning step of the Wrights' engineering approach to human flight was to become acquainted with the work of previous experimenters. By the time the brothers began their study of flight at the close of the nineteenth century, a growing community of aeronautical experimenters had emerged. As the field slowly organized, publication and dissemination of aeronautical research grew more widespread. Through contact with several key individuals and sources of information, the brothers were able to digest the work of generations of experimenters. Familiarization with these prior developments aided the Wrights in defining the basic obstacles to human flight and outlining their initial approach to the problem. Their literature search enabled them to take advantage of already established principles and to avoid dead-end paths pursued by others.

Merged with this basic engineering perspective and its associated practices were a number of conceptual capabilities and approaches present in the Wrights' method that in large measure explain why they were able to invent the airplane. Among the most important was their capacity for developing conceptual models of a problem that could then be transformed into practical hardware. Both brothers were adept at moving back and forth between the abstract and the concrete. This is seen most notably in the wind tunnel experiments they performed. The test instruments the Wrights designed and built to gather aerodynamic data on lifting surfaces mirrored the conceptual and mathematical models they developed to represent the physical forces generating lift and drag on a wing. These devices were mechanical analogs of the equations the Wrights used to calculate the size and the projected performance of their flying machines. As such, the information yielded by these instruments could be incorporated directly into the design of their aircraft. The brothers' ability to turn abstract concepts into workable machinery reveals itself in several other crucial areas as well, such as in their development of an effective control system and their design of an efficient aerial propeller.

Another feature of the Wright brothers' creative thought process that figured prominently in their advance toward powered flight was the great extent to which they used graphic mental imagery to conceptualize basic structures and mechanisms, even aerodynamic theory. In recent years, historians have pointed increasingly to the role of nonverbal thought in engineering and invention. A great many of the objects surrounding us were designed in part by mental visualizations. Even though there may be fundamental mathematical relationships or articulated scientific principles that underlie the creation of a new machine or structure, there is invariably a distinct facet of the design that is aesthetic in nature, an aspect that results from the maker's intuitive sense of what will or will not work, or what "looks" right or wrong.

This aesthetic element is not limited merely to the object's appearance. The more important contribution centers on the technical feasibility and the physical arrangement of components that leads to the design's success or failure. Especially creative and productive inventors and engineers quite often have an acutely developed ability to think pictorially and spatially in addition to facility in the use of verbal forms of thought. They can visualize an object in their mind, turn it over, form new images of it, incorporate old forms from other designs, and, finally, arrive at a much-improved device or something totally original that will accomplish new goals. This part of the creative process cannot be reduced to unambiguous verbal descriptions. The designer literally has a vision of what the object or structure should look like and how it will work and, in conjunction with verbal forms of knowledge, produces a tangible article based upon what has already been seen in the mind's eye.

Individuals who are adept at this mental manipulation of images are often the ones who conceptualize useful and practical combinations of component parts, or modifications to individual devices, that result in original inventions or more sophisticated technological systems. They and the fruits of their creativity stand out because they are able to see a workable arrangement of the essential elements of a proposed invention or existing device in ways that have eluded others.

Samuel F. B. Morse, for example, built his successful electromagnetic telegraph in 1837 after all the basic scientific principles and technical components necessary for transmitting intelligence electronically were in place. His unique accomplishment was the first working, practical arrangement of these critical elements. He had no greater understanding of the scientific principles involved than other contemporary experimenters in the field, nor was he more skillful. In fact, Morse was rather inept mechanically and turned out to be a poor telegraph operator. What he did possess was an ability to visually conceptualize a workable interrelationship of the basic elements of the telegraph. His capacity to puzzle through the problem using concrete mental imagery was central to his making the primary breakthroughs that opened the door to instantaneous long-distance communication.

Design is a process that is characterized by numerous evolving combinations of alternative forms. Spatial thinking and mental manipulation of graphic images are clearly at the heart of this activity. Examples such as Morse and the telegraph demonstrate that, frequently, truly groundbreaking technological innovations are not based solely on articulated scientific or engineering principles, mathematical calculations, or other forms of knowledge that can be expressed verbally. Wilbur and Orville's facility for nonverbal thought was among the most prevalent and salient aspects of their inventive method.

The brothers' emphasis on continuity of design was another key to their success. Their path to practical flight moved through an evolving series of gliders and powered machines of a single basic design, each incorporating what was learned from the previous craft. Haphazard, mercurial approaches to flight research were common among their contemporaries, and rarely productive. The Wrights' aeronautical work, on the other hand, was a coherent program of experimental development that finally led to success.

The Wrights' persistent attention to the overall goal of a completely successful flying machine during every phase of the work was also an important aspect of their inventive method. Each experimental glider and powered airplane they built, as well as every individual element of each aircraft, was seen and valued in terms of the ultimate aim of building a practical aircraft. The Wrights' approach was distinct among aeronautical experimenters in that they believed no specific component to be more important than any other. They recognized that every aspect of a workable flying machine must be designed to coordinate with every other. No matter how advanced the wing, without an adequate control system, an aircraft will not fly. And so on. Wilbur and Orville understood that an airplane is not a single device, but a series of discrete mechanical and structural entities that, when working in proper unison, resulted in a machine capable of flight. Moreover, realizing that the pilot is a part of this system, they devoted as much attention to learning to fly their aircraft as they did in designing and building them.

The Wright brothers are frequently described as having been good mechanics. Their talents in this regard, however, went well beyond such mundane characterization. They had a particularly acute sense of materials, knowing instinctively which worked best and how to manipulate them, and a highly developed, sensuous affinity for machines. They possessed an uncommon intuitive ability to see how various mechanical components and assemblies worked and how they fit together. With a sort of tactile ease, they could modify technological devices to improve their operation or turn them into something new.

A telling example of their mechanical aptitude dates from the late 1880s, when as young men the Wrights improved a printing press Orville was using to turn out a small local newspaper he started. To make even copies they needed to devise a way of putting the exact amount of pressure required on the type each time. After rummaging around the Wright barn, Orville stumbled upon an old family buggy with a folding top. The mechanism that supported the top stretched it just enough to put it in proper position. This was precisely what was needed for the press. With Wilbur's help, the buggy frame was mated to the press bed. Even though some of Wilbur's suggestions for improving the press appeared to violate basic mechanical principles, the system worked perfectly. Some time later, a visiting foreman from the pressroom of a Denver newspaper came by to see the homemade press. After a thorough inspection he remarked, "Well, it works, but I certainly don't see how it does the work." This kind of mechanical ingenuity appeared time and time again in the Wrights' work and was another critical component of their inventive effort.

The Wrights' ability to draw upon their experience with other technologies also proved valuable to their invention of the airplane. They excelled at deriving significant connections between seemingly unrelated technologies. On numerous occasions, concepts and even basic hardware garnered from other fields were incorporated into their aeronautical work. Their familiarity with bicycles is a conspicuous example.

The Wrights are commonly described as bicycle mechanics turned airplane builders, yet the highly influential role bicycles played in their inventive work is rarely emphasized. More than a few late nineteenth-century prognosticators suggested that the ultimate resolution to the flying problem would rest with bicycle makers. One such forecaster, James Means, editor of the widely read aviation journal *The Aeronautical Annual,* published an article in the 1896 edition pointing to the links between bicycles and airplanes. "Wheeling is just like flying," he wrote. "To learn to wheel one must learn to balance; to learn to fly one must learn to balance."

Bicycles had existed in various forms since the early nineteenth century. But they had no significant impact in the United States until the mid 1870s, when the famous high-wheel, or *ordinary,* bicycle was introduced from England by a Boston merchant named Albert A. Pope. In 1878, he contracted the Weed Sewing Machine Company of Hartford, Connecticut, to produce an American-made version of the British ordinary. Within a decade, Pope had produced a quarter of a million high-wheelers.

In 1887, the bicycle craze in America began in earnest with the introduction, again from England, of the safety bicycle. The safety, with its two wheels of equal size, a sturdy frame, and a chain-driven transmission system, did not require quite the degree of athletic ability to ride as the ordinary. It therefore made the freedom of wheeling accessible to a much wider market. At the height of the 1890s bicycle boom, the industry was comprised of over three hundred companies and was producing more than a million bicycles per year.

Like so many other Americans, Wilbur and Orville were quite taken by this new form of locomotion. In the spring of 1892, Orville bought a brand-new Columbia safety for the then-considerable sum of 160 dollars. A short time later, Wilbur purchased a used Eagle for half that price. The brothers quickly became avid cyclists. Orville demonstrated his prowess with many successful performances in local races. Their skill at riding, matched with an already established local reputation as skillful mechanics, prompted the brothers to go into the bicycle business before the year was out. They opened their first shop in December of 1892.

The Wrights were not the only bicycle makers in their hometown of Dayton, Ohio. By the mid-nineties, there were no fewer than fourteen shops in the city doing a brisk business in response to the safety-bicycle craze that was sweeping America, and the Wrights' shop was by no means the biggest. Initially they only sold and repaired bicycles. But by 1895, with competition growing stiff, they decided to begin manufacturing their own line. By this time there were four other shops within two blocks of the Wrights'. The brothers' inaugural model was called the Van Cleve, in honor of their pioneering ancestors, who had been among Dayton's first settlers in the late eighteenth century.

While the major bicycle manufacturers were employing mass production techniques adopted from the firearm and sewing machine industries, the Wrights remained small scale and continued to produce handmade originals. At a time when manufacturing was becoming increasingly mechanized and rapidly rushing toward the twentieth century, the Wrights stayed firmly within the classic artisan tradition of handcrafted, carefully finished individual pieces. This kind of attention to detail and craftsmanship would be a hallmark of their flying machines. Every component of their aircraft was designed and built with great care and served a specific and essential function. It is a bit ironic that an invention that has been so influential in the twentieth century was the product of men whose approach was so firmly anchored in the nineteenth century.

Bicycles possess a number of significant conceptual links to the airplane, strongly suggesting that it was not coincidental that the invention of mechanical flight emanated from the minds of experimenters knowledgeable of these two-wheeled vehicles. One of the primary breakthroughs the Wrights made was the realization that a positive means of controlling, or balancing, an aircraft must be devised before any significant progress on the flying machine could be made. The bicycle is an unstable vehicle, but despite this characteristic it can still be balanced and kept under control. The Wrights' transference of this important concept to the airplane is clear, and it was central to the design of their aircraft. Their understanding of the operating principles of the bicycle prevented them from being hampered by the erroneous, though widely held, notion that control and instability were incompatible.

This was just one of several connections between bicycles and airplanes that the Wrights astutely saw. The engineering demands of light-weight, but strong, structures important in bicycle design would be even more crucial with aircraft. Their adaptation of the chain-drive-and-sprocket transmission system of the safety bicycle to link the engine and the propellers on their later powered airplanes is unmistakable. Even concerns regarding wind resistance and aerodynamic shape that are fundamental to aircraft design were addressed by bicycle makers. Of course, of the thousands of bicycle mechanics in America at this time, only two invented the airplane. Clearly there were many other elements critical to the Wrights' success with flight. A familiarity with bicycles, however, was certainly one of the important ingredients in the mix of factors leading to their achievement.

Beyond these approaches to technical investigation and their innate talents, the Wrights possessed a number of character traits and personal experiences that had a bearing on their being the inventors of the airplane.

Much has been made of the collaborative aspect of the Wrights' work. So intertwined were their ideas and their contributions to the airplane, it has become difficult to distinguish them as individual personalities. From a historical perspective, they have become a single entity. This image was in part fostered by the brothers themselves. In April of 1912, only a few weeks before his sudden death from typhoid, Wilbur wrote,

> From the time we were little children my brother Orville and myself lived together, played together, worked together and, in fact, thought together. We usually owned all of our toys in common, talked over our thoughts and aspirations so that nearly everything that was done in our lives has been the result of conversations, suggestions and discussions between us.

This close interaction was a genuine and essential component of the Wrights' inventive work. It is unlikely that either Wilbur or Orville would have achieved alone what they did as a team. Even so, Wilbur's later reflection upon his relationship with his brother is a little overly romantic. As children their relationship was much like any pair of siblings four years apart, interested and caring but somewhat distant.

As they approached adulthood, not much changed. Following a debilitating skating accident sometime late in 1885 or early 1886, Wilbur became extremely withdrawn. For several years he spent nearly all of his time reading and caring for his mother, who was dying of tuberculosis. He cut himself off from almost everyone and everything. One of Wilbur and Orville's older brothers, Reuchlin, wrote to their sister Katharine with growing concern: "What does Will do? He ought to do something. Is he still cook and chambermaid?"

It was not until 1888, when Wilbur assisted Orville with the improvements to his printing press, that he began to emerge from his self-imposed confinement. After helping his younger brother redesign the press, he contributed articles and editorial assistance to the short-lived neighborhood newspaper. It was at this point that the brothers began to interact in the cooperative way that was so important to their later success with flight. There would be several more collaborative efforts on local newspapers over the next few years. Then, in 1892, they opened their first bicycle shop, firmly establishing the teamwork and close relationship that would be such a significant factor in the creation of the airplane.

In the summer of that year, a dispute erupted between the brothers that offers an interesting insight into their working relationship. The disagreement arose over the division of the proceeds garnered from the construction of a press for another local printing firm and from a rush printing job that had interrupted progress on the press. Initially it was decided that the profits from the jobs were to be divided evenly. But later on Orville felt that he was doing the lion's share of the work and believed the original agreement to be unfair.

What is telling about the incident is how the conflict was resolved. The family set up a mock "court," and the "complainant" and the "defendant" each wrote up formal depositions stating their positions. Wilbur argued for the "court," to determine a fair and equitable distribution of the earnings from both jobs, to order Orville to "apologize for his insulting conduct," and to request him "to keep his mouth shut in the future, lest he should again be guilty of befouling the spotless and innocent character of others." The results of the proceedings are unknown, but the affair reveals something about the way the brothers approached interpersonal conflicts between them, and how they dealt with others in general. As the brothers conducted their aeronautical work, there were many differences of opinion that produced heated discussions. But they never let these disputes interfere with their progress, always settling them in a constructive manner. In fact, these arguments often helped to forge a collaborative answer to a difficult problem.

In addition to the closeness between the brothers, their relationships with their father, Milton, and their sister, Katharine, also played an important role in their inventive success. Wilbur and Orville were two of seven children born to Milton Wright and Susan Koerner Wright, married in Indiana in 1859. Their first child, a son named Reuchlin, was born in 1861. The following year, Susan gave birth to another son, Lorin. Wilbur was next, born on April 6, 1867, near Millville, Indiana. After giving birth to a set of twins that died in infancy, Susan delivered another healthy son, Orville, on August 9, 1871, in Dayton. The Wrights' last child, a daughter named Katharine, was born three years to the day after Orville, in 1874.

By the time Wilbur and Orville began to think seriously about flight, only they, Milton, and Katharine still lived in the family home at 7 Hawthorn Street in Dayton. The older children had moved out and started families of their own. In 1889, Wilbur and Orville's mother, Susan, succumbed to tuberculosis. Katharine had taken over the responsibility of caring for the family when her mother became ill, and she formally adopted that role after her death. The remaining four Wright family members became an extremely tight-knit group. They shared everything with one another and provided a network of support that enabled them to weather all manner of crises. When any one of them was away, they corresponded almost daily, even if the absence was only for a few days.

This supportive home life provided Wilbur and Orville with a belief in themselves that gave them the confidence to reject the theories of well-known and experienced aeronautical researchers when they felt their own ideas were correct. The path to invention is littered with stumbling blocks and confusing dead ends. It takes a powerful belief in oneself to work through immensely perplexing problems and stand firm on personal conclusions, even if they run contrary to accepted wisdom. On a number of occasions, the Wrights were so confounded by the complexity of the aerodynamic and design problems they faced that they nearly gave up. At one point during their early glider experiments, Orville wrote home to Katharine,

> We tried it with tail in front, and every other way. When we got through, Will was so mixed up he couldn't even theorize. It has been with considerable effort that I have succeeded in keeping him in the flying business at all.

Often it was the emotional anchor provided by their strong family ties that helped the Wrights persevere when things looked bleak. On a more pragmatic level, their father and Katharine assisted the brothers by looking after the bicycle shop while they were away experimenting with their aircraft and helping them prepare for the trips. If the role of Wilbur and Orville's home life is considered, it would not be entirely inaccurate to credit these four Wright family members for giving humans their wings.

Strong personal self-confidence was particularly important with respect to inventing the airplane because the brothers had to solve so many of the fundamental problems almost from scratch. After they familiarized themselves with the work of the major aeronautical experimenters prior to their own entrance into the field, the Wrights realized how little real progress had been made toward the resolution of the problem of mechanical flight. Once they began their work in earnest, it became apparent to them that they were quite on their own. They invented the airplane in a much truer sense than Edison the electric light or Morse the telegraph. The majority of the critical elements in the airplane were original to the Wrights, whereas with the electric light and the telegraph, the inventors achieved final success based on a much sounder, better-developed foundation of prior research. Without a deep reservoir of self-confidence, the Wright brothers would likely have been unable to conquer the many daunting challenges presented by the problem of human flight.

Another significant factor in their success was timing. One of the most striking things about the brothers' invention of the airplane was the relative speed with which they defined the problems, devised solutions, and took to the air. It took the Wrights only six years to progress from their first experimental kite to a fully practical powered airplane. Their phenomenal pace was largely a result of the creative approaches, the innate abilities, and the personal circumstances thus far described. But it was also partly attributable to their tackling the problem at a propitious moment.

When Wilbur and Orville emerged on the aeronautical scene in the late 1890s, a crucial phase of the prehistory of flight had drawn to a close. By that time, flying machines were no longer merely the domain of dreamers and visionaries. During the last half of the nineteenth century, mechanical flight had gained legitimacy as a worthwhile field of scientific and engineering research. A community of professional engineers and researchers interested in flight had evolved and were collectively amassing a body of aeronautical knowledge and technical data that provided the first definitive steps toward solving the problem of mechanical flight. This research was also being disseminated through publications and through gatherings of interested experimenters, further expanding and strengthening the reputation of aeronautics as a serious area of endeavor.

As the century wound down, this building momentum slowed. Greater advancement had been made in the years since 1860 than in the preceding millennium. But despite all the promise shown during the last decades of the nineteenth century, final success remained elusive. Major barriers still existed, and the progress of the leading experimenters had reached a plateau. Many had come to the logical conclusion of their work, some had simply given up, and others had lost their lives in accidents.

Despite this lull, the phase of aeronautical development just prior to the Wrights' entry into the field had yielded much productive research and had laid a foundation of critical inquiry that would be invaluable to the next generation of experimenters. The status of the invention of the airplane was still much like searching for a needle in a haystack, but now at least it was known in which haystack to look.

It was at this point that Wilbur and Orville began serious study of flight. The experience of their predecessors did more to reveal fundamental questions than to provide answers, but wading through the failures and the misunderstandings of others aided the brothers in focusing quickly on the basic problems that needed to be addressed. Much of what the Wrights accomplished was highly original, but the findings of the late nineteenth century definitely gave them several useful pieces to the puzzle, as well as saving them from many unfruitful avenues of research. If the brothers had been a generation older, it is not at all certain that they would have avoided the stumbling blocks of those who were working in the second half of the nineteenth century. The Wrights were especially talented to be sure, but there is no reason to believe their genius operated in a vacuum, and that they would have invented the airplane no matter when they took up the problem.

As we trace the Wrights' inventive work, it will become apparent that each advance was grounded in one or more of the principal elements of their methodology outlined in this chapter. It will become clear that the invention of the airplane was the product of a complex interaction of the Wrights' engineering techniques, creative abilities, and personality traits. It was the combination of these factors that distinguished them from their peers and led them to success. The term *genius* is often loosely applied to the Wrights' achievement. But if its use has any real meaning, it has more to do with these general aspects of the brothers' approach to invention than with their specific creation of the airplane. The following analysis of the brothers' inventive work from the perspective of their methodology therefore provides the clearest insight into how they produced the world's first airplane and yields the most enlightening answer to the question: Why Wilbur and Orville?

20

THE BIRTH OF A NATION

Leon F. Litwack

INTRODUCTION

Motion pictures are a powerful communications medium, impressing audiences with a wonderful array of sight and sound. Who can forget the burning of Atlanta from *Gone with the Wind* or the enigmatic black monolith from *2001: A Space Odyssey* or the panorama of the Austrian foothills at the beginning of *The Sound of Music?* Like all media, motion pictures structure their messages in subtle ways consistent with the nature of the technology. The director tries to use camera angles, color (or lack thereof), lighting, and background to underscore and enhance the meaning of the film. In some films actors, dialogue, and script seem to have been reduced to ancillary components, present only to complement the dramatic sweep of the imagery.

Movies function on various levels—as art, entertainment, and information. They can also be forceful propaganda tools. In Hitler's Germany, for instance, the film industry became a vital part of the Nazi propaganda machine, burnishing the image of the Third Reich's dubious accomplishments in politics, industry, the arts, and sports. Less obvious, but equally effective were the American films of the World War II and Cold War eras. To build patriotism and bolster commitment to the struggles against totalitarianism and communism, American movies depicted the Japanese as subhumans worthy of only contempt, the Germans as mindless automatons fixated on world domination, and the Soviets as Godless communists bent on overthrowing the American way of life at all costs.

Where movies depict history, it is often difficult for the audience to separate fact from fiction and art from propaganda. D. W. Griffith's epic *The Birth of a Nation* (1915) is just such a motion picture. Regarded by historian Tino Balio as "the most important single film ever made," *The Birth of a Nation* was Griffith's vision of how the searing experience of the Civil War and Reconstruction shaped our country. Millions saw the film, coming away from theaters convinced of the truth of Griffith's portrayal of black people as predatory and evil and the Ku Klux Klan as champions of white virtue. Largely as a result of this motion picture, a whole generation of Americans believed that the Civil War was really a struggle for states' rights and that Reconstruction was a black reign of terror imposed on a proud and undeserving South. Only by the intense efforts of historians in the 1960s and 1970s were these myths dispelled, and even then there still lingers in the popular culture disturbing misconceptions about these epochal events in American history.

———

With the release of *The Birth of a Nation* in 1915, the motion picture as art, propaganda, and entertainment came of age. Reviewers were ecstatic in their praise, audiences unrestrained in their enthusiasm. This was the movie everyone had to see, a unique and awesome experience for Americans, the first film spectacular, technically and artistically superior to anything they had ever viewed on the screen. Employing a multiplicity of cinematic techniques, director D. W. Griffith profoundly influenced filmmaking throughout the world. His epic film proved to be an extraordinary success, the first—and one of the greatest—box-office attractions in the history of motion pictures. From 1915 to 1946, some two hundred million people viewed the film in the United States and overseas, where it scored particularly impressive triumphs in Germany and South Africa. President Woodrow Wilson had a private showing of *The Birth of a Nation* in the White House. It was the first feature film shown there and an appropriate one for a president who embraced the ideology of racial segregation and maintained a discreet silence on the triumph of white terrorism in his native South. "It is like writing history in lightning," he reportedly said of the film. "My only regret is that it is all so terribly true." (Some years later, after the film had inflamed racial tensions, Wilson called it an "unfortunate production.")

From the very outset, the film mesmerized and misled Americans, revealing the extraordinary power of the cinema to "teach" history and to reflect and shape popular attitudes and stereotypes. Earlier public entertainment—such as minstrel shows, "coon" songs, and vaudeville—depicted blacks as clowns and buffoons, as essentially passive objects. *The Birth of a Nation,* however, introduced still another dimension: the grinning and obsequious demeanor of black men often masks a vicious bestiality, at no time more vividly manifested than after emancipation. The film is based on *The Clansman,* a novel by Thomas Dixon, Jr., a native of North Carolina and popular Baptist preacher who wanted to awaken the American people to the nature of the Black Peril. To Dixon, this was a national problem. The presence of the Negro, North and South, endangered American civilization and the sanctity of white womanhood, and it posed as great a threat in 1900 as it did in 1868. "There is enough negro blood here," a Dixon character warns, "to make mulatto the whole Republic." That obsession consumed Dixon, and the film—true to his intentions—plays on the presumed primitive sexuality of the subhuman black man and its implications for the survival of the Anglo-Saxon race. The message is driven home in imagery no audience could easily forget. Before riding off to redeem the white South, klansmen dip their emblem into the blood of a blonde white virgin who has been terrorized to death by a black brute.

The credits do not list Dixon or President Wilson as consultants, but their influence hovers over the film. Dixon supplied the plot; Wilson, the scholarly footnotes. Intent on assuring the public of the film's historical credibility, Griffith went to extraordinary lengths. On Reconstruction, Wilson's *A History of the American People* was cited to underscore and authenticate the vivid scenes depicted on the screen. The end result was not simply a flawed but a profoundly perverted history. It was a history, however, that Americans found easy to absorb. "My object," Dixon said of the earlier stage version of his novel, "is to teach the North . . . what it has never known—the awful suffering of the white man during the dreadful

Reconstruction period . . . to demonstrate to the world that the white man must and shall be supreme."

The Birth of a Nation appeared during the most repressive and violent period in the history of race relations in the South. Between 1890 and 1915, in the face of racial tensions heightened by growing evidence of black independence and assertiveness (the New Negro), whites acted on the prevailing racial orthodoxy to ensure their absolute supremacy and the permanent political, economic, and social subordination of the black population. To achieve this objective, the white South systematically disenfranchised black men, imposed rigid patterns of racial segregation, corrupted the judicial system, and sustained extraordinary and unprecedented levels of violence and brutality, culminating in the public burnings and lynchings of black men and women. At the same time, the findings of "science" and the learned professions and the dissemination of dehumanizing caricatures reinforced and comforted whites in their racial beliefs and practices.

This was the America *The Birth of a Nation* explained, vindicated, and celebrated. What more effective way to awaken the American people to the nature of the Black Peril and justify their racial atrocities than to remind them of what had happened during Reconstruction? Through the lives and relationships of two families—the Camerons of South Carolina (the plantation ideal) and the Stonemans of Pennsylvania (the abolitionist Radical Republican impulse), *The Birth of a Nation* depicts a tragic era in the history of "the Aryan race," when a misguided North, under the spell of radical zealots like Austin Stoneman (a thinly disguised Thaddeus Stevens) and mulatto demagogues like Silas Lynch (Stoneman's protégé), along with their carpetbag and scalawag colleagues, used the votes of duped and ignorant newly freed slaves to fasten a black despotism onto the South.

Through its vivid and unforgettable images, the film impressed on Americans a certain version of reality. Reconstruction, proclaimed one of the intertitles, was "the agony which the South endured that a nation might be born." The camera graphically captures the lurid details of that "agony": impudent, ungrateful, venal black men, their ambitions bloated by emancipation and civil rights, terrorize helpless whites, shoving them off the sidewalks, blocking their access to the ballot boxes, and leering at their women. Blacks brandish signs reading, "Equal Rights, Equal Politics, Equal Marriage." They ridicule and chain their old masters. They abuse those "faithful souls" (the Cameron servants) who still take pride in their white folks. They make a mockery of democratic government, sitting shoeless in legislative chambers, drinking whiskey from bottles, and eating chicken off the bone while enacting a statute legitimizing interracial marriage. Finally and inevitably, maddened by power and lust, blacks strike out at the most valued possessions of white men—their women. Gus, a depraved "renegade Negro" and former Cameron slave, forces a white girl (the Cameron's youngest daughter) to leap to her death in order to preserve her purity. And Silas Lynch, whose election as lieutenant governor only heightens his lust, seeks to force marriage on a virginal, limp, gagged, and helpless young white woman (none other than Austin Stoneman's daughter). "I will build a Black Empire," he tells her, "and you as my queen shall rule by my side."

Barely suppressing a nostalgia for slavery, *The Birth of a Nation* paints its black characters literally and figuratively. While exploiting every traditional racial stereotype, most of them passive and unthreatening, the film introduces the relatively new image of the Negro as aggressor ("the bad nigger"), assuming in this picture the guises of revolutionist (Lynch) and sexual brute (Gus). No matter whether black people are depicted as evil or sympathetic, they are all dehumanized, from the blindly faithful, submissive, and pampered house servants to the wretched, dim-witted, insolent, and brutish mass of newly freed slaves. Yet the ultimate and most dangerous villain is unmistakably the mulatto (Silas Lynch), who combines the sexuality and lust of the savage Negro with the intellectual and organizing prowess that could be explained only by his white blood.

Like an "Anglo-Saxon Niagara" (as Vachel Lindsay called it), the Ku Klux Klan (the freedom fighters of the 1870s) mobilize and pour down the road to rescue the South from the "anarchy of black rule" and to reestablish white supremacy. Clearly, this film suggests, only the end of Reconstruction deserves to be commemorated—a triumphant redemption of honor, virtue, and race, when, in the words of Woodrow Wilson, "Negro rule under unscrupulous adventurers was finally [ended], and the natural, inevitable ascendancy of the whites, the responsible class, established."

Evoking the film's spirit and principal theme, the beleaguered Cameron family finds refuge in a log cabin occupied by two Union veterans, and they join forces to resist pursuing black soldiers. The intertitle says it all: "The former enemies of North and South are united again in common defense of their Aryan birthright." By the conclusion of the film, even those naive and misled northerners (the Stonemans) who had initially embraced Reconstruction come to see their folly. The redemption of the South—and the nation—is given a biblical sanction as well, with Jesus Christ in the "halls of brotherly love" overseeing (or so it seems) the glorious triumph of the Ku Klux Klan and white supremacy. In this redemption, according to Dixon and Griffith, the American nation is truly born: that is, only after whites regained absolute supremacy on the basis of a nationalized racial consciousness, and only after the North acquiesced in the South's "final solution" to the "race problem."

Stripped of complexity, the history reenacted in *The Birth of a Nation* is easy and simpleminded. It took another generation to expose the myths, falsehoods, and fantasies on which the film is based. Few historians still accept the perverse view of Radical Reconstruction as an unrelieved orgy of black misrule. The motives and conduct of the much-reviled carpetbaggers and scalawags were as varied as their social makeup. The much-publicized corruption of the era was biracial and bipartisan, polluting politics in both the North and the South, and the principal beneficiaries everywhere were businessmen and speculators, among them members of some of the South's most distinguished families. While in power, the Radical state governments, even those tainted with corruption, enacted much needed democratic reforms, including universal manhood suffrage, equal access to the courts, and the first public school systems. The black legislators and officeholders, although initiated into the political process during a period of corruption, learned the uses of political power and ruled as competently—and, in some instances, as incompetently—as their white counterparts. The Radical governments were overthrown not because they were corrupt but because the reforms they instituted threatened the supremacy of whites and the subordination of black labor.

Few if any films in the history of the cinema had such tragic and far-reaching consequences. "Chicago went wild," one observer wrote. "It started people to thinking. . . . The people of Chicago saw more in *The Birth of a Nation* than a tremendous dramatic spectacle. They saw in it the reason the South wants to 'keep the Negro in his place.' They saw in it a new conception of southern problems." More than any historian or textbook, the vivid images conveyed by *The Birth of a Nation* shaped American attitudes toward Reconstruction and the "Negro problem." With that version of history firmly fixed in their minds, most Americans could readily understand why black southerners were unfit to exercise political rights and why the white South had to go to such extraordinary lengths to control and contain its black population. And for much of the twentieth century, *The Birth of a Nation* molded and reinforced racial stereotypes, distorting the physical appearance of black men and women, making a mockery of their lives and aspirations, and fixing in the public mind the image of a race of inferiors—sometimes amusing and comical, sometimes brutal and subhuman, but in either case less than white men and women.

"Art is always revolutionary," D. W. Griffith remarked in 1915, "always explosive and sensational." He left his generation with a classic example. Yet for African Americans, the film remains one of the principal artifacts of a racial ideology that denied them their very humanity. With *The Birth of a Nation,* Ralph Ellison wrote, "the propagation of subhuman images of Negroes became financially and dramatically profitable. The Negro as a scapegoat could be sold as entertainment, could even be exported. If the film became the main manipulator of the American dream, for Negroes that dream contained a strong dose of such stuff as nightmares are made of."

21

AMATEUR OPERATORS AND AMERICAN BROADCASTING

SHAPING THE FUTURE OF RADIO

Susan J. Douglas

INTRODUCTION

Before the advent of television, radio had no rivals among mass communications media for immediacy and impact. Another technology with roots in the nineteenth century, radio appeared to many Americans as the apotheosis of scientific and technological progress. Marvelous as it was, early radio, based on spark technology, was suitable only for telegraphic transmissions of Morse Code. Transmission of voice and music was impossible before the advent of so-called continuous-wave technology, made practical by the introduction of the vacuum tube or audion by Lee De Forest in 1906. Even then, few of the pioneers recognized the revolutionary implications of broadcasting, whereby news and entertainment programming reached millions of people. Remarkably, this new medium was "free," subsidized by advertisers who bought air time to market various products and services. No one at the turn of the century could have predicted that within twenty years radio would form the basis for today's huge electronics and entertainment industry.

Susan Douglas uses radio to demonstrate how a general climate of enthusiasm led to major technological change. In contrast with the telegraph and telephone, both controlled by large companies, radio could be mastered by individuals with little money and much zeal. At its heart, radio was a democratic technology, open to any and all who had enough interest and expertise. Under such circumstances, it is not surprising that Frank Conrad (1874–1941), an avid radio enthusiast, and not his employer, giant electrical manufacturer Westinghouse, led the way with radio broadcasting. Only after Conrad had demonstrated that there was a market for radio programming and had attracted advertisers, did it dawn on Westinghouse executives that they were sitting on a resource waiting to be tapped for corporate profit.

This article also demonstrates that not all technology emerges from the identification and meeting of a need or requirement. Communication in the first two decades of the twentieth century—dominated by the telegraph, telephone, and spark-technology radio—was adequate for most people's immediate and future needs. Broadcasting came not from necessity but from the curiosity, shared knowledge, and mutual enthusiasm of a talented group of amateur operators who literally wanted to have their voices heard.

"If any of the planets be populated with beings like ourselves," wrote William Preece in 1898, "then if they could oscillate immense stores of electrical energy to and fro in telegraphic order, it would be possible for us to hold commune by telephone with the people of Mars." Preece, the engineer-in-chief of the British Post Office and a radio experimenter, was one of the first of many to predict that intergalactic "wireless" signaling would, in the near future, connect us with others across the great expanse of the universe. His comments, circulated in American magazines and newspapers, were reiterated by some and ridiculed by others. But although Preece's heady vision may have seemed farfetched to some, it was only the ultimate extension of other more earthbound yet highly enthusiastic predictions surrounding radio at the turn of the century. From its first public unveiling and through the next 25 years, the invention evoked a range of prophecies—some realistic, some fantastic, and nearly all idealistic—of a world improved through radio.

Radio both fitted into and extended Americans' notions of how the future would be made better, maybe even perfect, through technology. Not all technology was so embraced. The factory system, with its large, noisy, seemingly autonomous machines, had produced a range of complicated social problems that profoundly frustrated most Americans. At the turn of the century, the American press was filled with self-congratulatory assessments of how far the country had come in 100 years, but just beneath that veneer of optimism was a deep anxiety about the dislocations and vulnerabilities that had accompanied industrialization. Radio was not only exempt from this anxiety, it was also meant to relieve it. Like certain other inventions, radio was seen as delivering society from a troubled present to a utopian future. What was it about radio that evoked both idealistic and fantastic visions of the future? What influence, if any, did these highly publicized and richly embellished predictions exert? Who, if anyone, believed them? Did they influence the course of broadcasting's early history?

Although other scientists and inventors had been experimenting with the wireless transmission of electrical energy and signals, it was Guglielmo Marconi, an Irish-Italian inventor, who first sought to make such signaling practicable and commercially available. In 1896 he introduced British government officials to his method of sending dots and dashes through "the air." Marconi intended to provide point-to-point communications between ships and between ship and shore. He called his invention a wireless telegraph, and he saw it as an adjunct to and a potential competitor with the telegraph and the transatlantic cables. Thus, radio began not as a method of broadcasting speech and music to a vast audience but rather as an analogy to and an extension of the telegraph. Telegraphy had revolutionized first domestic and then international communications, but its reliance on a network of wires physically limited the range and scope of its use. In remote areas, on islands, or aboard ships, where wires were not or could not be connected, people were unable to take advantage of the new invention. Thus, there were still potential customers left out of the communications revolution.

In 1899 Marconi brought his apparatus to the United States and demonstrated its potential for ship-to-shore signaling and for news-gathering during the highly publicized America's Cup races. Having installed his invention aboard a small ship, he followed the progress of the race and "wirelessed" the day's results to newspaper reporters on shore. News of his achievements inspired awe and wonder; to people still getting accustomed to the telegraph, cables, and the telephone, signaling without any wires—without any tangible connection at all—was fantastic and incredible.

Wireless telegraphy made its debut at the close of what the press often referred to as the "Century of Science." Invention was celebrated in the nineteenth century as the handmaiden of cultural progress; inventors were exalted as the discoverers and interpreters of nature's secrets. Popular magazines showed little restraint in describing recent advances in scientific and technical knowledge. Technological progress and social progress seemed intertwined in an ineluctable upward spiral. In the words of a *Scientific American* writer, "The railroad, the telegraph, and the steam vessel annihilated distance; people touched elbows across the seas; and the contagion of thought stimulated the ferment of civilization until the whole world broke out into an epidemic of industrial progress." While words such as *contagion* and *epidemic* suggested that industrialization was like a disease, the implied cure was better inventions more in tune with natural forces. Noting that the scientific movement was "at its maximum of vigor and productiveness," *Popular Science Monthly* nonetheless felt that, because of the recent advances in scientific inquiry, nature would "go on revealing herself to us with greater and greater fullness." These were expressions of an America that still believed the right technical advances would bring a utopia closer. Those advances that unraveled nature's mysteries and tied them to practical applications found particularly warm reception in the popular press.

Reporters responded to wireless telegraphy with unprecedented awe. On December 15, 1901, when Marconi reported to the press that he had successfully transmitted the letter S from England to Newfoundland, he garnered bold front-page headlines and effusive praise. The press lionized the inventor-hero and compared him to Edison. Popular magazines sent reporters to interview him and featured illustrated stories detailing in often melodramatic style the delays, doubts, and hardships that had preceded his success. With optimistic and excited rhetoric, these articles celebrated the new invention. "Our whole human existence is being transformed by electricity," observed the *North American Review.* "All must hope that every success will attend Marconi and the other daring adventurers who are exploring this comparatively unknown scientific region." Success was so important, continued the magazine, because no invention was "more pregnant with beneficial possibilities or calculated to be a more helpful factor in advancing the existing order of the world's life." *Current Literature* declared: "Probably no other modern scientific discovery has had so much romantic coloring about it as wireless telegraphy." Wireless held a special place in the American imagination precisely because it married idealism and adventure with science: "The essential idea belongs to the realms of romance, and from the day when the world heard with wonder, approaching almost incredulity, that a message had been flashed across the Atlantic . . . the wonder of the discovery has never decreased." Ray Stannard Baker, writing for *McClure's,* tried to transport his readers to this romantic realm by putting them in Marconi's position: "Think for a moment of sitting here on the edge of North America and listening to communication sent *through space* across nearly 2000 miles of ocean from the edge of Europe! A cable, marvelous as it is, maintains a tangible and material connection between speaker and hearer; one can grasp its meaning. But here is nothing but space, a pole with a pendant wire on one side of a broad, curving ocean, an uncertain kite struggling in the air on the other—and thought passing between." *World's Work* asserted: "The triumph of Marconi remains one of the most remarkable and fruitful that have ever crowned the insight, patience, and courage of mankind."

Celebration quickly led to prediction. In contrast with the forecasts for other technologies, however, there were few, if any, forecasts of how wireless equipment would look or how it would change the American landscape. There were no speculations on wireless sets of the future, no fantastic drawings of modernistic equipment. Rather, the predictions focused on where the messages might go and on what wireless would do for society and for individuals.

Reporters, often repeating the pronouncements of inventors eager to sell apparatus, began anticipating how wireless would make the world a happier, less risk-filled, and more civilized place. Some prophecies, though over-enthusiastic, were realistic and quickly came true—for instance, the following: "On shipboard a word from shore or from another ship will give warning of a neighboring reef or an ice floe, or tell of a dangerous change in an ocean current or herald a coming tempest. Steamer may communicate with steamer throughout the whole course of an ocean lane, forfending all risk of collision." P. T. McGrath, a newspaper editor who interviewed Marconi shortly after his transatlantic experiment, predicted in *Century Magazine* that wireless would "play a great part" in future military operations and would facilitate the exploration of places as remote and forbidding as the "arctic solitudes." These forecasts reflected the early marketing goals of those who, like Marconi, sought to model wireless after the telegraph system and thus offer a similar but competing communications network. But such a circumscribed vision, focusing on the existing market, could not contain the hopes and dreams wireless evoked. The possibilities seemed so much grander, and they extended beyond the advantages that might be enjoyed by ships' passengers, soldiers, and explorers. In the eyes of the press, wireless held the promise of being a truly democratic invention, benefiting millions instead of a few hundred.

The introduction of wireless renewed hopes for the possibility of eventually securing world peace. *Popular Science Monthly* observed: "The nerves of the whole world are, so to speak, being bound together, so that a touch in one country is transmitted instantly to a far-distant one." Implicit in this organic metaphor was the belief that a world so physically connected would become a spiritual whole with common interests and goals. The *New York Times* added: "Nothing so fosters and promotes a mutual understanding and a community of sentiment and interests as cheap, speedy and convenient communication." Articles suggested that this technology could make men more rational; with better communications available, misunderstandings could be avoided. These visions suggested that machines, by themselves, could change history; the right invention could help people overcome human foibles and weaknesses, particularly rivalry and suspicion brought on by isolation and lack of information.

The most stirring prophecies, however, envisioned individual rather than social benefits. A sonnet published in the *Atlantic Monthly* entitled simply "Wireless Telegraphy," traced the flight of a word "over the wilds of ocean and of shore" until it reached its intended destination:

Somewhere beyond the league-long silences,
Somewhere across the spaces of the years,
A heart will thrill to thee, a voice will bless,
Love will awake and life be perfected!

Love and life would be "perfected" as wireless communication would ease loneliness and isolation. The *New York Times* foresaw a time when "wireless telegraphy would make a father on the old New England farm and his son in Seattle . . . neighbors—perhaps by the use of their own private apparatus." *The Century Magazine,* reporting "vastly greater things are predicted for the future" of wireless, offered this rather poignant prophecy:

> . . . if a person wanted to call to a friend he knew not where, he would call in a very loud electromagnetic voice, heard by him who had the electromagnetic ear, silent to him who had it not. "Where are you?" he would say. A small reply would come "I am at the bottom of a coal mine, or crossing the Andes, or in the middle of the Atlantic." Or, perhaps in spite of all the calling, no reply would come, and the person would then know that his friend was dead. Think of what this would mean, of the calling which goes on every day from room to room of a house, and then think of that calling extending from pole to pole, not a noisy babble, but a call audible to him who wants to hear, and absolutely silent to all others. It would be almost like dreamland and ghostland, not the ghostland cultivated by a heated imagination, but a real communication from a distance based on true physical laws.

The rhetoric of this vision gets at the heart of what excited people about wireless. It was the potential autonomy and spontaneity of such communication that gripped Americans' imaginations: people could talk to whomever they wanted whenever they wanted, no matter how much distance or how many obstacles intervened. This technology would help them transcend the social and economic forces—particularly, and ironically, industrialization—that had driven them apart.

America's population was in the midst of an accelerated shift from country to city living, resulting in more frequent separation of family members and friends. To communicate over distances, individuals could either write letters or go through corporate intermediaries. Using the networks operated by the Bell Company or Western Union could be expensive, and privacy was compromised; both the telegraph and the telephone relied on operators, who were, either by necessity or inclination, privy to the contents of the message. Wireless seemed to promise something different: instant communication, through "the air," free from both operators and fees. In addition, wireless seemed the technical equivalent of mental telepathy. Intelligence could pass between sender and receiver without tangible connection. Thus, to many, wireless bridged the chasm between science and metaphysics, between the known and the unknown, between actual achievement and limitless possibility.

Though there were few predictions about how the wireless apparatus of the future would look, one recurring image was that of the "pocketsized" wireless kit that could be taken and used anywhere. The small size of such a device and its detachment from a corporate network contributed considerably to its appeal. Finally, the articles suggested, here was an invention people themselves could handle and control. Thus it was very different indeed from other technologies, such as factory machinery, railroads, the telegraph, or the telephone. If a better future was to be attained through particular technologies, and if this invention was one that all could master, then couldn't individuals, through radio, shape their own futures? This was one of the unarticulated yet central aspects of the allure of wireless.

Why did the press print and encourage all these prophecies, naive and farfetched as some of them seemed? The success of utopian novels in the late nineteenth century indicated that visions of the future, which offered escape from the problems of the present, were what the public wanted. Such popularity was one of the keys to the continued appearance of prophecy in journalism. Circulation wars among newspaper publishers during the 1880s and the 1890s contributed to an increased reliance on sensationalism in headlines, stories, and illustrations to attract yet more readers. Given the prevailing celebration of technological progress, which was perpetuated by the press, reporters looked for scoops on the latest technical feat or for predictions of feats to come. The grander the prophecy, the more dramatic (and beneficial) the changes envisioned, the better; caution did not sell newspapers.

Most important, newspaper publishers sought to promote wireless because they believed the invention would accelerate and cheapen newsgathering. The press considered the transatlantic cable rates for foreign news onerous; the *New York Times* once referred to the cable companies as "monopolistic serpents." Marconi predicted that wireless would shortly provide a transatlantic news service at much cheaper rates than those imposed by the cable companies, and the press reiterated this forecast frequently. One reporter said simply, "Cables might now be coiled up and sold for junk." Thus, there were economic as well as social and cultural stimuli generating the proliferation of these visions.

However, the enthusiasm of the press was not matched in either the corporate world or the armed services, for there was still a great discrepancy between present potential and predicted promise in the wireless field. The appealing predictions in the newspapers and magazines envisioned invisible, point-to-point connections between an unlimited number of senders and receivers. Implicit in these forecasts was the belief that there would be room for all potential users in "the air" and that these point-to-point conversations would be private. But in reality, Marconi and others were still struggling to eliminate interference between messages and ensure secrecy. These disadvantages, which inventors kept predicting would soon be corrected, explained the hesitancy of military and commercial clients to purchase wireless equipment. In addition, a combination of erratic equipment performance, poor marketing strategies, and corporate indifference or wariness about the potential value of wireless in general left the invention with no definite niche in the American marketplace. The two major communications companies, Western Union and American Telephone and Telegraph, concentrated on preserving the hegemony of their own systems and did not see any immediate advantage to acquiring and promoting the new technology. Only the most prestigious ocean liners, such as those of the Cunard line, installed wireless; smaller steamship companies were slow to adopt the invention. The American inventors Lee DeForest and Reginald Fessenden, who made the most significant technical contributions to American radio development, failed to find steady customers and a regular clientele. From a business standpoint, wireless was a failure.

Yet from 1906 to 1912, as American wireless companies were on the verge of or in fact declared bankruptcy, the United States experienced its first radio boom. Thousands of people, believing in a profitable future for the invention, bought hundreds of thousands of dollars' worth of stock in fledgling wireless companies. Others took even more decisive action and began to construct and use their own wireless stations. Thus, while the leaders of American corporate and bureaucratic institutions regarded the various prophecies with a skeptical eye, other individuals began translating vision into action. These Americans—primarily white middle-class boys and men who built their own stations in their bedrooms, attics, or garages—came to be known as the amateur operators, and by 1910 their use of wireless was being described in newspapers and magazines around the country. *The Outlook* outlined the emerging communications network:

> In the past two years another wireless system has been gradually developing, a system that has far outstripped all others in size and popularity. . . . Hundreds of schoolboys in every part of the country have taken to this most popular scientific fad, and, by copying the instruments used at the regular stations and constructing apparatus out of all kinds of electrical junk, have built wireless equipment that in some cases approach the naval stations in efficiency.

The amateurs were captivated by the idea of harnessing electrical technology to communicate with others, and were not deterred by lack of secrecy or interference. In fact, these features, considered such a disadvantage by institutional customers, increased the individual amateur's pool of potential contacts and the variety of information he could send and receive.

It is impossible to establish a causal relationship between the eager early predictions and these subsequent activities on the part of the amateurs. We cannot know how many wireless enthusiasts were inspired by what they read in newspapers or magazines. But we do know that there was a climate of enthusiasm, which the press reflected, embellished, and fanned. And we see the emergence of a widely dispersed group of individuals trying to accomplish what the journalistic visions had promised: communication over sometimes great distances with whomever else had a wireless set. The ways in which the amateurs came to use wireless—to contact strangers, to make friends, to provide communication during disasters, and to circumvent or antagonize private and governmental organizations—were enactments of the previously articulated visions.

The favorable social climate, though conducive to the development of the amateur wireless network, cannot fully explain the invention's proliferation. How were the amateurs able to master this particular technology? The first and most tangible development was the availability, starting in 1906, of the simple, inexpensive crystal set, a device that could, for some unexplained reasons, detect radio waves. Inventors did not understand how the crystal worked, but they knew that it was a sensitive, durable, inexpensive receiver that was simple to operate and required no replacement parts. At the time, how and why the crystal worked was not as important as its simplicity and its very low cost. (The crystal was placed between two copper contact points, which were adjustable so that the pressure could be regulated and the most sensitive portion of the mineral selected. To keep the contact as small as possible, often a thin wire, known popularly as the "catwhisker" was used.) The importance of the introduction of the crystal detector cannot be overemphasized. More than any other component, it contributed to the democratization of wireless, the concomitant wireless boom, and the radio boom of the 1920s.

The amateurs' ingenuity in converting a motley assortment of parts into working radio sets was impressive. With performance analogous to that of an expensive detector now available to them in the inexpensive crystal, the amateurs were prepared to improvise the rest of the wireless set. Before 1908 they had to, for very few companies sold equipment appropriate for home use. Also, one of the crucial components, the tuning coil, was not supposed to be available for sale because it was part of the patented Marconi system. As the boom continued, however, children's books, wireless manuals, magazines, and even the Boy Scout Manual offered diagrams and advice on radio construction. As one author instructed, "You see how many things I've used that you can find about the house."

In the hands of the amateurs, all sorts of technical recycling and adaptive reuse took place. Discarded photographic plates were wrapped with foil and became condensers. The brass spheres from an old bedstead were transformed into a spark gap, and were connected to an ordinary automobile ignition coil cum transmitter. (Model T coils were favorites.) Tuning coils were made out of curtain rods, baseball bats, or Quaker Oats containers wound with wire. One amateur described how he made his own rotary spark gap from an electric fan. Another recalled that he "improvised a loudspeaker by rolling a newspaper in the form of a tapered cone." Another inventor's apparatus was "constructed ingeniously out of old cans, umbrella ribs, discarded bottles, and various other articles." Amateurs used umbrella ribs as well as copper or silicon bronze wire to erect inexpensive and fairly good aerials. The one component that was too complicated for most amateurs to duplicate, and too expensive to buy, was the headphone set. Telephones began vanishing from public booths across the United States as the amateurs lifted the earpieces for their own stations. Thus, the amateurs didn't just adopt this new technology; they built it, experimented with it, modified it, and sought to extend its range and performance. They made radio their own medium of expression.

The size of this burgeoning wireless network is hard to gauge. Estimates vary, but Clinton De Soto, in his history of amateur radio, asserts that "it was the amateur who dominated the air." In 1911, *Electrical World* reported: "The number of wireless plants erected purely for amusement and without even the intention of serious experimenting is very large. One can scarcely go through a village without seeing evidence of this kind of activity, and around any of our large cities meddlesome antennae can be counted by the score." The *New York Times* estimated in 1912 that the United States had several hundred thousand active amateur operators.

Although the availability of the crystal set was a prerequisite for the proliferation of wireless, the technology alone cannot account for the dramatic increase in the invention's use. Complementary cultural and social forces were at work, and their power becomes more apparent when we look at a very different sort of historical artifact: the contemporary popular culture. It is in the popular culture that the spirit and the zeal of amateur radio are revealed.

Articles and books published between 1907 and 1922 captured enthusiasm and extended the visions first articulated in the press at the turn of the century. Radio was portrayed as an invention that provided entrée into an invisible realm unfamiliar to the less technically adventurous. This hint of exclusivity further romanticized the amateur's activities while implying that they were helping to shape and bring about the future. In a feature article on the amateurs in November 1907, the *New York Times* evoked the mystery surrounding radio and hinted at what lay ahead: "For intrigue, plot and counterplot, in business or in love of science, take to the air and tread its paths, sounding your way for the footfall of your friends' or enemy's message. There is a romance, a comedy, and a tragedy yet to be written." A more ethereal note was struck by Francis Collins in his children's book *Wireless Man:* "On every night after dinner . . . the entire country becomes a vast whispering gallery." Most effusive of all was the assessment of radio offered by a character in the *Radio Boys* book series: "But honestly, I think radio is the greatest thing in this whole Universe . . . What hasn't it done? What can't it do? . . . It's enough to make a dumb man eloquent." It is difficult to establish how widely distributed these books glorifying radio's potential were, but a review of the *New York Times* index and the *Reader's Guide* indicates an escalating number of practical, popular, and visionary articles about the invention during this period.

These breathless accounts of the adventures awaiting the enterprising enthusiast had special appeal for the young. Unlike their suspicious elders, who thought wireless too fantastic, too impractical, or too unremunerative, certain boys believed earnestly in the new marvel and were eager to explore its possibilities. Many were at the age when they could most easily learn a new technical "language." To them, radio promised excitement, fraternity, and new scientific knowledge. Through dime novels, vaudeville shows, and children's books, these youngsters witnessed, unhindered by any acquired disbelief, the unrefined and unselfconscious aspirations of the culture, especially the hope that technology would solve society's problems. Businessmen and military men were not part of this world, and they no doubt would have considered the fictional celebrations of wireless unrealistic.

By 1910, the prevailing theme in vaudeville and popular literature was man's mastery of and alliance with technology. This had supplanted western themes glorifying the white man's victory over the wild frontier. For an era that no longer had a frontier, the western motif became less compelling than the more urban, technological themes. A famous and popular vaudeville routine performed during the first decade of the century consisted of a team of men taking apart and reassembling a Ford on stage in 8 minutes. Youthful heroes of popular fiction, such as Frank Merriwell, Nick Carter, and Tom Swift, were able to meet any technological challenge. Technology provided a new realm of adventure and conquest.

Fictional characters' lives were transformed with the advent of radio. *The Radio Boys with the Iceberg Patrol* described the exciting achievements of Bob and Joe, two amateur operators. With their radio sets, they track down a "rascal who had defrauded an orphan girl." They are "instrumental in rescuing people who had been run down by a stolen motorboat." Shortly after this, Bob and Joe "overhear and expose a scoundrelly plot of financial sharpers" and "secure the return to jail of desperate escaped convicts." Because their apparatus is small and portable, it goes everywhere with them. While relaxing at the shore, they learn of a "terrible storm" out at sea, and they are "able by a message to save the vessel on which their own people were voyaging." All these adventures are recounted in just one of the book's action-filled paragraphs. In *Tom Swift and His Wireless Message,* Tom saves himself and his companions from a volcanic island by devising a wireless set and sending for help. "Would help come? If so, from where? And if so, would it be in time? These are the questions that the castaways asked themselves. As for Tom, he sat at the key clicking away, while, overhead, from the wires fastened to the dead tree, flashed out the messages." Finally, "from somewhere in the great void," a reply comes back and all are rescued.

Early accounts, both fictional and journalistic, portrayed young radio amateurs as having the sort of physical features and personality traits previously extolled in the highly popular Horatio Alger stories. Bob, one of the Radio Boys, "was a general favorite because of his frank and sunny nature and his straightforward character. The elder people liked him, and among the younger element he was the natural leader. . . . He was tall for his age, of dark complexion and with eyes that always looked straight at one without fear or favor." The *New York Times* described J. Willenborg, an amateur from Hoboken, New Jersey, as "gray-eyed, clear-cut of feature, intent, and with his brow furrowed." The reporter noted that although Willenborg's father was "well-to-do," Willenborg did not rely on his father's wealth. "He is so frequently called as an expert witness in so many important suits over electrical matters that his fees give him ample resources."

The press emphasized that many of these industrious amateurs, after graduating from high school, became operators on ships and saved their salaries to pay for college or technical school. Contemporary celebrations of the "ambition and really great inventive genius of American boys" no doubt lured new recruits. Parents were advised to encourage the hobby: "This new art does much toward keeping the boy at home, where other diversions usually, sooner or later, lead him to questionable resorts; and for this well-informed parents are only too willing to allow their sons to become interested in wireless." As these various expressions of encouragement for the amateurs appeared, the amateurs, according to their reminiscences, took them to heart. As one amateur recalled, "We were undoubtedly romantic about ourselves, possessors of strange new secrets that enabled us to send and receive messages without wires." This romantic self-image was heightened whenever real-life operators became heroes. In January 1909, when all but five passengers of the ships *Republic* and *Florida* were saved after the two ships collided in a thick fog, Jack Binns, the wireless operator, who had sent the distress signals, became a hero. Later, Binns was asked by vaudeville agents and book publishers to demonstrate his talents and tell his story. He agreed to write the forewords for the Radio Boys books, and through these he emphasized that adventure and celebrity could happen to any boy at any time. While he acknowledged that "the escapades of the boys in this book are extremely thrilling," he added, "but not particularly more so than is actually possible in everyday life." Binns further advised his readers that "radio is still a young science, and some of the most remarkable advances in it have been contributed by amateurs—that is, by boy experimenters. . . . Don't be discouraged because Edison came before you. There is still plenty of opportunity for you to become a new Edison, and no science offers the possibilities in this respect as close radio communication."

Though such promises of fame and adventure may have been overenthusiastic, these popular accounts were simply embellishing reality. A young man's life was indeed made more exciting by involvement in radio. The amateurs came to feel that their lives were intertwined with truly significant events as they overheard messages about shipwrecks or political developments and transmitted these messages to others. Those amateurs who heard Jack

Binn's distress signals became celebrities by association. One remembered that "the few boys in school in the area who claimed to have received the distress call were local heroes for a time, and they made a number of converts to the radio amateur hobby among the more technically minded youngsters." Hearing "the news" first, the night before other Americans would read the story in the newspapers, imbued the amateur with an aura of being "in the know." As Francis A. Collins wrote in *The Wireless Man,* "Over and over again it has happened that an exciting piece of news has been read by this great audience of wireless boys, long before the country has heard the news from the papers . . . a wide awake amateur often finds himself independent of such slow-going methods of spreading the news as newspapers or even bulletin boards." The amateurs could feel part of an inner circle of informed people because they heard the news as it happened and because they were tapping point-to-point messages meant only for certain ears, not broadcasts intended for just anyone.

Equally important was the novelty of contacting strangers across the miles. Although many operators hoped to hear dots and dashes coming from thousands of miles away, making contact over a distance as small as 10 or 15 miles was reportedly a "thrilling experience." In a culture that was becoming more urbanized and in which social networks were becoming increasingly fragmented, many strangers became friends through wireless. The fraternity that emerged possessed the fellowship felt among pioneers. These young men were exploring and comparing their findings on relatively uncharted and mysterious territory. As one amateur explained, "The eagerness and frankness in distributing the results of our findings undoubtedly molded the form of fellowship which is such a striking quality of the amateurs."

An unusual social phenomenon was emerging. A large radio audience was taking shape that, in its attitude and its involvement, was unlike traditionally passive audiences. Collins summarized the development in *The Wireless Man:* "An audience of a hundred thousand boys all over the United States may be addressed almost every evening by wireless telegraph. Beyond doubt this is the largest audience in the world. No football or baseball crowd, no convention or conference, compares with it in size, nor gives closer attention to the business at hand." This was an active, committed, and participatory audience. Out of this camaraderie emerged more formal fraternities, the wireless clubs, which were organized all over America. By 1912, the *New York Times* estimated that 122 wireless clubs existed in America. Most of the club meetings took place "in the air" on a prearranged wavelength. The chairman called the meeting to order by sending out his call letters, and the members signified their attendance by answering with their own. During these meetings, the amateurs usually shared technical problems and solutions and drilled each other on transmission skills. A Chicago wireless club broadcast a "program" every evening "as a matter of practice for amateur operators in receiving." "The bulletin usually consisted of an article of some electrical or telegraphic interest . . . sometimes the program was varied by sending passages in foreign languages, to quicken the receiving ears of the amateur operators."

Gradually, an informal wireless network was established as the different clubs relayed messages for each other to points too far to reach with most amateur sets. "Message handling—for pleasure, for friends, in time of emergency—was rapidly becoming the predominant theme in amateur radio." In March 1913, the midwest was hit by a severe windstorm that blew down the telegraph and telephone lines. The local amateurs handled the region's communications by relaying messages in and out. Such impromptu public-service gestures led some amateurs to advocate the establishment of better-organized communication among operators. One radio enthusiast, Hiram Percy Maxim, believed that the amateurs needed a national organization to establish a formal relay system or network to serve all amateurs. Through his Hartford Radio Club, he sent out invitations in March 1914 to amateurs to join a league and have their stations become official relay stations. The name of his organization was the American Radio Relay League (ARRL), and response to his invitations was so enthusiastic that within four months the league boasted 200 official relay stations across the United States. Thus, in 1914, a grassroots, coast-to-coast communications network existed. Upon the formation of the ARRL, *Popular Mechanics* noted: "The coming of wireless telegraphy has made it possible for the private citizen to communicate across great distances without the aid of either the government or a corporation, so that the organization of the relay league actually marks the beginning of a new epoch in the interchange of information and the transmission of messages."

People were becoming invisibly bound together by and in the airwaves, not by necessity, but for fun, to learn, and to establish contact with others. Those involved in the new hobby saw larger-than-life reflections of themselves in popular books, magazines, and newspapers. We cannot tell whether popular culture helped increase participation, but we do know, from the reminiscences of amateurs alive at the time, that the popular culture articulated the hopes and dreams invested in wireless. The technology gave the amateurs the means to communicate without wires. The popular culture sustained their visions of being on the cutting edge of technological progress. By now, the amateurs were not so much envisioning the future as they were laying the groundwork for it.

What did the amateurs' ever-increasing activity in the airwaves portend? The emergence of the amateurs and their often unrestrained fervor influenced both the immediate and the long-range regulatory, technical, and social developments in broadcasting. As increasing numbers of amateurs took wireless communication into their own hands, their activities became a nuisance to wireless companies and the government. In contrast with the early visions, which suggested there would be room for all in "the air," it was sadly discovered that the spectrum could accommodate only so many transmitters in a given area, especially when many of the sending stations emitted highly damped waves from crude spark gaps. Experimenters also learned that point-to-point, directional signaling was, at the time, impossible to achieve. And while some amateurs were skilled operators, devoted to serious experimentation, others were novices who clogged the airwaves with inconsequential and slowly sent messages. Francis Halt, a wireless operator in New York City from 1907 to 1911, described the congestion in his log book: "The different kids around here raise an awful noise, all try to talk at once, call when anybody is in and never use any sense, half can't read 4 words a minute and sit calling everybody within 20 miles and can't hear 800 feet from another station." He commented on one amateur's conversations: "FH is a very good reader, but he tries to say too much at one time then the poor reader makes him repeat it and they keep that blooming business up for hours." As this sort of interference increased, so did "malicious" interference, which began to give the amateurs a bad reputation. Posing as military officials, some amateurs dispatched naval ships on fabricated missions. Navy operators received emergency messages warning them that a ship was sinking off the coast. After hours of searching in vain, receivers heard the truth: the supposedly foundering ship had just arrived safely in port. Navy operators at the Newport Navy Yard complained that amateurs sent them profane messages. Others reportedly argued with Navy operators over right-of-way in the air. *The Outlook* reported that during what Navy operators claimed was an emergency situation, amateurs refused to clear the air, "some of the amateurs even arguing with the Navy men over the ownership of the ether." In another instance, when a Boston amateur was told by a naval operator to "butt out," he reportedly made the following classic remark: "Say, you Navy people think you own the ether. Who ever heard of the Navy anyway? Beat it, you, beat it."

What had developed was the inevitable situation of too many people wanting access to the airwaves at the same time, with no guidelines for establishing priority. Too many people had embraced the invention and its possibilities. During this era, before 1912, no spectrum allocation had occurred, and all operators—amateur, commercial, and naval—vied with each other for hegemony. Military lobbyists in Washington, citing safety at sea and national security as reasons, advocated legislation that would ban amateurs from transmitting over the then-preferred portion of the spectrum.

The amateurs could not accept that the Navy should suddenly step in and claim the airwaves for itself in the name of national security when the Navy had done little to develop or refine wireless. The amateurs asserted that they had as much if not more right to transmit, because they had worked and experimented to earn that right. While the Navy relied on outdated apparatus and unskilled or disinterested operators, the amateurs claimed to promote technical progress and individual commitment. The airwaves were a national resource, a newly discovered environment, and the amateurs claimed that their early enthusiasm and their technical work had entitled them to a sizable portion of the territory. They asked where the Navy had been when they were translating vision into practice. Much as the nineteenth century pioneers had obtained squatters' rights by cultivating the land on which they had settled, the amateurs had developed a proprietary attitude toward the airwaves they had been working for the past five years. They granted that there were a few outlaws in their midst, but they argued that the alleged violations did not justify the exclusion of all individual operators by the government.

Ultimately, the amateurs lost. During the *Titanic* disaster of April 1912, interference from amateur stations trying to relay as well as elicit news was so great that within four months the Congress banished their transmissions to a portion of the spectrum then deemed useless: short waves. The Radio Act of 1912 also required that amateurs be licensed, and imposed fines for "malicious interference."

What impact, then, could a group of operators have on radio broadcasting who were, by 1912, banished to this etheric reservation? One scholar who has studied how Americans have managed the airwaves points out that "relatively deprived users" were "virtually forced to innovate spectrum-economizing, spectrum-developing technology." It was the amateurs, the recently deprived users, who would pioneer one of the biggest breakthroughs in radio: shortwave broadcasting. One of the more famous amateurs, Edwin Armstrong, developed the regenerative or feedback circuit, which amplified the often feeble signals coming in over the receiving antenna. Thus, the amateurs' technical contributions remained significant. Also, less creative amateurs, by reporting results to others, provided the more serious experiments with valuable data on performance and results.

In the years after the Radio Act of 1912, the amateurs not only advanced radio technology but also anticipated broadcasting and even advertising. Between 1910 and 1920, amateur stations began to broadcast music, speech, and even advertising. By 1917, amateurs were relaying messages not just regionally but from coast to coast, demonstrating the benefits of a national communications network. Some of the early amateur stations became commercial stations in the 1920s. Frank Conrad of Pittsburgh, a radio amateur and a Westinghouse employee, operated in his garage a small amateur station that is usually credited with inaugurating the broadcasting boom. In 1920, Conrad's station was moved to a portion of the Westinghouse plant and became KDKA. It was the amateurs who demonstrated that, in an increasingly atomized and impersonal society, the nascent broadcast audience was waiting to be brought together. Using the airwaves to inform, entertain, and connect the general public was, before 1920, still not in the corporate imagination. Institutions continued to view radio as merely a substitute for cables, a technology that would provide long-distance, point-to-point communications. The Radio Corporation of America, which was formed to establish an American-controlled international network, was compelled to reconsider its purpose and its goals shortly after its formation in 1919. The industry that would come to control radio broadcasting by the late 1920s had to respond to a way of using the airwaves pioneered by the amateurs.

In their fight to retain access to the preferred portion of the spectrum in 1912, the amateurs claimed to be surrogates for "the people," who, they declared, were the rightful heirs to the spectrum. In congressional testimony and letters to magazines and newspapers, the amateurs insisted that individuals, not the Navy or big business, should determine how the airwaves were used. This democratic ideology, manifested both in rhetoric and in practice throughout the teens and the twenties, contributed to the legitimation of the public's claim to and stake in the air. The Communications Act of 1934, which established the Federal Communications Commission and required the licensing of all radio stations, mandated that these stations serve "the public interest, convenience, and necessity."

The turn-of-the-century predictions about radio's future applications had not come true. They had been based on a misunderstanding of how the invention worked, and they assumed that radio, by itself, could change the world. Yet even dreams that do not come true can have an effect. By encouraging and romanticizing the amateurs' hobby, these visions fostered experimentation among members of a subculture who had neither a corporate nor a political agenda. The predictions also articulated and reinforced the belief that this technology could and should be accessible to the greatest possible number of Americans.

Such dreams did not die in the 1920s. They simply transformed to accommodate the new reality of institutional management. Radio was now indeed firmly embedded in a corporate grid, and the new visions of the 1920s, while still very enthusiastic, made concessions to this centralized control. Just as Frank Conrad's radio station moved from his garage to Westinghouse, so too did visions of radio's uses and benefits begin to reflect corporate agendas. In the 1920s there was little mention of world peace or of anyone's ability to track down a long-lost friend or relative halfway around the world. In fact, there were not many thousands of message senders, only a few. The theme of isolation was still central, but instead of the separation of one individual from another the predictions of the 1920s focused on certain individuals' separation from the mainstream of American culture. "All isolation can be destroyed," proclaimed Stanley Frost in a 1922 article entitled "Radio Dreams That Can Come True." Now radio had the potential to be a "tremendous civilizer" that would "spread culture everywhere" and bring "mutual understanding to all sections of the country, unifying our thoughts, ideals, and purposes, making us a strong and well-knit people." This audience would be passive: "We do not even have to get up and leave the place," exclaimed a *Collier's* contributor. "All we have to do is to press a button." Thus, through radio, Americans would not transcend the present or circumvent corporate networks. In fact they would be more closely tied to both. Visions and reality were merging.

Yet at least one vision of how radio would bring about a utopian future persisted. In the spring of 1919, Marconi announced that several of his radio stations were picking up very strong signals "seeming to come from beyond the earth." Nikola Tesla, another prominent inventor, believed these signals were coming from Mars. Articles in newspapers and magazines speculated about the signals and, reiterating Preece's prediction of 20 years before, asked "Can we radio a message to Mars?" *Illustrated World,* a magazine that popularized recent technical developments, urged that America try; only then would the Martians know that "their signals were being responded to, and that intelligent beings actually inhabit the earth." The writer then added: "We can imagine what excitement this would cause on Mars." But the most important reason for trying to contact Mars was to learn what it was assumed they must know about improving, even perfecting, the quality of life. As *Illustrated World,* put it, "It is not unreasonable to believe that the whole trend of our thoughts and civilization might change for the better." Martians would not only view our civilization with considerable detachment, but they would also presumably give us all the secret answers. Once again, through radio, we might be able to escape the institutions in which we found ourselves ensnared.

The idea of sending radio signals to Mars was in many ways the most revealing and poignant of the visions surrounding radio. It exposed a sense of isolation, insecurity, and dissatisfaction over things as they were. It revealed that, despite the failure of past predictions, many Americans were still inclined to view certain technologies as autonomous, as possessing superhuman or magical powers. This willingness to invest certain inventions with individual hopes and cultural aspirations has permitted the corporate sphere to exploit a range of technologies to profitable ends, but it has led certain Americans, such as the amateur operators, to take technology into their own hands and, in the process, profoundly influence the course of technical change.

AFRICA

Charles Okigbo

INTRODUCTION

Like radio, television was a science-based technology, originating in studies of light and electricity in the late nineteenth century. And, like radio, the vacuum tube made practical television possible. Boris Rosing's use of the cathode-ray tube (CRT) as a receiver in 1907, and Vladimir Zworykin's demonstration of the CRT as a transmitter by 1931 pointed the way to all-electronic television before World War II. The war interrupted efforts by RCA and other companies to realize the commercial potential of television, but when peace came in 1945, the way was clear for the new technology to grow into the dominant mass communications medium we are familiar with today. Television touches nearly all aspects of our lives, so much so that what remains of dialogue is dictated by the "sound bite," the brief, attention-getting device designed like the television commercial to "sell" us on an idea or a point of view. Those of us brought up in the television age—now covering two generations—have found our attention span bound by the actual length of a half-hour program—twenty-two minutes, given a second or two either way. Beyond that, our minds drift off and our eyes glaze over, causing all manner of problems for professors and students alike trapped in fifty-minute classes.

In this selection by Charles Okigbo from the comprehensive edited work, *Television: An International History,* the focus is on the effects of television in Africa. Hailed by many as a means of educating the masses in the Third World, television has not lived up to its idealistic promise. Part of the problem is economic; most Africans cannot afford a television set, and there is an average of only 25 sets per 1,000 people across the continent. Another dimension of the problem is that television has become part of the African political kaleidoscope. Throughout the continent, political leaders understand the power of television as a propaganda and agitational tool and do all they can to exploit it as such. It is no accident that the first military coups in Africa came on the heels of the introduction of television and that the first target in any political takeover is the national television broadcasting service. Africans accept that news and entertainment on television carry with them a degree of political content that Westerners would find totally unacceptable.

Satellite uplinks and downlinks appeared at first to be the means of bringing about what some hoped would be a "global village," whereby virtually instantaneous worldwide communication would permit the free and open exchange of ideas and culture from people to people. Unfortunately, the African experience is that this communication is one-way only, with Africa the recipient of the dominant Western culture of Europe and the United States. This unidirectional flow of information and programming threatens to overwhelm the indigenous development of television and prolong Africa's dependency on the West. Television, along with newer technologies like the personal computer and the Internet, despite all their promise as liberating and uplifting international technologies, may fall far short of their potential and devolve into other means of subjugating and exploiting the Third World.

TELEVISION AND NATIONAL INDEPENDENCE

Africa—that sprawling continent that will never cease to amaze both natives and foreigners alike—is not one unit. Historically, geographically, and politically, it is the epitome of diversity. Above all else, it is characterized by contrapuntal attributes. For instance, though it is the oldest continent, the study of its history "came of age" only in the 1960s, coinciding with the emergence of many newly independent modern African states. One can only attempt therefore a somewhat cursory and arbitrary excursion into the history, role, and future of television in certain African countries.

There is evidence that Africa is the birthplace not only of the human species, but also of many technological innovations of the ancient world of human prehistory. The reality today is that Africa is not leading in any area of modern technology, least of all television, which, among the modern mass media, is a latecomer to the continent. Other parts of the developing world beat Africa in the race for introducing television.

Mexico had its first television in 1950, and two years later Venezuela and the Dominican Republic got theirs, followed by the Philippines in 1953, Colombia in 1954, with Guatemala, Nicaragua, and Uruguay achieving that status in 1956. In 1958 Chile, Peru, and Iran established their first television stations.

Some African countries did not lag far behind. In many cases, television seemed to be the handmaiden of political independence. In 1954 Morocco established its television station, followed two years later by Algeria. Nigeria, the giant of Africa, established hers in 1959, on the eve of her independence in 1960. Between 1962 and 1965 television was introduced to Kenya, Uganda, the Congo (Brazzaville), the Sudan, Zambia, Upper Volta, Gabon, Côte d'Ivoire, Senegal, and Ghana. Making the link between the new television stations and the political developments of the period, Dietrich Berwanger rightly argues that "it was the time when most of the colonies in Africa were becoming independent, and quite often a television station found its way into the colonial powers' farewell gifts." That might well be the case for some countries, but in a great many others local initiative and the desire to use television as a political weapon played vital roles.

Considering the relatively low technological developments in most of the African countries at the time, it is amazing that so many of them were able to afford the initial high costs involved in introducing television. In this respect, African countries were not far behind more prosperous and modernizing countries, among which Korea and Taiwan established their television stations in 1961 and 1962 respectively, only after Morocco, Algeria, and

Nigeria. Singapore and Malaysia joined the club in 1963, the same year as Ghana. Kenya beat them to it by one year, establishing its first television station in 1962, a year before independence, as with Nigeria. But unlike Nigeria, where a regional government in opposition had taken the lead, in Kenya it was the central government that did this, primarily for the settler community of Europeans and Indians.

In Zambia, television came in 1961 at the instance of a private firm, London Rhodesia Company (Lonrho), which established its television operations at Kitwe. Realizing the political impact of the medium, which can be used for mass mobilization of even illiterate viewers, the government bought the facility in 1964 and subsequently opened another station at the capital city of Lusaka. From the most humble beginning, television broadcasting in Zambia developed fast to the point that by 1986, as Francis Kasoma explains, most of rural Zambia could, technically, watch television, although many of the people could not afford the sets and, in some cases, electrical power was not available. Microwave links had brought the television signal to the provincial centres of Chipata, Kasama, Solwezi, Mongu, and Livingstone.

The introduction of television in many African countries takes a coloration that in some respects reflects the geopolitical culture and/or commercial character of the states. For instance, in Nigeria, with its wide variety of ethnic groups and highly developed social organizations, many of which compete with the federal government for power and influence, television first came at the instance of a regional government. Following the removal of broadcasting from the exclusive (central government) list as a result of the 1953 constitutional conference, the 1954 Constitution provided that regional governments could establish broadcasting stations.

Thus it was that the Western Nigerian government, in association with a British firm, Overseas Re-Diffusion Limited, established the Western Nigeria Broadcasting Service-Western Nigerian Television (WNBS-WNTV) to operate a radio station and also a television station, the latter becoming operational just a year before national independence on 1 October 1960. WNTV's slogan was: "First in Africa" (notwithstanding that Algeria and Morocco already had operational television stations). The stage was set in Nigeria for interregional rivalry in television operations.

Thus, one year after the establishment of WNTV, the Eastern Nigerian government established its own television station, appropriately called the Eastern Nigerian Television Service (ENTV), with the slogan "Second to None." This was later to make a historic contribution in the prosecution of the Nigeria-Biafra war that raged between 1967 and 1970. Many objective Nigerians agree with Biafrans and international observers that Biafra won the propaganda war, which was orchestrated by Radio Biafra, the wartime name of the Eastern Nigerian Broadcasting Service, an amalgamation of the radio and television operations.

The other political region in Nigeria—the North—accepted it was lagging behind in the race for television operations, but was determined to improve its position. In March 1962 it established its television station, Radio Television Kaduna, as an arm of the Broadcasting Company of Northern Nigeria (BCNN), and with that, the war of the regions temporarily cooled down. In April 1962 the federal government balanced the equation by establishing the federal television station, the Nigerian Television Service (NTS) on Victoria Island, Lagos.

The strong hand of foreign partners was everywhere evident in the early attempts to establish television stations. In the case of the Nigerian Television Service (NTS) the foreign partner was the American giant RCA, which outbid Siemens and Marconi in the tenders for the establishment of national television services. The contract with RCA was signed on 23 February 1961, though actual telecasting started in April 1962 on Channel 10, Lagos.

The history of television in Nigeria is intimately linked to the political history of the country, not only in the sense that the regions pre-empted the federal government and thereby set the agenda for managing television, but also in respect of the control and use of the medium as a political weapon. New structures of state administration invariably led to new structures of television establishment, control, and use. With the abolition of the regional governments and the subsequent creation of states in 1969, the new states that did not inherit television stations felt the first need was to establish one. A further balkanization exercise in 1975 left the country with a nineteen-state structure, instead of the original twelve-state arrangement. The new states again felt they had to have their own television (and radio) stations, and they now have.

The federal government, always trailing behind, in April 1976 promulgated Decree No. 24 to establish the Nigerian Television Authority (NTA), the umbrella organization for managing all federal government-owned television stations in the federal and state capitals. Today the federal government in Nigeria controls television and radio stations located in the old and new federal capitals of Lagos and Abuja, as well as those located in the individual capital cities of the thirty states in the country. Additionally, nearly all the thirty states have their own state-controlled radio and television stations—as these are now accepted as the first order of business for any newly created state.

Another African country that has an interesting history of television is the People's Republic of the Congo, a largely French-speaking Central African country located on the Atlantic Coast and with a modest population of about 2 million people. Congo is reputed to be the first French-speaking African country to establish a television station, and the third country in tropical Africa to do so, after Nigeria and Kenya. Congo started transmission on 28 November 1962, twenty-seven years after it had established its first radio station in 1935.

The reasons for establishing a television station in the Congo were neither to preempt the federal government, as was the case in Nigeria, nor to satisfy the needs of foreigners, as was the case in Kenya. It was not a marriage of the private and public sectors as was the case in Zambia, where Lonrho initiated and government took over. Rather it was uniquely French in conception. It was France's intention to deck out the Congo as a showcase of its post-colonial policy in Africa. But even when that policy changed a short while later, the television service remained. The Congolese Radio and Television Service (Office de Radio-diffusion et Télévision Congolaise—ORTC) was originally run by French staff until indigenous personnel who had gone to France for training returned a few months later. Within one year, all but three staff members were Congolese nationals.

Television use is very popular in the Congo, where there is now, in the 1990s, about one television set per fifty inhabitants, with more than 10 percent of all sets being colour receivers. Part of the rapid development of television in the Congo is attributable to the rivalry occasioned by the clarity of transmissions from Kinshasa (Zaïre), which provides the viewing public in Brazzaville with a second channel using the same languages in addition to Kiswahili and Tchilouba.

Though television was already firmly established in some African countries in the early 1960s, there was still a pocket of countries where the novel medium was not established even in the 1980s. Today, mainland Tanzania still lacks a television station, though it receives signals from neighbouring Zanzibar. Among those countries that have been classified as the laggards are Niger, which launched her television station in 1980, Lesotho and Cameroon (1985), and Chad (only in 1987).

The promise of television has not been realized yet as the medium is still the least active medium, with many stations running somewhat haphazard operations that are remarkable only in their failure to inspire any strong following. The difficulty is compounded by the paucity of television sets, now aggravated by the poor economic conditions. Taking the continent as a whole, 1965 showed there were 1.9 television sets per 1,000 inhabitants. In 1975, this increased to 6.2, and in 1986 it went up to 25, but even at this, it was a far cry from what obtained in other parts of the world. There was also a wide disparity between individual countries, with Egypt posting the highest figure at 83 receivers per 1,000, followed by prewar Sudan with 52. Congo and Gabon (both French-speaking) recorded 20, while Ghana was 10, Uganda 6.2, Kenya 5.4, Nigeria 5.6, and Niger 2.4.

THEMES ON AFRICAN TELEVISION

The themes on African television are as varied as the motives and philosophical principles that undergird the stations. In some cases, these change as often as the managements of the individual stations change; and often station management changes with the government. It is a standing joke among the staff of the Organization of African Unity (OAU) that no Minister of Information in any of the member states has managed to attend three successive meetings of the OAU Council of Ministers. This is because of incessant cabinet changes, and, in some cases, changes of government.

Politics

Regardless of what type of government an African state might have, a permanent theme on African television is politics. It is safe to assume that the apolitical television station in Africa does not exist, for it is in the nature of the general mass media in Africa to be seen and used as political tools, if not on the offensive, at least for warding off the inevitable personal attacks that are part of African politics.

In the typical case of Nigeria, the seed was sown when the Premier of the Western Region, the late Chief Obafemi Awolowo, was denied permission "to air his views through the national radio services" in reply to allegedly false accusations leveled against his party by the Governor, Sir John Stuart MacPherson. According to Mike Egbon:

> Chief Awolowo was disappointed by this denial of access. He considered [that] the only way out of such a dilemma in the future would be to have his own regionally controlled mass medium. The idea was nursed and it grew until the Western Region of Nigeria decided to set up its own broadcasting services . . . October 31, 1959.

Politics has continued to be a major variable informing many decisions, about establishing television stations as well as about choosing events and news makers to cover. Many Africans accept this without apology, as the rightful role for television. According to Chen Chimutengwende, Zimbabwean Minister of Information and Broadcasting, "the purpose of broadcasting in underdeveloped [sic] societies is not merely to educate, inform and entertain as is the case in the West. Mass Communication has a direct political mission . . . the 'agitational' or 'propaganda' element has to be there if mass mobilisation is to take place."

The political import has now taken a new dimension with the critical role broadcasting stations play during military *coups d'état*. The vicinity of radio and television stations in Africa is usually full of tanks and artillery always in readiness to ward off coup makers who know that their success or failure probably depends on how soon they take control of the broadcasting stations.

It may not be purely accidental that the era of the first military coups in Africa coincides with the introduction of television in the 1960s. The first Nigerian coup of January 1966, as well as the second one of July 1966, made good use of the broadcasting stations, and in both cases the young officers were emboldened by the success stories of their colleagues in other developing countries where military regimes had replaced elected governments. Among these are Zaïre (Congo Brazzaville), where Mobutu successfully led the military revolt of 25 November 1965; Upper Volta (now Burkina Faso), where Lamizana overthrew the civilian government on 3 January 1966; Algeria, where Boumedienne came to power on 19 June 1965; and Benin Republic, where Christopher Soglo led the revolt of 22 December 1965; while in the Central African Republic Jean Bedel Bokassa took over power on 1 January 1966.

It may be argued that radio plays a more critical role in attempts to take power by force, but it is also true that television stations play decisive roles in supporting or refusing to go along with the radio messages. In Nigeria, for instance, supportive television stations fly the national flag on the screen, play military music, and intermittently broadcast the message of the mutineers. Whenever coups occur, government agencies, ministries, departments, and parastatals are always found to be in great disarray as a leadership vacuum is created, and the broadcasting stations become the *de facto* government.

Though the military is becoming more unpopular as a political actor in Africa, its love affair with television is not about to cool, as military dictators now use the medium more than ever before in their new-found strategy of resigning their military positions only to run for the Presidency and declare themselves winners. All across the continent, the picture of the incumbent President is the most permanent icon in television news. So the theme of politics will probably remain an evergreen in African television programming.

Education

Next in importance to the political is the educational role of television. Education is always a vote catcher and all governments are also genuinely altruistic towards education to some extent. Thus the politicians present the education argument to the people in order to secure their massive approval and support for the introduction or expansion of television. In recognition of the educational role of television, Chief Obafemi Awolowo, the first politician to canvass for the establishment of a television station in tropical Africa, argued that "television [would] serve as teacher and entertainer, and as a stimulus to us all to transform Nigeria into a modern and prosperous nation."

Early television in Africa was a strong instructional medium which was used for both formal training in academic subjects and general information on civics, health, agriculture, and even morals. In addition to instructional academic programmes imported from the United States and Europe, some African television stations now have locally produced lessons in mathematics and the natural sciences. Other instructional packages come in the form of quizzes or school competitions for college students. Television is being used extensively for public service and civic behaviour campaigns.

Referring to the situation in Nigeria, Sylvanus Ekwelie has argued that it is no longer in doubt, if ever it was, that the mass media can and do supplement existing educational facilities, nor that the media (including television) can at times supplant these facilities. Wilbur Schramm once reported, at the time when many African countries were launching their television stations, that television could be as good (sometimes better) a teacher as conventional classroom instructors. According to his report of 1964 "out of 393 experimental comparisons of classes taught chiefly by television with classes taught by conventional classroom methods, there was no difference (in what the pupils could do in the final examination) in the case of 65 percent of all the comparisons; in 21 percent of the cases, the television class wrote significantly better examinations than the conventional class, and only in 14 percent was the conventional class superior."

On the whole, the promise that television is supposed to hold for educational purposes in Africa has gone largely unrealized because of the inherent limitations of the medium (limited reach) and also the motive behind television use (fun, games, and play). Tapio Varis in his 1985 study of the structure of television programmes in six African countries (Côte d'Ivoire, Kenya, Nigeria, Senegal, Uganda, and Zimbabwe) found that "on the whole, educational and cultural or generally developmental broadcasts do not appear to have gained significant attention." He noted further that "the improvement of production standards is constrained by lack of trained personnel and other necessary resources."

Joseph Mbindyo's study of Kenyan television viewers did not show any habitual viewing of educational programmes. Rather it showed that, whereas 22 percent "had no particular favourite programme," 18 percent mentioned news as their favourite, 15 percent chose sports, and 8 percent chose movies. Zambia had an ambitious programme when in October 1964 it established the Educational Broadcasting Service (EBS), which produced its first programmes for schools in February 1965. According to Francis Kasoma, "EBS was set up to help improve the quality of teaching and learning for teachers and students and in schools and colleges . . . Thousands of radio and television sets were distributed to schools throughout the country." Teachers were recruited to present the lessons on radio and television. But in spite of all these, by 1986 "both the television equipment in Kitwe and the sound recording studios in Lusaka were not operational," and thus the educational television project died naturally (though the radio wing survived).

In the Congo, though the two vernacular languages of Lingala and Munukutumba are used for the evening news, nutrition, education, and health programmes, the Congolese audience was found to have a decided preference for American action series and some local productions. In many parts of Africa today, educational television is not the instant university that the early advocates of instructional electronic media hoped it would be.

Entertainment

African television is primarily an entertainment medium, much in the character of such traditional forums as the village square, the community market, and the age-grade gathering, which are all communication situations that facilitate the common exchange of information and sharing of values. The entertainment motive was not lost on the early advocates of television in Africa. Not surprisingly, traditional dances and other forms of entertainment were some of the most common contents. Central to the entertainment functions of television is this taxonomy provided by Denis McQuail for all media: "escaping, or being diverted from problems, relaxing, getting intrinsic cultural or aesthetic enjoyment, filling time, emotional release and sexual arousal."

From its inception, the entertainment function of television and other electronic media in Nigeria as in other African countries was not in doubt. According to Ekwelie, "the bulk of media entertainment comes from radio, television and the cinema. As is well known, entertainment is the selling point of all three." In his earlier (1968) study of broadcasting in Nigeria he found that Eastern Nigerian Television devoted 62.49 percent of its broadcast time to entertainment, as against 73 and 60.75 percent on Western Nigerian Television and Radio Nigeria.

Television in the Congo is remarkable in its celebration of entertainment, which comes in many guises, especially, in the words of a 1990 UNESCO report by Peter Larsen, "variety shows, video-taped performances of traditional dancing and singing, concerts by well-known dance bands, coverage of public events to be considered of national importance such as the arrival and departure of visiting presidents and reporting of civic, social and economic affairs." In addition to these local programmes, Congolese television screens some popular foreign entertainment programmes such as *Dallas* (which was a huge success before it was discontinued due to financial reasons), *Starsky and Hutch, Derrick,* and *Der Alte.*

A certain number of entertainment programmes, especially variety shows, are exchanged with those of other African countries. Such exchanges are now promoted by regional bodies like AIDEC, which is based in Ouagadougou (Burkina Faso). In the film areas, though the three French-speaking countries of Mali, Senegal, and Burkina Faso have achieved enviable heights in international film culture, their popularity is more noticed beyond Africa, and least of all in African television. This is mostly because many African television stations find it cheaper to receive foreign films, which usually have more than paid their way, unlike African films, which may not have had a wide enough distribution to ensure they break even and turn in a profit.

Television is well patronized by youth, with young women seeming to prefer entertainment to news or public affairs. An empirical and qualitative study of television use by young Nigerians found that 63.9 percent reported watching television daily while 23.3 percent said they watched only occasionally. But by far the most dominant factor determining their preference among TV programmes was "entertainment," followed by "national affairs." Whereas the boys preferred national affairs, the girls voted overwhelmingly for entertainment. Though popular TV programmes were watched for their entertainment value, television news still got the highest rate of approval.

All across the continent there is a wide variety of entertainment programmes available for the local television audience. In Nigeria, Kenya, Ghana, and the French-speaking countries of Congo, Côte d'Ivoire, and Senegal, local audiences are thrilled by drama series, situation comedies, and live performance by indigenous or popular music groups, with most of these being in the national languages of the individual countries.

The foreign often appears to the African to be more exotic than the indigenous, and so, even with official policies that require up to 70 percent of local programming in many African stations, there is still considerable play given to American soap operas (*Another Life, General Hospital,* and *As the World Turns*) and British comedies, especially those using many black artists. On Nigerian television, late night movies, which are usually reruns of old American films, are popular on state-owned television stations and the NTA2 Channel 5, Lagos.

In Kenya, the establishment in 1991 of a private-enterprise television station (KTN) has seen the unrestrained presentation of entertainment programmes, nearly all of which are imported from the United States and Europe. Though the local audience is not complaining, such unbalanced programming is usually the focus for charges of new media imperialism from nationals concerned at the uncontrolled importation of foreign entertainment programmes.

Languages and cultural differences as well as infrastructural poverty make it difficult to engage in inter-country exchange of television programmes of the magnitude one would expect, considering that there are long-standing regional blocs that should have facilitated this. A report on the possibilities for such exchange of programmes in Africa showed that "programme exchange . . . has a long way to go" for these reasons:

1. lack of adequate personnel to produce or put together programmes for exchange;
2. stations are too preoccupied with day-to-day problems of broadcasting to pay attention to the needs of programme exchange;
3. lack of adequate resources to cope with programme exchange;
4. the reasons for programme exchange are vague and remote as far as practicing broadcasters are concerned;
5. many broadcasters do not feel that what they produce for their stations is good enough or relevant for the needs of other stations.

Though the Union des Radiodiffusions et Télévision Nationale d'Afrique (URTNA) is working vigorously to promote inter-country exchange of programmes, there is a great need for more action by national governments and national broadcasting unions to augment its efforts in this direction. There is a regional monthly exchange between Gambia, Sierra Leone, Ghana, and Nigeria (English-speaking West African states with a common colonial background). The Nigerian Television Authority also uses a lot of footage in its news and screens some entertaining programmes from Afrovision. But the extent of exchange is still less than desirable. Though the URTNA Programme Exchange Centre in Nairobi has studied the exchange situation and problems, it is still hampered in its operations by poor financial resources and ageing equipment for dubbing and translating entertainment programmes. So, even when the will is there the might to make exchange possible is often lacking.

In recent years, many African television stations have started treating their viewers to international live programmes, many of which are pure entertainment. In this respect, sport and musical shows dominate, with occasional state visits involving the Pope or some other international personality sometimes qualifying for telecasting. This is made possible by the ground satellite-receiving facilities in nearly all the television stations in Africa. These can allow for the exchange of programmes, though despite the availability of these facilities, not many programmes are exchanged through the satellite systems in Africa because the tariff in using satellites is prohibitive. It is only in the case of a few international sports events that URTNA, the Commonwealth Broadcasting Association (CBA), and/or the European Broadcasting Union (EBU) facilitate the sharing of costs to bring the coverage—either live or recorded—to African viewers.

CULTURAL IDENTITY AND UNITY

Of all the modern media of communication, none has a more serious implication for cultural development than television, which has the unique advantage of sight and sound, and whose range of creative manipulation is limited only by the aptitude of its users. Referring to culture as an anchor for society, Ogbu Kalu has argued that Africa has witnessed "a shell-burst from foreign cultures [and] much of her history is . . . imprisoned within European histories"; some historians like Hugh Trevor-Roper even suggest that Africa has no history. Culture covers all aspects of life, from the technological and economic to language and religion, and can provide the anchor to prevent a changing society from drifting: television must be central to it.

The era of the earliest television in Africa was also the period of the nationalist struggles that culminated in political independence in many countries. The nature of the European occupation of each African country and the character of the independence struggle that led to political autonomy have tended to colour the cultural use and impact of television, even up to the present. In Kenya, for instance, known as the East African Protectorate until 1920, the British viewed the territory as a colony for white settlement. This was because the area offered a favourable climate and fertile soils and was served by the newly completed Uganda Railway. It took the ferocity of the Mau-Mau freedom struggle to establish the principle of African majority rule for Kenya in 1960. Independence eventually came in December 1963. But that early British policy of permanent settlement coupled with a large presence of Indians whose ancestors came for the railway projects has left an indelible mark on the culture of Kenyans and on the main contents of Kenyan television.

Early Kenyan television catered more to the tastes of the foreigners who controlled the economy than to the indigenous population, who suffered deliberate marginalization. Apart from the use of Kiswahili in some programmes, there is not much of Kenyan traditional culture evident on television. The greatest shock for a first-time West African visitor to Nairobi is the realization that the English suit and tie (the blouse and skirt) appear to be the national dress for this independent African country.

Nigeria took a different route to independence, and also to the establishment of her television stations. The hot and humid climate, abundant mosquitoes that threatened every European with fatal malaria, and the rancour of an indeterminate number of local ethnic groups which were locked in perpetual battles with each other, all combined to impress on the British colonial administration that it had a limited tenure in that West African territory, which before 1 January 1900 was administered by the Royal Niger Company, a British enterprise. Not only were the British ready to relinquish power easily without imposing British culture on the people, but the indigenous people were notoriously proud of their African cultural heritage. Not surprisingly, this found expression in the earliest television programmes, and has continued to the present, in spite of the increasing influence of foreign cultural values arising from the globalization and Americanization of communication generally, and the electronic visual media in particular.

At independence, the task for television was simple. It was to portray a true picture of the people's culture and accurately render an account of the political climate, which showed Nigeria to be vastly diversified and blessed with enormous wealth, natural resources, and manpower. She was perceived as the greatest, the most promising, and the best hope for the black man and as having the fewest tensions. This dual mandate of promoting the cultural heritage while depicting the political promise was ably handled by the early managers of Nigerian television. However, in a vast country of about 80 million people, 256 ethnic groups, and 400 different languages, it is impossible to achieve the promotion of cultural unity through only three regional television stations, and so by 1966 the television stations were part of the political machinery for aggravating the civil strife that ensued.

In the French colonies, the situation was closer to what obtained in Kenya. By deliberate policy the French originally sought to "assimilate" their colonial subjects into being cultural Frenchmen, regardless of their skin colour. They were to have the full legal and political rights of French citizenship, including the right to send representatives to the French parliament in Paris. This proved impractical because of large-scale colonization and thus was later abandoned except for some Senegalese towns and a select few highly educated, French-speaking Africans, though "potential assimilation" was held as an ideal which all French-speaking Africans should strive for. This colonial policy has affected the cultural role of television in the former French colonies, where much of indigenous African culture has been subjugated and suppressed by the desire of the native people to be more French than their colonizers. This is more evident in a bilingual country like Cameroon, where the French-speaking *indigènes* are more foreign in outlook and orientation than their English-speaking counterparts, who appear more African (though these perceptual differences are definitely subjective, there being no truly empirical measures of Africanness, apart from such arbitrary characteristics as clothes, food, and language use).

The expectation that television in Africa would help bind the various ethnic groups together has largely gone unrealized from one country to another, regardless of whether the people suffered from the British maltreatment of Indirect Rule or the French policy of Assimilation or the Portuguese version (*assimilado*) or the Belgian *évolué*. Television must be seen as a mirror that reflects what is happening in society. This passivist perspective needs to be balanced, however, with an activist one which posits that television can be used as an agent for cultural development.

In this regard, each society must decide for itself how it sees its culture and how television can play a positive role in the management and promotion of that culture, including national cultural unity, if this is one of the goals it has set for television. The experience of the Western world does not support the view that television can easily bring about cultural unity, even among nationals of a country. This is not to discount the role of the media (including television) in the propagation of culture. In Nigeria the early newspapers, and television also later on, created and sustained Nigerian culture. If television in Africa has not lived up to its expectations in the promotion of African culture, it is because the programmers have not applied themselves seriously to that task, nor has the audience demanded it. What is not in doubt is that the medium can rise to this challenge. If it can be used as a major source of local, national, and international news, as is usually the case, it can also be a source of cultural values and education.

NEWS CONTENT

The news function of television is one of its most critical roles, and, because this usually has political implications, it attracts considerable attention from both television operators and the owners, mostly governments in the case of African countries. News on African television is as predictable and routinized as what we have in any other part of the world. Commenting on this feature of television news generally, Denis McQuail once noted that "what is striking is the extent to which a presumably unpredictable universe of events seems open to incorporation, day after day, into much the same temporal or spatial frame." Though there might be deviations from this routine (e.g., during crises), "the news form is posited on the notion of normality and routine and might be thought to reinforce the notion of normality through its regularity," McQuail concluded.

Allied to the routinized presentation is the indication of significance suggested by the arrangements of news items on television. All across the continent, television news starts with the President or some activity at Government House, continues with focus on the most important cabinet ministers, before it is spiced with some remote events, including international news. This is not a unique African feature, as it obtains in most television news operations world-wide. The Glasgow Media Group referred to this in 1980 as "Viewers' Maxims," by which is meant the principle that first-appearing items are more important than those that come later. Much of the news on African television can be classified as protocol news since it arises mostly from the comings and goings at Government House. This kind of coverage has also been noticed in the presentation and news selection styles of Third World news agencies.

Whereas Western journalists strive for objectivity and neutrality, many African television journalists have a view of the world which is essentially ideological—reflecting the positions of the governments of the day. It is amazing how this worldview changes immediately when a new regime comes to power, especially when this results from a *coup d'état*. There is a very thin line dividing news and propaganda, and credibility is not one of the strongest attributes of African television news. Some aspects of television news on the continent are absurd and ludicrous, bordering on pure entertainment or pedantic nonsense. This is more often the case during election campaigns, when the airwaves are put to greatest use by the incumbent heads of government, most of whom cannot distinguish between "state" and "party." The result is erosion of the medium's credibility.

The coverage of the world on African television varies from country to country, though one can easily identify a pattern of old colonial ties still influencing the nature of foreign news reporting in each African country. Erwin Atwood found from his study of how the international press covers Africa that British and French media coverage of sub-Saharan African countries is strongly associated with the country's membership in the British Commonwealth and the French Community. Similarly, the content of African television stations is directly related to the historical ties of individual countries. There is more about Nigeria on Kenyan television than about other African nations, and vice versa. There is also more about Côte d'Ivoire on Senegalese television, and vice versa. On the other hand, there is not much about former British colonies in the television of former French colonies, and vice versa.

The proportion of foreign news in African television has been found to be higher than obtains in some other regions of the world. This can be explained by the historical and commercial linkages many African countries share with the West and East. But even in this there are regional variations, with former French colonies and East African countries giving more play to foreign news. On Kenyan television, Western countries account for about 32 percent of foreign news, followed by African countries, which account for 21.9 percent.

In the case of Nigerian television, it has been found that (as with the Nigerian press generally) foreign news is not given much attention. It has been reported that as much as 82.9 percent of Nigerian television news is local while only 17.1 percent is foreign. The Third World accounts for a disproportionately high percentage of the news stories (94.3 percent), with the Western world providing only 4.1 percent. Eastern Europe and other parts of the world provide only 1.6 percent of the television news on the whole. The dominant contents all across the continent are usually politics, business, and human interest. Because of the commonality of training programmes, the presentation of the news is usually similar right across the continent, and in fact is the same as in Europe and America, except that there is less "sweet talk" among news presenters on African television. Lately, some African stations have started experimenting with weather reports on television, but these weather men/women are not as effective as characters as their counterparts on American television.

AFRICAN TELEVISION CULTURE

In spite of the wide variety of television stations in Africa, and also the different colorations of television use, there is general agreement that the medium should be deployed in the forefront of the war for accelerated development. This expectation that television should be given a serious and purposive role in the social engineering process in Africa runs in the face of both empirical and episodic evidence of how people (Africans and all others) react to television. There is hardly any African television station that does not incorporate educational and mass mobilization elements in its programme structure, even though entertainment is the dominant fare and the main attraction.

It is very difficult to come up with one notion of African television culture, because there is no one African people unified in a common approach to television, nor is there one single methodology of television in Africa. It is not only possible, but also instructive, to consider the proposition that, right across the continent, television content is predominantly skewed towards foreign or local plays, drama, soap opera, story-telling, and sport. There is also an increasing incidence of religious and political programmes which tend to be so similar that it is sometimes difficult to distinguish between them. Both preachers and politicians harangue their audiences at religious and political rallies in much the same manner and style.

A review of the programme schedule of many African television stations shows that, among local programmes, fictional content, in the form of drama in local languages, soap opera in English or French, and story narration by or for children, is some of the commonest fare. In Kenya, weekend viewers are treated to long hours of entertainment that start at noon with such programmes or films as *Wild Rose, The Littlest Hobo Year, Joy Bringers,* and *Rambo* (on Saturdays).

On Sunday, the menu includes *Disneyland, Children Variety,* and *Classical Music.* Weekend programming is incomplete without sport, for which there are usually three programmes on Saturday (*Football Coaching, KBC Sport Hour,* and *Premier League*). On Sundays, sports fans are treated to *Sports Machine* and *Gillette World Sports Special.* The programmes on the independent and private-enterprise television station (KTN) are almost entirely foreign, with the following being some of the most popular: cartoons, *Desmond's, Beauty and the Beast, Neighbours, Knotts Landing, Oprah Winfrey,* and *Showbiz Today.*

Among the local entertainment drama are: *Shulko Mawaidha, Kinimacho Baloonology,* and *Hukuma.* There is usually a thrilling feature film late every night, before the prayers that precede closedown at 11:33 p.m. African television culture is evidently entertainment-oriented.

The final picture that emerges shows that television is regarded as the modern equivalent of many traditional media forms which are used mostly for entertainment and the transmission of the cultural heritage. Many Africans make a clear distinction between serious use of the traditional/modern mass media as instructional channels and their use for enjoyment. Television use is more for the latter. This has informed not only how African viewers react to or use the medium, but, equally importantly, how African programmers package the daily television menu. The popularization of satellite networks is more on the basis of pure entertainment than for education. This has serious implications for the future of television in Africa, though the use of the medium for instructional and mobilizational purposes should not be completely discounted.

THE FUTURE OF TELEVISION IN AFRICA

All over Africa, even within those countries that established their television stations as long ago as the 1950s and 1960s, television is still a novelty. In the beginning, all the television sets were black and white, but now they are mostly full colour. The recent developments are in the sizes of the sets, some of which now approximate cinema screens. Of great significance also is the popularization of satellite channels. Though a regional satellite system (the Regional African Satellite Communication System—RASCOM) was launched in early 1987 to develop an efficient, reliable, and economic means of telecommunications, including sound and television broadcasting, intercountry exchange of television news and programmes is yet to develop beyond the trial stage.

By far the greatest impact of satellite broadcasting is coming from direct transmissions from European and American stations. All across the continent, a wide variety of foreign stations are received either directly or through diffusion arrangements with local stations. For instance, in April 1989 the French television network Canal France International started a daily four-hour direct satellite transmission to television stations in twenty-four French- and Portuguese-speaking African countries, among which are Benin, Côte d'Ivoire, Niger, and Senegal. Kenya's private television channel (KTN) relays regular satellite programmes from the American Cable News Network (CNN) on an hourly basis, creating the impression that its local programmes are fillers. In Nigeria, satellite antennae that make it possible to receive CNN, BBC, UK Gold, Sky, MTV, C-Span, and at least six other channels are now so cheap that nearly every household in the big cities has one. They have also become so popular that there is now a microversion that is specially designed for folding and fitting in a travelling bag for weekend trips to the villages.

The result of the introduction of satellite television among African states has been an increase in the one-sided flow of information, from the developed countries to Africa. The satellite news and programmes that are now becoming the common content of African television do not reflect African realities, and, if anything, they paint a negative picture of Africa as a continent that is at war, hunger-stricken, or drought-ravaged. The uncontrolled flow of satellite television programmes from European and American stations is a serious threat to the future development of television in Africa. Many urban dwellers in Africa prefer the foreign programmes to their local competitors', which suffer from the usual sicknesses of modern African mass media: lack of money, poverty of creativity, inadequate equipment, political pressure, and bureaucracy, among others. African governments need to invest more in regional satellite systems that will promote inter-country exchange of resources and television programmes; otherwise they will remain forever at the receiving end of the global satellite networks, leading to a perpetuation of the media dependency syndrome.

Unfortunately, the poor economic health of many African countries means that not much can be achieved in the immediate future, no matter how well intentioned the governments might be about television development. The gloomy outlook has forced the World Bank to the view that the sub-Saharan region is more underdeveloped even than South Asia. Some of the predicaments for tomorrow's Africa are rapid population growth and scarce water resources, two problems that can slow down the rate of development.

According to United Nations projections, the population of Africa is expected to quadruple before stabilizing at the end of the twenty-first century. The perennial drought in parts of the continent is another major handicap to development. Much of the African continent lies in a zone which for part of the year is arid and where recurrent drought severely disturbs agriculture, leading to a chain of adverse reactions that ultimately results in underdevelopment.

In these circumstances, growth and expansion in communications, including television, are likely to be frustrated. Even the expansion in population is not yet of much advantage to television development since there is usually no equivalent expansion in advertising revenue. The challenge to policy-makers in Africa is to turn the growing population of the continent to advantage.

One observer has pointed out that the populations of the less developed world have made no vow of permanent poverty while their economic policies are oriented toward maximum feasible material growth. Television in Africa has to be placed within a new vision of expanded development and growth. Television stations have yet to realize the potentials of the medium as a strong advertising revenue earner. In 1985 Tapio Varis found that, on many stations, advertisements account for as little as 1.6 percent of the overall total broadcasts and 3.3 percent during prime time. About a third of all television advertisements were found to be foreign. The low volume of advertisements leads to reduced revenue in many countries. On Ethiopian television, for example, advertisements account for only 3.8 percent of total revenue. In Algeria advertisements on radio and television combined account for only 5 percent of total revenue but the figures for Ghana and Benin are 11 percent and 26 percent respectively.

Mauritius and Zimbabwe point to the possibility that African stations cannot only be self-sustaining in future, but might also be significant profit centres. Unesco figures for Zimbabwean television reveal that advertisements yield 52 percent of total revenue while the figure for radio and television stations in Mauritius is 47.3 percent. If the potential is to be realized, the managers of African television stations need to be more businesslike in their advertising sales operations. Many still behave like civil servants and expect advertisers to beg for their time.

The distinctive feature of American broadcasting is the marketing abilities of even the smallest stations. American radio and television stations are primarily marketing tools, and, not surprisingly, there is a deliberate effort to position each station according to the consumer outlook for the area. Because of the paucity of radio and television stations in Africa, the marketing approach to programming, station positioning, and promotion has not yet been adopted. African television stations now need to target their programmes for defined market segments. This was not the habit of government-owned television but the new privately-owned stations will usher in an era of aggressive marketing and bring about a revolution in television management. In recent times, there has been a serious call for countries of the south to co-operate more among themselves. One of the pressure groups for this is the South Commission, formally established in 1987, after years of informal discussion among intellectual and political élites of the south. In its manifesto, *Challenge to the South,* the Commission analysed the problems of southern development and proffered far-reaching solutions, many of which have serious implications for the media, especially television.

According to the Commission, "it is important that the Public should have access to information on the activities of the government. In this respect, the role of the media becomes vital." It goes further, recommending that "the existing cooperation among the media of developing countries should be greatly intensified and diversified, and the necessary infrastructural links improved . . . The South has to act collectively so as to minimize its dependence on Northern sources." Information is a key resource that needs to be managed for the protection and promotion of southern interests. In this regard, television, especially its satellite operations, must be employed in the strategic task of ensuring public access to vital government information, the promotion of south-south development, and the enhancement of the cultural dimension of development.

In its expansive view of culture the Commission includes "values, attitudes, beliefs, and customs of a society" as well as "activities . . . which express and enrich, while at the same time transforming those values, attitudes, beliefs, and customs." Television must be sensitive to the cultural roots of African societies and at the same time must include as a goal the development and sustenance of African culture itself—not an easy task.

The future of television cannot be divorced from the future of African societies. In the daily struggle of the medium to be a relevant actor in the socio-political and technological development of Africa it has to find a solution to the one-sided flow of satellite programmes and thus to reduce dependence on the north. It has to capitalize on the growing size of African populations, and it has to orient itself to the task of marketing while at the same time fulfilling its mission as an agency of sustainable development.

African television is so varied in its nature and characteristics that one cannot describe it in simple terms. At one end there are developed systems like the Nigerian Television Authority with a network of thirty federal and state stations linked to the central station for network news and special programmes. At the other end, there is Tanzania, just about to establish her first mainland station, and there is Lesotho, where television was established in 1986, but transmits its programmes for only one hour a day from 6:00 to 7:00 p.m. with the evening news taking the last fifteen minutes of broadcasting. With three South African channels (TV.1, CCV, and MNET) available, one cannot see much future for the expansive growth of Lesotho Television in this country of 1.6 million people. Television in Africa is largely a political weapon, not a tool of marketing as in the West. It is this that makes the ownership and control of the medium so important to African governments. Like Western education and religion, it arrived at the instance of colonial powers who left their mark.

In an era of political armies, radio and television stations as well as the people who work there have acquired added significance because of their roles during *coups d'état*. Not surprisingly, some radio and television stations now have more tanks than government houses and barracks. In the future of politics in Africa, the role of television cannot be disguised. The mismanagement of the medium is the beginning of failure for any regime.

Africa's dwindling economic fortunes will have severe results in the development of the medium, which every African likes, but only few can now afford. Unesco figures show that television has become nearly invisible in some African countries, especially Angola, with 5.3 sets per 1,000 people; in Tanzania with 0.6; in Burundi with 0.2; and in Mali with 0.1. Many countries are establishing community viewing centres as a way of overcoming the diminishing presence of television.

In spite of its promise in Africa, television has not lived up to people's expectations, and after more than thirty years on the continent it is still largely foreign in orientation. An Africanization revolution is inevitable if the medium is ever to realize its potential as an instrument of culture; without this it will continue to be only a filler of time.

AUSCHWITZ OBSERVED: REPORT OF TWO ESCAPED EYEWITNESSES

Lucy S. Dawidowicz

INTRODUCTION

In the recent past, nothing can rival the Holocaust for the sheer scale of its horror. During the course of World War II, the Germans systematically exterminated 6 million Jews during a massive campaign of genocide. Here was the mass production of death, carried out with ruthless efficiency. Auschwitz, Buchenwald, Belsen, Dachau, Maidanek, and scores of other previously obscure villages became huge death factories, "processing" hundreds of thousands of men, women, and children in gas chambers and crematoria. Consider the implications within the context of the history of technology. Gassing evolved from early experiments with carbon monoxide to more sophisticated chemical poisons derived from insecticides and rodenticides developed by Germany's premier chemical manufacturing firms. At the other end of the spectrum of death, the Germans designed and built crematoria to provide continuous operation, fulfilling the demands for continuity and synchronization central to mass production technology. Finally, by 1942, the two technologies came together at Auschwitz, which in the interests of efficiency, became the focal point of a coordinated extermination system designed by architects, developed by engineers, and administered by technocrats in the SS to carry out the "Final Solution" to the "problem" of the Jews.

This selection, the recollections of two survivors of the death camp at Auschwitz, provides only a glimpse of the tragedy. It is almost chilling in its objective, matter-of-fact treatment of the events. How is it possible for witnesses to such inhumanity to describe it without resorting to emotion-filled cries of anguish? The answer is that the enormity of the misery they witnessed was so monstrous and so shocking as to be at the outer limits of comprehension.

On April 13, 1942, our group of 1,000 men was loaded onto railroad cars at the assembly camp at Sered. The doors were sealed, so that nothing would reveal the direction of the journey. When they were opened after a long while, we realized that we had crossed the Slovak frontier and were in Zwardon.[1] Until then the train had been guarded by Hlinka men,[2] but it was now taken over by SS guards. After a few cars had been uncoupled from our convoy, we continued on our way, arriving at night at Auschwitz, where we stopped at a siding. . . . Upon arrival, we were counted off in rows of five. There were 643 of us. After a walk of about twenty minutes with our heavy packs—we had left Slovakia well equipped—we reached the concentration camp of Auschwitz.

We were led at once into a huge barracks, where we had to deposit all our luggage on one side and on the other undress completely, leaving our clothes and valuables behind. Naked, we then proceeded to an adjoining barracks, where our heads and bodies were shaved and disinfected. At the exit, every man was given a number, beginning with 28,600. With this number in hand, we were then herded to a third barracks, where so-called registration took place. Here the numbers we received in the second barracks were tattooed on the left side of our chests. The extreme brutality with which this was done made many of us faint. The particulars of our identity were also recorded. Then we were led by hundreds into a cellar and later to a barracks, where we were issued striped prisoners' clothes and wooden clogs. This lasted until 10 a.m. In the afternoon our prisoners' outfits were taken away from us and replaced by the ragged and dirty remains of Russian uniforms. Thus equipped, we were marched off to Birkenau.

Auschwitz is a concentration camp for political prisoners under so-called "protective custody." At the time of my arrival, that is, April 1942, about 15,000 prisoners were in the camp, the majority Poles, Germans, and civilian Russians under protective custody. A small number of prisoners came under the categories of criminals and "work-shirkers."

Auschwitz camp headquarters also controls the labor camp of Birkenau as well as the farm-labor camp of Harmense. All the prisoners arrive first at Auschwitz, where they are provided with prisoners' registration numbers and then are kept there, or are sent either to Birkenau or, in very small numbers, to Harmense. . . .

There are several factories on the grounds of the camp of Auschwitz: a war production plant of *Deutsche Ausrustungswerke* (DAW), a factory belonging to the Krupp works, and one to the Siemens concern. Outside the camp's boundary is a tremendous plant covering several square kilometers named Buna.[3] The prisoners work in all the aforementioned factories.

The prisoners' actual living quarters, if such a term is at all appropriate, covers an area approximately 500 by 300 meters, surrounded by a double row of concrete posts about three meters high, interconnected, inside and out, by a dense netting of high-tension wires fixed into the posts by insulators. Between these two rows of posts, at intervals of 150 meters, there are five-meter-high watchtowers, equipped with machine guns and searchlights. The inner high-tension ring is encircled by an ordinary wire fence. Merely to touch this fence is to draw a stream of bullets from the watchtowers. This system is called the "small" or "inner ring of sentry posts."

---

1. Zwardon was on the Polish side of the Polish-Czech frontier.

2. These were members of the Hlinka Guard, the paramilitary arm of the Hlinka People's party, a right-wing Catholic nationalist party, the only legal party in Slovakia after March 1939. The Hlinka Guard collaborated with the SS.

3. *Deutsche Ausrustungswerke* (German Armament Works) was an SS enterprise founded in 1939. Krupp and Siemens were among Germany's largest industrial manufacturers, with plants all over Europe. The Buna plant at Auschwitz, part of the vast network of I. G. Farben industrial enterprises, produced synthetic rubber.

The camp itself is composed of three rows of houses. The camp thoroughfare lies between the first and second row. A wall used to stand between the second and third row. Up to mid-August 1942, the over 7,000 Jewish girls deported from Slovakia in March and April 1944 lived in the houses separated by this wall. After these girls had been removed to Birkenau, the wall was removed. The road into the camp bisects the row of houses. Over the entrance gate, always, of course, heavily guarded, stands the ironic inscription: "Work brings freedom."

At a radius of some 2,000 meters, the whole camp is encircled by a second ring called the "big" or "outer ring of sentry posts," also with watchtowers every 150 meters. Between the inner- and outer-ring sentry posts are the factories and other workshops. The towers of the inner ring are manned only at night when the high-tension current is switched into the double row of wires. During the day the garrison of the inner-ring sentry posts is withdrawn, and the men take up duty in the outer ring. Escape—and many attempts have been made—through these sentry posts is practically impossible. Getting through the inner-ring posts at night is completely impossible, and the towers of the outer ring are so close to one another that it is out of the question to pass unnoticed. The guards shoot without warning. The garrison of the outer ring is withdrawn at twilight, but only after all the prisoners have been ascertained to be within the inner ring. If the roll call uncovers a missing prisoner, sirens immediately sound the alarm.

The men in the outer ring remain in their towers on the lookout, the inner ring is manned, and hundreds of SS guards and bloodhounds begin a systematic search. The siren brings the whole surrounding countryside to a state of alarm, so that if by miracle the escaping man has succeeded in getting through the outer ring, he is almost certain to be caught by one of the numerous German police and SS patrols. The escapee is furthermore handicapped by his clean-shaven head, his striped prisoner's outfit or red patches sewn on his clothing, and the passiveness of the thoroughly intimidated population. The mere failure to give information on the whereabouts of a prisoner, not to speak of extending help, is punished by death. If the prisoner has not been caught sooner, the garrison of the outer-ring sentry posts remains on the watch for three days and nights, after which it is presumed that the fugitive succeeded in breaking through the double ring. The following night the outer guard is withdrawn. If the fugitive is caught alive, he is hanged in the presence of the whole camp. If he is found dead, his body—wherever it may have been located—is returned to camp (it is easily identifiable by the tattooed number) and seated at the entrance gate, a small notice clasped in his hands, reading: "Here I am." During our two years' imprisonment, many attempts at escape were made, but except for two or three, all were brought back dead or alive. It is not known whether those two or three actually managed to get away. It can, however, be asserted that among the Jews who were deported from Slovakia to Auschwitz or Birkenau, we are the only two who were lucky enough to save ourselves.

As stated previously, we were transferred from Auschwitz to Birkenau on the day of our arrival. Actually there is no such district as Birkenau. Even the word Birkenau is new in that it has been adapted from the nearby Brzezinki.[4] The existing camp center of Birkenau lies four kilometers from Auschwitz, though the outer borders of Birkenau and Auschwitz adjoin. . . .

---

4. "Birch tree" in Polish is *brzezina;* in German, *Birke. Brzezinki* is the plural diminutive, hence, a wood of small birches; the German equivalent was Birkenwald.

When we arrived in Birkenau, we found only one huge kitchen there for 15,000 people and three stone buildings, two already completed and one under construction. The buildings were encircled by an ordinary barbed-wire fence. The prisoners were housed in these buildings and in others later constructed . . . All are built according to a standard model. Each house is about 30 meters long and 8 to 10 meters wide, [divided into tiny cubicles] . . . too narrow for a man to lie stretched out and not high enough for him to sit upright. There is no question of having enough space to stand upright. Thus, some 400–500 people are accommodated in one house or "block." . . .

After three days I was ordered, together with 200 other Slovak Jews, to work in the German armament factories at Auschwitz, but we continued to be housed in Birkenau. We left early in the morning, returning at night, and worked in the carpentry shop as well as on road construction. Our food consisted of one liter of turnip soup at midday and 300 grams of bad bread in the evening. Working conditions were inconceivably hard, so that the majority of us, weakened by starvation and the inedible food, could not endure. The mortality was so high that our group of 200 had 30–35 dead every day. Many were simply beaten to death by the overseers—the *Kapos*⁵—during work, without the slightest provocation. The gaps in our ranks caused by these deaths were replaced daily by prisoners from Birkenau. Our return at night was extremely painful and dangerous, as we had to drag, over a distance of five kilometers, our tools, firewood, heavy cauldrons, and the bodies of those who had died or had been killed during the working day. With these heavy loads we had to maintain a brisk pace, and anyone incurring the displeasure of one of the Kapos was cruelly knocked down, if not beaten to death. Until the arrival of the second group of Slovak men some fourteen days later, our original number had dwindled to 150. At night we were counted, the bodies of the dead were piled up on flat, narrow-gauge cars or in a truck and brought to Brzezinki, where they were burned in a trench several meters deep and about fifteen meters long. . . .

Until the middle of May 1942, a total of four convoys of Jewish men from Slovakia arrived at Birkenau and all were given treatment similar to ours.

From the first two transports 120 men—90 Slovak and 30 French Jews—were chosen, including myself, and placed at the disposal of the administration of the camp of Auschwitz, which needed doctors, dentists, intellectuals, and clerks. As I had in the meantime managed to work my way up to a good position in Birkenau—being in command of a group of fifty men, which had brought me considerable advantage—I at first felt reluctant to leave for Auschwitz. However, I was finally persuaded to go. After eight days, eighteen doctors and attendants as well as three other persons were selected from this group of 120. The doctors were used in the so-called *Krankenbau* ("patients building" infirmary) at Auschwitz. . . . The remaining 99 persons were sent to work in the gravel pits where they all died within a short time.

Shortly thereafter a Krankenbau was set up. It was destined to become the much dreaded Block 7, where I was first chief attendant and later administrator. The "infirmary" chief was

---

5. *Kapo* (sometimes *Capo*) was concentration-camp slang for a foreman of a labor gang, who was himself a camp inmate. The origin of the word is obscure. It may be an abbreviated form of the French *caporal,* a term used in the German army during the Second World War. *Kapo* was also used long before the war among carpenters as a German slang word for a foreman. Another hypothesis is that *Kapo* is a borrowing from the Italian *capo,* "head" or "chief."

a Pole. This building actually was nothing but an assembly center of candidates for death. All prisoners incapable of working were sent there. There was no question of any medical attention or care. We had some 150 dead daily and their bodies were sent for cremation to Auschwitz.

At the same time, the so-called "selections" were introduced. Twice weekly, Mondays and Thursdays, the camp doctor indicated the number of prisoners who were to be gassed and then burned. Those selected were loaded onto trucks and brought to Brzezinki. Those still alive upon arrival were gassed in a big barracks erected near the trench used for burning the bodies. The weekly contingent of dead from Block 7 was about 2,000, 1,200 of whom died a "natural death" and about 800 by "selection." For those who had not been "selected," a death certificate was issued and sent to the central administration at Oranienburg, whereas a special list was kept of the "selectees" with the indication "S.B." (*Sonderbehandlung*— special treatment). Until January 15, 1943, up to which time I was administrator of Block 7 and therefore in a position directly to observe the events, some 50,000 prisoners died of "natural death" or by "selection."

As previously described, the prisoners were numbered consecutively, so that we can reconstruct fairly clearly their order of succession and the fate which befell each individual convoy on arrival.

The first transport of Jewish men reaching Auschwitz for Birkenau was composed, as mentioned, of 1,320 naturalized French Jews bearing approximately the following numbers: 27,400–28,600

28,600–29,600	In April 1942 the first convoy of Slovak Jews (our convoy).
29,600–29,700	100 men (Aryans) from various concentration camps.
29,700–32,700	3 complete convoys of Slovak Jews.
32,700–33,100	400 professional criminals (Aryans) from Warsaw prisons.
33,100–35,000	1,900 Jews from Cracow.
35,000–36,000	1,000 Poles (Aryans)—political prisoners.
36,000–37,300	In May 1942–1,300 Slovak Jews from Lublin-Majdanek.
37,300–37,900	600 Poles (Aryans) from Radom, a few Jews among them.
37,900–38,000	100 Poles from the concentration camp of Dachau.
38,000–38,400	400 naturalized French Jews with their families.

This whole convoy consisted of about 1,600 individuals, of whom approximately 200 girls and 400 men were admitted to the camp, while the remaining 1,000 persons (women, old people, children, as well as men) were sent without further procedure from the railroad siding directly to Brzezinki, and there gassed and burned. From this moment on, all Jewish convoys were dealt with in the same way. Approximately ten percent of the men and five percent of the women were assigned to the camps and the remaining members were immediately gassed. This process of annihilation had already been applied earlier to the Polish Jews. During long months, without interruption, trucks brought thousands of Jews from the various ghettos directly to the pit in Birkenwald. . . .

48,300–48,620	320 Jews from Slovakia. About 70 girls were transferred to the women's camp, the remainder, some 650 people, gassed in Birkenwald. This

	convoy included about 80 people who had been transferred by the Hungarian police to the camp at Sered. . . .
49,000–64,800	15,000 naturalized French, Belgian, and Dutch Jews. This figure certainly represents less than ten percent of the total convoy. This was between July 1 and September 15, 1942. Large family convoys arrived from various European countries and were at once directed to Birkenwald. The Sonderkommando, employed for gassing and burning, worked day and night shifts. Hundreds of thousands of Jews were gassed during this period.
64,800–65,000	200 Slovak Jews. Of this transport, about 100 women were admitted to the camp, the rest were gassed and burned. . . .
65,000–68,000	Naturalized French, Belgian, and Dutch Jews. Not more than 1,000 women were "selected" and sent to the camp. The others, 30,000, at the least, were gassed.
71,000–80,000	Naturalized French, Belgian, and Dutch Jews. The prisoners brought to the camp hardly represented ten percent of the total transport. A conservative estimate would be that approximately 65,000 to 70,000 persons were gassed. . . .

Number 80,000 marks the beginning of the systematic annihilation of the Polish ghettos.

80,000–85,000	Approximately 5,000 Jews from various ghettos in Mlawa, Makow, Ciechanow, Lomza, Grodno, Bialystok. For fully thirty days truck convoys arrived without interruption. Only 5,000 persons were sent to the concentration camp; all the others were gassed at once. The Sonderkommando worked in two shifts, twenty-four hours daily, and was scarcely able to cope with the gassing and burning. Without exaggeration, it may be said that some 80,000–90,000 of these convoys received Sonderbehandlung. These transports also brought in a considerable amount of money, valuables, and precious stones.
85,000–92,000	6,000 Jews from Grodno, Bialystok, and Cracow, as well as 1,000 Aryan Poles. The majority of the Jewish convoys were directly gassed and about 4,000 Jews daily were driven into the gas chambers. During mid-January 1943, three convoys of 2,000 persons each from Theresienstadt arrived. . . . Only 600 men and 300 women of these 6,000 persons were admitted to the camp. The remainder were gassed.
99,000–100,000	End of January 1943, large convoys of French and Dutch Jews arrived; only a small proportion reached the camp.
100,000–102,000	In February 1943, 2,000 Aryan Poles, mostly intellectuals.
102,000–103,000	700 Czech Aryans. Later, those still alive were sent to Buchenwald.
103,000–108,000	3,000 French and Dutch Jews and 2,000 Poles (Aryans). During the month of February 1943, two contingents arrived daily. They included Polish, French, and Dutch Jews who, in the main, were sent to the gas chambers. The number gassed during this month can be estimated at no smaller than 90,000.

At the end of February 1943, a new modern crematorium and gassing plant were inaugurated at Birkenau. The gassing and burning of the bodies in Birkenwald were discontinued, the whole job being taken over by the four specially built crematoria. The large ditch was filled in, the ground levelled, and the ashes used, as before, for fertilizer at the farm labor camp of Harmense, so that today it is almost impossible to find traces of the dreadful mass murder which took place.

At present four crematoria are in operation at Birkenau, two large ones, I and II, and two smaller ones, III and IV. Those of type I and II consist of three parts, i.e.: the furnace room, the large hall, and the gas chamber. A huge chimney rises from the furnace room around which are grouped nine furnaces, each having four openings. Each opening can take three normal corpses at once, after an hour and a half the bodies are completely burned. Thus, the daily capacity is about 2,000 bodies. A large "reception hall" adjoins, so as to give the impression of the antechamber of a bathing establishment. It holds 2,000 people and apparently there is a similar waiting room on the floor below. From there, a door and a few stairs down lead into the very long and narrow gas chamber. The walls of this chamber are also camouflaged with simulated entries to shower rooms in order to mislead the victims. The roof is fitted with three traps which can be hermetically closed from the outside. A track leads from the gas chamber to the furnace room.

The gassing takes place as follows: the unfortunate victims are brought into the reception hall where they are told to undress. To complete the fiction that they are going to bathe, each person receives a towel and a small piece of soap issued by two men in white coats. Then they are crowded into the gas chamber in such numbers that there is, of course, only standing room. To compress this crowd into the narrow space, shots are often fired to induce those already at the far end to huddle still closer together. When everybody is inside, the heavy doors are closed. Then there is a short pause, presumably to allow the room temperature to rise to a certain level, after which SS men with gas masks climb on the roof, open the traps, and shake down a preparation in powder form out of tin cans labelled "Zyklon— For use against vermin," manufactured by a Hamburg concern. It is presumed that this is a cyanide mixture of some sort which turns into gas at a certain temperature. After three minutes everyone in the chamber is dead. No one is known to have survived this ordeal, although it was not uncommon to discover signs of life after the primitive measures employed in Birkenwald. The chamber is then opened, aired, and the Sonderkommando carts the bodies on flat trucks to the furnace rooms where the burning takes place. Crematoria III and IV work on nearly the same principle, but their capacity is only half as large. Thus the total capacity of the four gassing and cremating plants at Birkenau amounts to about 6,000 daily.

On principle only Jews are gassed; Aryans very seldom, as they are usually given Sonderbehandlung by shooting. Before the crematoria were put into service, the shooting took place in Birkenwald and the bodies were burned in the long trench; later, however, executions took place in the large hall of one of the crematoria which has been provided with a special installation for this purpose.

Prominent guests from Berlin were present at the inauguration of the first crematorium in March 1943. The "program" consisted of the gassing and burning of 8,000 Cracow Jews. The guests, both officers and civilians, were extremely satisfied with the results and the special peephole fitted into the door of the gas chamber was in constant use. They were lavish in their praise of this newly erected installation.

At the beginning of 1943, the political section of Auschwitz received 500,000 discharge certificates. We thought, with ill-concealed joy, that at least a few of us would be liberated. But the forms were simply filled out with the names of those gassed and filed away in the archives. . . .

Cautious Estimate of the Number of Jews Gassed in Birkenau Between April 1942 and April 1944, by Country of Origin

Poland (tranported by truck)	*ca.*	300,000
" (" " train)	"	600,000
Holland	"	100,000
Greece	"	45,000
France	"	150,000
Belgium	"	50,000
Germany	"	60,000
Yugoslavia, Italy, and Norway	"	50,000
Lithuania	"	50,000
Bohemia, Moravia, and Austria	"	30,000
Slovakia	"	30,000
Various camps for foreign Jews and Poland	"	300,000
	ca.	1,765,000

24

THE ROCKET MAN

Curt Wohleber

INTRODUCTION

One of the outstanding characteristics of technological change in the twentieth century is the predominance of teamwork in research and development. The success of the Wright brothers, for example, was due in large part to their ability to work together and with their sister Katharine as a team. Mass communications technologies, radar, advanced weapons systems, new medicines and medical techniques, the transistor, the laser, and the computer all emerged from coordinated research and development efforts and not from the labors of individual scientists and engineers. This article on rocket pioneer Robert Goddard illustrates the power of inspiration and the limitations of secrecy and isolation. Goddard was a man of vision and genius. He understood the immense possibilities for exploring the universe using liquid-fueled rockets. At the same time, he preferred to work alone and, fearing that others would steal his ideas and inventions, refused to share his discoveries with colleagues. The consequences were that he achieved significant results with fuels, oxidizers, pumps, and control and guidance systems—nearly every feature of the modern rocket—but that after more than a decade of work his devices failed to perform up to expectations.

It is useful to compare Goddard's approach to that of the Wright brothers. Whereas the Wrights saw the airplane as a complex system and pursued solutions to each problem in rational succession, Goddard failed to view the rocket as an overall package. Instead of making a mental picture of what he wanted the rocket to look like and, from that, gaining an understanding of what was an achievable level of performance, he leapt from one detail to another and attempted to resolve multiple variables with each experiment. In other words, Goddard's work was a poor example of "engineering and the mind's eye."

Nevertheless, despite all of his shortcomings, Goddard represents innovation at its most basic, visionary level. Certainly Thomas Edison was right that invention was 90 percent perspiration and 10 percent inspiration, but there is a level at which all technology must start. Someone has to have the idea, and there must be the "Eureka moment," where the engineer or scientist has "got it." Put in the context of the studies of engineering knowledge by historian and aerospace engineer Walter Vincenti, Goddard was dealing with what is known as "radical design," in which the innovator has never seen the device and is not sure whether or not it will work. Up to 1926, no one, including Goddard, had ever seen a liquid-fuel rocket, much less succeeded in making it fly. Understanding that, Goddard's achievement takes on new meaning and significance.

It all began on an autumn day in 1899 behind the family home in Worcester, Massachusetts. The seventeen-year-old Robert Goddard had climbed a cherry tree to trim some dead branches with a saw and hatchet. Up in that tree he was possessed by an idea that was to propel him on a lifelong path.

I imagined how wonderful it would be to make some device which had even the *possibility* of ascending to Mars, and how it would look on a small scale, if sent up from the meadow at my feet," the adult Goddard recorded in a 1927 autobiographical sketch. "I was a different boy when I descended the tree from when I ascended, for existence at last seemed very purposive." Thereafter Goddard referred to October 19 in his diaries as Anniversary Day. He kept photos of the cherry tree and the ladder he had used to climb it, and he would visit the cherry tree each year on October 19 when he was in the area.

Robert Hutchings Goddard labored almost his entire adult life to bring the heavens within reach. He patented most of the basic features of the rockets that have carried astronauts to the moon and robot probes to Mars and beyond. He showed that rockets could operate in a vacuum, launched the first liquid-fueled rocket, and even invented a prototype of the bazooka. Today he is often called the father of modern rocketry. History places him with Konstantin Tsiolkovsky of Russia and Hermann Oberth of Germany in the triumvirate of visionaries credited with laying the conceptual and practical foundations of space travel.

Yet Goddard's career was one of promise unfulfilled. His best rockets rose less than two miles, and he lived to see his achievements eclipsed within a few years by a group of German scientists, whose V-2 of 1944 reached altitudes of nearly seventy miles—the very edge of space.

Goddard was one of the last of the big-time lone-wolf inventors. He seldom published his results and refused to collaborate, working only with a handful of hired technicians. His concern for secrecy bordered on the paranoid. Indeed, his insistence on working alone may have ensured his place as the undisputed father of modern rocketry, but that insularity seems also to have sharply limited his experimental success and his concrete contributions to technology.

He was born in 1882 to Nahum and Fannie Hoyt Goddard. The family spent his early years in the Boston suburb of Roxbury. His father co-owned a company that manufactured machine knives, and during his career he invented a new type of machine knife for cutting rabbit fur as well as a flux for welding steel and iron. Nahum Goddard encouraged his son's interest in science, supplying him with a telescope, a microscope, and a subscription to *Scientific American*.

When Fannie fell ill with tuberculosis in 1898, a doctor recommended fresh air and rest, so the Goddards moved to the family farmhouse in Worcester. They shared the house with Goddard's great-aunt and with George and Ella Boswell, friends of the family. Bob called Boswell "Uncle George" and said he "could do wonderful little things about the house with wire and pieces of zinc, and his neat little workshop and tool cabinet in the shed were an unending feast to my eyes."

Later that year Goddard made his fateful ascent of the cherry tree. With the call of the stars ringing in his head, he immediately began making plans: "It seemed to me then that a weight whirling around a horizontal shaft, moving more rapidly above than below, could furnish lift by virtue of the greater centrifugal force at the top of the path." A college student he met on a trip to Boston pointed out the problem with his planned device, but Goddard remained unconvinced until he conducted his own experiments with rubber bands and floats, at which point he "began to think there might be something after all to Newton's laws."

Clearly he would have to give the problem more thought. "It made me realize that if a way to navigate space were to be discovered—or invented—it would be the result of a knowledge of physics and mathematics. . . . I resolved forthwith that I would shine in these subjects." He aced physics and led his class in geometry. He spent free time in the school's laboratory and received advanced instruction from his physics teacher. Though not exactly outgoing, Goddard was no socially inept science nerd. He served two terms as class president, edited the school newspaper, played the piano, acted in school plays, and sang in a quartet.

He entered Worcester Polytechnic Institute in the fall of 1904 (his schooling had been prolonged by repeated illness) and plunged eagerly into his studies. While at WPI he wrote an article called "The Use of the Gyroscope in the Balancing and Steering of Airplanes" that was published in *Scientific American*. In his notebooks he scrawled voluminous speculations on space flight, including the use of solar and atomic energy to power spacecraft. To minimize a spacecraft's weight, he conceived a series of nested cannons, essentially an embryonic version of the idea of multistage rockets.

In 1908 he embarked on graduate studies in physics at Clark University, also in Worcester. After earning his Ph.D. in 1911 and staying on for a year as a research fellow, he accepted a fellowship at Princeton University to study electricity, magnetism, and atomic theory. He worked diligently during the day on his assigned research and devoted evenings and many late nights to rocket propulsion. While visiting his family in Worcester for Easter in 1913, he came down with what he shrugged off as a slight cold. He treated it with an old family remedy: snuff and lard. It turned out to be tuberculosis. A doctor told his parents that he had about two weeks to live.

Goddard was bedridden for several weeks but failed to die on schedule. In the spring his doctor reluctantly gave him permission to work for an hour each afternoon. He recovered, but his health remained fragile for the rest of his life. During his long convalescence Goddard completed two applications for patents, which were granted the following year. These landmark patents described multistage rockets and rockets powered by liquid and solid fuels and outlined methods of feeding fuels into a rocket's combustion chamber.

"Blue-sky patents," his lawyer, Charles Hawley, called them. "They covered the universe, pretty near." In essence they described fundamental features of the rockets that would later carry satellites, probes, and astronauts into space. The basic principle of rocket propulsion—in which a rapidly burning fuel shoots out one end of a cylinder, pushing it in the opposite direction with great speed—was not new in itself, of course. Fireworks and weapons using the effect had been known since the Middle Ages. But these were all solid-fuel rockets burning black powder. They were fine for reaching heights of a hundred feet or so, but too heavy to go much higher, and there was no way to keep the powder burning for more than a few seconds. The vastly greater energy density of liquid fuels, combined with Goddard's ideas for multiple stages and sustained feeding of fuel into the combustion chamber, would one day allow rockets to leave the earth's atmosphere entirely.

In the fall of 1914 Goddard joined the physics faculty at Clark as a part-time instructor, turning down offers from Princeton and Columbia because the light teaching load would give him more time to pursue his rocket studies. He proved to be a popular and dedicated teacher, his lectures sometimes concluding with a cheer from his students. One of his students was Edwin Aldrin, Sr., the father of astronaut "Buzz" Aldrin, the second human being to walk on the moon. Goddard also embarked on a series of experiments aimed at supporting and extending the theoretical work covered in his patents. First he measured the efficiency of ordinary black-powder rockets, including fireworks and signal flares used by ships at sea. The best he found, Coston rockets, which were used to fling lifelines to ships in distress, had an efficiency of only 2.5 percent, meaning that 97.5 percent of the energy in the fuel was wasted. He got better results by switching from black powder to smokeless powder and packing it more tightly.

In a series of static tests, Goddard measured the thrust obtained by using various kinds of nozzles and a steel combustion chamber, which permitted higher pressures. After several dozen experiments he managed to achieve ejection velocities of nearly 8,000 feet per second. Goddard's static rockets were the most efficient heat engines of his day, more efficient by far than the best steam and internal combustion engines.

Goddard had no doubt that rockets could reach the edge of the earth's atmosphere. But what about the airless void beyond? Some scientists maintained that a rocket could not function in a vacuum because it would have nothing to push against. Goddard sought to demonstrate otherwise: he built a vacuum chamber and tested the efficiency of a rocket engine in *vacuo*. The rocket engine not only worked in the vacuum; it worked some 20 percent better than in air.

In the fall of 1916 Goddard wrote to the Smithsonian Institution, outlining his rocket research and its importance to science, especially meteorology, as well as to warfare. He asserted that with funding for equipment and assistants he could develop a rocket capable of reaching an altitude of several hundred miles. He received a grant of $5,000.

Though a rocket fueled by liquid hydrogen and oxygen seemed the most promising approach, using those chemicals would be expensive and dangerous. Goddard focused his efforts instead on rockets fueled by smokeless powder. He envisioned a sort of vertical machine gun involving an elaborate loading mechanism that would continually feed blocks of solid fuel into a combustion chamber. The scheme turned out to be a bit too complicated. In a discouraging series of tests, his loading mechanism kept jamming, warping, blowing up, or doing nothing at all.

Meanwhile, in the spring of 1917, the United States entered the war in Europe. Goddard offered his services to the military, suggesting that he could develop powerful artillery rockets and even a sonar-like "submarine detector." The U.S. Army Signal Corps, working through the Smithsonian, upped Goddard's research grant by $20,000.

After working in Worcester for the first half of 1918, Goddard and two assistants relocated to the Mount Wilson astronomical observatory in Pasadena, California, in June. There they continued to work on the problematic loading mechanism as well as a series of small single-charge rockets. One of these could be launched from a lightweight tube—a forerunner of the bazooka introduced in World War II. It gave a single soldier the same fire-power as a field cannon, and since the projectile was self-propelled, there was little recoil.

The weapon greatly impressed military observers, who assured Goddard that more funds would be headed his way. Four days later the armistice was signed in Europe. With peace at hand the military lost interest in developing exotic new weapons. Goddard went back to Worcester and his original $5,000 grant, which was nearly depleted.

At the urging of Arthur Webster, head of the physics department at Clark, Goddard used some of his Smithsonian money to publish a detailed account of his research to date. The 1919 report, entitled "A Method of Reaching Extreme Altitudes," laid out Goddard's theoretical and experimental work in painstaking detail, arguing that if a rocket could be made light enough, so that most of its weight was in the form of fuel, it could accelerate sufficiently to break free from earth's gravity and hurtle forever through space, to what Goddard called "infinite altitude."

This highly technical document would probably have generated little interest among the general public had it not been for a Smithsonian publicist who wrote a press release highlighting Goddard's hypothetical discussion of sending a rocket loaded with flash powder to the moon, where it would ignite on impact, providing visible confirmation that the device had reached its target.

Front-page newspaper stories across the nation in early 1920 seized on the fantasy that Goddard was about to launch such a rocket. Reporters dogged him, and dozens of people from around the world volunteered to be passengers or protested the possibility of killing the moon's inhabitants. An amusement park in the Bronx offered the use of its facilities to host the first moon shot. An editorial in *The New York Times* commented that Goddard seemed to be unaware that a rocket could not function in a vacuum. "Of course," the editorialist wrote, "he only seems to lack the knowledge ladled out daily in high schools." (In July 1969, with astronauts about to land on the moon, the *Times* printed a retraction.)

"From that day, the whole thing was summed up, in the public mind, in the words 'moon rocket,'" Goddard wrote. To quell the sensation, he released a statement reporting on the actual state of his research. He added that $50,000 to $100,000 would go a long way toward advancing his work. A second report to the Smithsonian, unpublished until after Goddard's death, contained even more extravagant speculations: manned space flight, remote-operated space probes, solar sails, ion propulsion, and even communication with extraterrestrial intelligences.

While Goddard's imagination ranged widely, he was nowhere near actually launching a rocket to infinite altitude. He was still struggling with his mechanism to feed cartridges of fuel into a rocket's combustion chamber. "One thing would go wrong after another," said his mechanic, Nils Riffolt. "He'd come in with pencil sketches on the backs of envelopes and we'd talk over ways to handle the problem. After a while, we knew we were running down rabbit trails, that a workable cartridge rocket was at least a long way off." In addition to his work at Worcester, Goddard spent weekends and school vacations from 1920 to 1923 at the Navy's Indian Head Powder Factory in Maryland, developing depth-charge and armor-piercing rockets for the Bureau of Ordnance.

Around 1921 he gave up on building a high-altitude solid-fuel rocket and set his sights on developing a rocket engine using a liquid propellant, usually ether or gasoline, with pure liquid oxygen as oxidizer. While dangerous to work with, liquid fuels generated far more energy per pound than smokeless powder. And feeding two liquids into the combustion chamber presented a simpler mechanical challenge than perfecting his complicated apparatus for loading solid-fuel charges.

Goddard secured a less-than-adequate supply of liquid oxygen, or "lox," from the Linde Air Products Company, which produced it as a by-product of manufacturing supplies for oxyacetylene welding. He and Riffolt set up shop in a sheet-iron shack outside the basement of the physics department building at Clark. "We figured that if anything went wrong," said Riffolt, "we would merely blow up the outbuilding and not the whole department of physics."

Meanwhile Goddard warded off requests for more information about his work and maintained tight security at his laboratory. He hired an armed watchman, got an unlisted telephone number for the lab, and made his assistants sign a pledge of secrecy. Hermann Oberth, in Germany, beseeched Goddard in 1922 to share his research because "only by common work of the scholars of all nations can be solved this great problem." The suggestion unnerved Goddard. When he received a copy of Oberth's 1923 treatise *Die Rakete zu den Planetenräumen* (The Rocket Into Interplanetary Space), Goddard suspected that Oberth had stolen some of his ideas. "I am not surprised that Germany has awakened to the importance and the development possibilities of the work," he wrote in an anxious memo to the Smithsonian, "and I would not be surprised if it were only a matter of time before the research would become something in the nature of a race."

Charles Abbot, assistant secretary of the Smithsonian, told Goddard in 1923 that his speculations "make very interesting reading. I am, however, consumed with impatience, and hope that you will be able to actually send a rocket up into the air some time soon. Interplanetary space would look much nearer to me after I had seen one of your rockets go up five or six miles in our own atmosphere."

While Goddard forged ahead with his lox rocket, his personal life took a new turn in 1924, when he married Esther Kisk, who at twenty-three was twenty years younger than Goddard. They had met in 1919, when he hired her to type the manuscript of "A Method of Reaching Extreme Altitudes." Esther, whose considerable intellect attracted Goddard as much as her youthful beauty, became an invaluable aide, working as his secretary, bookkeeper, photographer, firefighter, and laboratory assistant. She also put up with her husband's habit of spending much of the household budget on equipment for rocket research.

Goddard's first liquid-fuel rocket consisted of a skeletal framework of tubing, with the combustion chamber and nozzle at one end, the gasoline and oxygen tanks at the other, and several feet of empty space in between. The chamber and nozzle were positioned above the tank, so the nozzle expelled torch-bright exhaust gases onto the fuel tank, which had to be protected by a cone-shaped shield. (Goddard thought this awkward arrangement would provide greater stability.) In December 1925 he ignited the engine in a static testing rack, where it rose under its own power for about twenty-seven seconds.

The following March Goddard drove out to the farm of a family friend in the nearby town of Auburn, accompanied by his new machinist, Henry Sachs, who had replaced Riffolt. They spent the cold morning setting up the rocket and its launch frame on a snow-covered patch of ground. Around noon Esther Goddard showed up with Percy Roope, a physics professor at Clark. The farm's owner, Effie Ward, offered everyone cups of hot malted milk.

Goddard ignited the engine with the flame of an alcohol stove, then joined the others behind a sheet-iron barricade. "Even though the release was pulled," Goddard wrote, "the rocket did not rise at first, but the flame came out, and there was a steady roar. After a number of seconds it rose, slowly until it cleared the frame, and then at express-train speed, curving over to the left, and striking the ice and snow, still going at a rapid rate."

On its only voyage the world's first liquid-fueled rocket, which weighed six pounds empty and ten and a half when filled with fuel, reached a height of 41 feet. After a flight of two and a half seconds, it crashed 184 feet from the launch frame. It was a long way from infinite altitude, but Mrs. Goddard deemed the launch a success: "We slogged jubilantly through the mud of Aunt Effie's cabbage patch toward the broken and twisted wreckage."

Goddard's report to the Smithsonian urged Abbot to make no public announcement of the launch. He noted with concern the strong interest in rocket propulsion in Germany. "Rocket work is being made almost a national issue in Germany, a novel having been written, playing upon race feeling, in which Germany is urged to support the development of a German liquid-propelled rocket, which, the readers are given to understand, is a German idea. Nearly every day, I am in receipt of requests from Germany for information and details." The flight of the first liquid-fueled rocket remained secret until 1936, when Goddard published a second Smithsonian report on his research.

Goddard built a liquid-fueled rocket some twenty times the size of the first. Working on this scale introduced new problems. The challenge was to fashion a combustion chamber that was both light in weight and able to withstand the intense heat of the burning fuel. Goddard therefore devised a "curtain cooling" system that protected the inner surface of the chamber with an insulating film of liquid fuel, either gasoline or lox.

It was a brilliant innovation that would become standard in high-altitude rockets and missiles. Unfortunately Goddard himself never got curtain cooling to work very reliably, for the thin-walled combustion chamber kept burning through. Multifarious technical problems kept the new rocket from ever getting off the ground. In one discouraging test the gasoline tank exploded.

In 1929 Goddard tested a less ambitious and less costly rocket measuring 11½ feet in length and weighing 32 pounds without fuel. It was equipped with a thermometer, a barometer, a camera to photograph the instruments at the apex of the rocket's flight, and a parachute to bring the payload safely back to earth.

On the afternoon of July 17 the rocket roared out of the 60-foot launch tower Goddard and his assistants had built on Aunt Effie's farm. It climbed 90 feet before leveling off. The parachute failed to deploy and the rocket hit the ground with an impressive explosion.

While Goddard and the others poked through the wreckage, several police officers, two ambulances, and a couple of newspaper reporters converged on the scene, summoned by reports of a fiery plane crash. The state fire marshal declared Goddard's rocket tests a fire hazard and ordered him to carry out his experiments somewhere else.

For half a year Goddard worked at Camp Devens, a military installation twenty-five miles from Worcester, near an artillery range and a stagnant body of water called Hell Pond. The War Department let Goddard conduct tests only when the ground was rain-soaked or covered with snow. The rugged, unpaved road to the test site jarred Goddard's delicate equipment, often forcing him to spend hours on tedious repairs and adjustments. Soldiers sometimes stole apparatus as well.

Under these conditions Goddard made frustratingly little progress. In late 1929, however, he had gotten a call from Charles Lindbergh, who had become a national hero two years before by piloting *Spirit of St. Louis* on the first nonstop solo flight across the Atlantic. Lindbergh had read newspaper accounts of Goddard's run-in with the fire marshal. He was interested in the potential of rockets to increase the range and speed of aircraft, and he asked Goddard if he could visit him in Worcester the next day.

He agreed, and the normally secretive Goddard eagerly discussed his ideas with Lindbergh. He screened a brief movie Esther had taken of his July test flight. He talked about launching rockets out of the atmosphere and sending human passengers far into space, even to the stars.

Lindbergh asked Goddard what he needed to advance his work. Goddard told him that he required an out-of-the-way place to test his rockets. And he needed money, of course—enough to support himself and his wife so he wouldn't have to teach, and to pay for assistants and equipment. For the last decade and a half he had been limping along on erratic funding from Clark, the Navy, the Smithsonian, and the Carnegie Foundation. The lack of a steady source of money forced him to lead a hand-to-mouth existence. With an assured $25,000 a year, Goddard said, he might accomplish in four years what would otherwise take a lifetime.

Lindbergh recalled later that Goddard "spoke as though such an amount was part of a dream beyond realization." Lindbergh knew better. He went to Daniel Guggenheim, the copper tycoon and philanthropist, and persuaded him to support Goddard's research with a four-year $100,000 grant.

No longer tied to the Worcester area, Goddard searched for an ideal place to conduct his work. He needed level ground, good visibility, decent weather year-round, and lots of open space. A Clark University meteorologist suggested a high plateau in southeastern New Mexico. "You might try somewhere around the town of Roswell," he said.

For Goddard's tubercular lungs, the clear, dry air of Roswell was just what the doctor had ordered. The Goddards rented a large, run-down ranch from Effie Olds of the Oldsmobile family. Goddard got permission from a neighbor to launch his rockets on a 16,000-acre stretch of land called Eden Valley. He described the terrain as a "world of alkaline gray, holy, profane, grim although exquisite with a haunting stillness." On occasion he would set up an easel in the desert and try to capture the landscape on canvas.

Goddard's team rebuilt the 60-foot launch tower he had used in Auburn and Hell Pond. Beneath the tower they placed a large concrete trough to deflect the blasts of the rockets. He resolved to pull off at least one launch by the end of 1930. The new rocket, 11 feet long and weighing 33 1/2 pounds, blasted off on December 30 and soared to 2,000 feet—more than twenty times as high as any previous Goddard attempt.

The parachute failed to deploy completely, and the rocket crashed several hundred yards from the launch tower. Still, this was progress. "It seemed more like the operation of a vehicle than the flight of a rocket," Goddard wrote. "The sustained and effortless qualities of the flight were the most striking."

He continued his policy of strict secrecy. "Through the years, people would ask us where the Goddard tower was and we'd tell them stories," a neighbor named May Marley told Milton Lehman, a Goddard biographer. "I told so many lies, I guess I'll never get to Heaven. We'd send them south of Roswell, usually. If anybody heard a rocket shoot and asked about the noise, we'd say it was Indians up in the Capitan Mountains."

In his early years at Roswell, Goddard developed a stabilizing system to guide the rocket's flight. It consisted of a set of four gyroscopically controlled steering vanes. Any major deviation from the vertical would tilt one of the vanes into the wake of hot gas rushing from the nozzle and thus push the rocket back on course. Goddard described the system as "a veritable mechanical brain directing mechanical muscles."

On the first test flight of the control system, on April 19, 1932, the rocket rose a short distance and then plummeted to the ground. It was a pretty discouraging sight, but Goddard found cause for hope in the wreckage: "I rushed to the rocket and felt the four vanes. The one that should have been forced into the blast was warm—the others cold! Thus I knew that our idea was sound, and concluded that we merely needed larger vanes."

The next day he wrote a letter to H. G. Wells, who had been a source of inspiration for Goddard since childhood. He reread Wells's *War of the Worlds* nearly every Christmas season. "What I find most inspiring is your optimism," he told Wells. "It is the best antidote I know for the feeling of depression that comes at times when one contemplates the remarkable capacity for bungling of both man and nature." That same day he wrote in similar vein to Rudyard Kipling: "I have enjoyed your writings for many years. . . . The sordid side of life and the idealistic side, the rough-and-tumble fight, and the most pathetically delicate things are all written equally convincingly."

Of his own work, Goddard wrote to Wells: "How many more years I shall be able to work on the problem, I do not know; I hope, as long as I live. There can be no thought of finishing, for 'aiming at the stars,' both figuratively and literally, is a problem to occupy generations, so that no matter how much progress one makes, there is always the thrill of just beginning."

Two months later the deepening Depression cut off Goddard's Guggenheim funding and forced him to return to Worcester. He was reduced to begging the Smithsonian for a $250 grant. With this and small amounts from Clark, he managed to scrape by for two years, continuing his research in the laboratory since he could not make any flight tests. Goddard made the bureaucratic circuit of military and philanthropic donors and elicited effusive praise but no money. Dejected, he wrote in his diary in April 1933: "The rocket is very human. It can raise itself to the very loftiest positions solely by the ejection of enormous quantities of hot air."

Back at Roswell in early 1935, with his funding restored, Goddard launched rockets that broke the sound barrier and reached altitudes of more than a mile and a half. Later that year he invited Lindbergh and Harry Guggenheim (Daniel's son) to New Mexico to witness a test flight. A minor technical problem aborted one launch attempt; then rain delayed further tries for two days. When Goddard was at last able to try another launch, the combustion chamber burned through and the rocket merely smoldered in its tower.

Lindbergh, who later said that Goddard "was as mortified as a parent whose child misbehaves in front of company," sent Goddard a consoling letter, telling him that despite the failed launches, he and Guggenheim "came back with the feeling that the project is being managed with unusual efficiency and intelligence and that success was a matter of time rather than possibility." But how much time did Goddard have? A decade earlier he had estimated that a few years and a few thousand dollars would allow him to send a rocket hundreds of miles into space. He was still nowhere near that goal.

In his later years at Roswell, Goddard directed much of his efforts toward reducing the weight of his rockets. His first rockets launched from Eden Valley had used a tank of compressed nitrogen to force propellant and lox into the chamber, but this arrangement added a lot of weight to the rocket. To get rid of the nitrogen tanks, Goddard developed small, lightweight centrifugal pumps to force fuel into the chamber. The pumps were driven by turbines, which were started up before launch by a stream of nitrogen from an external tank. After ignition the tank was disconnected, and diverted exhaust gases kept the turbines in motion.

Building the pumps from scratch took years, during which flight testing progressed with agonizing slowness. Even when the pumps worked perfectly, a hundred other things might go wrong: a stuck lever, a broken connection, a burned-out combustion chamber. In June 1938 a tornado destroyed the launch tower and the latest version of "Nell" (as all Goddard's rockets were called by this point). Goddard and his men toiled all day in the desert heat, salvaging whatever they could.

"I shall not forget how Bob looked," Esther wrote. "Fatigue showed in every line of him especially his shoulders, bent forward, as they always are, to protect the weakness of his lungs. A man who 'should be in bed in Switzerland' [as a doctor had once told him] coming in at 7:30 at night after a day that began at 3 in the morning. . . . And as he came in last night, almost staggering, the undefeatable was still in his eyes, and made me ashamed."

That fall a monstrous hurricane lashed the Northeastern states, including Worcester, where it ripped Goddard's cherry tree out of the ground. "Cherry tree down," he wrote in his diary. "Have to carry on alone."

But Goddard was not alone in the rocket business, whether he liked it or not. He obstinately refused pleas to accept collaborators or farm out some of the work, but other researchers were more than willing to pool their talent and resources. In the early 1930s Germany's Society for Space Ship Travel launched several small liquid-fueled rockets. An almost complete lack of funding and the German government's opposition to civilian rocket research discouraged further experimentation until the German military's own program went into full swing in 1936.

"Until 1936, Goddard was ahead of us all," wrote Wernher von Braun, who served as technical director of German rocket development at Peenemünde, on the Baltic island of Usedom. The Nazi regime poured several billion dollars into rocket research, which paid off with the spectacular and fearsome V-2 rocket. Fueled by grain alcohol and liquid oxygen, the V-2 weighed twelve tons including fuel and towered nearly 50 feet high. The rocket had a range of 190 miles and reached a maximum altitude of 68 miles—more than 30 times the altitude of Goddard's most successful rocket. Several thousand V-2 rockets rained destruction on England in the waning months of the war.

While the German military buildup jump-started rocketry in that country, in the United States war diverted Goddard from his experiments. He could not persuade the government to fund research into long-range rockets, so he left Roswell in 1942 to serve as director of jet propulsion research with the Navy's Bureau of Aeronautics in Annapolis, Maryland. With his team from Roswell he developed and flight-tested a jet-assisted takeoff system. The group also developed a variable-thrust rocket motor intended for use in manned rocket planes. Meanwhile the Army resurrected Goddard's lightweight rocket launcher from World War I. U.S. troops used the weapon, modified and dubbed the bazooka, to take out German tanks.

In early 1945 Goddard had the opportunity to study a captured V-2. In a letter to Harry Guggenheim he outlined the similarities between the V-2 and his last version of Nell: both used lox as the oxidizer, incorporated turbine-driven centrifugal pumps, and employed a gyroscopic stabilizer that steered blast vanes to correct the rocket's flight. Unlike Goddard's rockets, the V-2 had a double-walled combustion chamber: fuel flowed between the two walls before entering the chamber itself. This served the twin functions of cooling the chamber and warming the fuel before combustion. Goddard had conceived this method of "regenerative cooling" decades earlier but had never used it in any of his rockets, preferring the troublesome but mechanically simpler curtain cooling method.

"I don't think he ever got over the V-2," one of Goddard's associates said. "He felt the Germans had copied his work and that he could have produced a bigger, better and less expensive rocket, if only the United States had accepted the long-range rocket."

The V-2 vindicated Goddard's designs, but it also served as a stark repudiation of his secretiveness, his refusal to collaborate, and his relentless focus on technical details at the expense of seeking record-breaking altitudes. Through their collective efforts, the German rocket scientists went far beyond what Goddard could accomplish on his own.

"It seems to me that he has a tendency to underemphasize the importance of actual rocket flights," Lindbergh wrote to Harry Guggenheim. ". . . No one but a specialist is in a position to judge the value of highly specialized work, unless it can be demonstrated by its effect on more easily understood accomplishments."

J. D. Hunley, a NASA historian, believes there is more to it than that: "Simply put, besides remaining a loner, he failed to follow the step-by-step procedures called for by standard engineering practice." Instead of adjusting one variable at a time, Hunley writes, "he usually changed several components on a given rocket in between separate tests." For example, when a 1931 rocket plummeted and exploded in midair after ascending only 200 feet, Goddard decreased gasoline flow into the combustion chamber, altered the chamber itself, modified the way the cooling curtain of liquid oxygen was applied to the inner surface of the chamber, changed the dimensions of the gasoline tank, and reduced the overall length of the rocket by more than two feet.

Goddard's health declined during the war, perhaps in part because of the damp Chesapeake climate. His voice grew weak and hoarse; he sometimes had to communicate with his subordinates by tapping a pencil stub against his desk in Morse code. He grew bored with his military work, which included developing components for small, short-range rockets, and became preoccupied with his patents and notes, intent on setting the record straight about his achievements in rocketry. He died of cancer on August 10, 1945, the day after the Allies dropped an atomic bomb on Nagasaki. He was sixty-two years old.

Shortly after the war von Braun, Hermann Oberth, and more than a hundred other German rocket scientists emigrated to the United States to develop missiles for the Army. In 1951 Esther Goddard and the Guggenheim Foundation sued the government for infringing on Goddard's patents. Nine years later the newly established NASA announced a $1 million settlement for rights to more than two hundred Goddard patents. The previous year Congress posthumously awarded Goddard the Congressional Gold Medal, the nation's highest civilian honor. In 1961 NASA dedicated the Goddard Space Flight Center in Greenbelt, Maryland. A Goddard postage stamp was issued in 1964. The site of Goddard's major work, Roswell, is now firmly associated with space travel—not because of Goddard but because UFO devotees believe that an extraterrestrial spacecraft crashed there in 1947.

The posthumous recognition of Goddard's work may have had as much to do with salvaging national pride—of putting an American in the pantheon with Oberth, Tsiolkovsky, and von Braun—as with his contributions to the development of rockets and space travel. Goddard accomplished many firsts, and his work served as an important source of inspiration for early rocket designers. But because of his secretiveness, others often had to blaze their own trails to get where Goddard had already been.

WAS THE RACE TO THE MOON REAL?

John M. Logsdon and Alain Dupas

INTRODUCTION

Politics and prestige, not science and technology, drove the American manned space program in the 1960s. President John F. Kennedy made it clear in 1961 when he committed the United States to landing a man on the moon by the end of the decade that the effort was part of the overall objective of countering Soviet communism whenever and wherever it challenged Western-style democratic capitalism. The Cold War was a struggle for survival, pure and simple, and it had to be waged on all fronts—military, political, economic, ideological, scientific, and technological. Manned space programs were ideal weapons in the war. Highly visible, they provided a showcase for engineering know-how and human courage and tangible proof that the ideals represented by the United States were superior to those of Soviet Marxist-Leninism. Kennedy and his advisers firmly believed that American success in space would have a strong psychological effect on the peoples of the so-called non-aligned nations and swing them away from communism, which, it appeared, had made major gains in Africa and Asia during the late 1950s.

The American Apollo project and other large-scale engineering programs were examples of what historian Walter MacDougall refers to as "command technology." That is, they received direction and funding from the government and became components of a technocracy, where an overweening political agenda subsumed all technological and scientific endeavors. Technocrats convinced many politicians and shapers of public opinion that state-sponsored science and technology could provide the answers to most, if not all, economic and social questions. The irony of this is obvious. In the name of freedom, liberty, and democracy, American political leaders willingly subverted those ideals to defeat what they considered to be the greater threat of Soviet communism. In the end, the United States won the Cold War, so it can be argued that this was a price that had to be paid, but it may also be true that it left a dangerous legacy of centralized political authority and disillusionment among the general public.

In this selection, John M. Logsdon and Alain Dupas examine the competition between the United States and the Soviet Union for dominance in space, focusing on the race to the moon. Using recently released Soviet documents, they find that the Soviet Union was as deeply committed to landing men on the moon as was the United States. But in contrast with the American Apollo program, which benefitted from bipartisan political support, excellent administration, and ample resources, the Soviet effort stalled, caught in a bureaucratic and political quagmire. The determinants of success in space technology, then, were not so much engineering factors as they were political and economic considerations within the broader context of Cold War ideology.

Twenty-five years ago, on July 20, 1969, Neil A. Armstrong took the first footsteps on the surface of the moon. That event marked a political and technological victory for the U.S. in its cold war rivalry with the U.S.S.R. In the years that followed, the Soviet government insisted that the Soviet Union had never planned a lunar landing. Hence, it argued, the contest to send humans to the moon was a one-sided exercise. The reality is otherwise; recently declassified information from that era and testimony of key participants in the Soviet space program under Khrushchev and Brezhnev prove that the moon race was indeed real.

New evidence reveals that personal rivalries, shifting political alliances, and bureaucratic inefficiencies bred failure and delays within the Soviet lunar-landing program. In contrast, the American effort received consistently strong political and public support. The National Aeronautics and Space Administration and its contractor teams also benefited from a pool of skilled and highly motivated workers and managers. Despite an early Soviet lead in human space exploration, these factors, along with more generous and effective allocation of resources, enabled the U.S. to win the competition to be first to the moon.

Soviet capability in space became clear to the world in October 1957, when the U.S.S.R. lofted *Sputnik,* the first artificial satellite. Two years later the Soviets launched a probe that returned close-up images of the lunar surface. And on April 12, 1961, cosmonaut Yuri A. Gagarin became the first human in space. Soviet officials cited each accomplishment as evidence that communism was a superior form of social and economic organization. The Soviet advantage in space rocketry underlined fears in the U.S. that a missile gap existed between it and its adversary, an issue that Kennedy belabored in the 1960 presidential campaign.

At first, the shape that a U.S.-Soviet space race might take was not clear. Indeed, if President Dwight D. Eisenhower had had his way, there might not have been one at all. Eisenhower rejected the idea that spectacular space achievements had anything to do with the fundamental strength of a country; he consistently refused to approve space programs justified on purely political grounds. In July 1958, however, he created NASA, an agency that brought together the resources to establish a U.S civilian space program. It was inevitable, perhaps, that NASA would argue that such a program should be ambitious.

Eisenhower's successor, President John F. Kennedy, perceived a much more direct link between space exploration and global leadership. Stimulated by the worldwide excitement generated by the Gagarin flight, Kennedy decided that the U.S. had to surpass the Soviets in human spaceflight.

On April 20, 1961, just eight days after the Gagarin flight, Kennedy asked Vice President Lyndon B. Johnson, "Is there any . . . space program that promises dramatic results in which we could win?" In particular, Kennedy inquired, "Do we have a chance of beating the Soviets by putting a laboratory in space, or by a trip around the moon, or by a rocket to land on the moon, or by a rocket to go to the moon and back with a man?" Johnson, whom Kennedy had named his primary adviser on space policy, promptly organized an intense two-week assessment of the feasibility of these and other alternatives. A series of memoranda trace the evolving response to Kennedy's questions.

One of the many people Johnson consulted was Wernher von Braun, leader of a team of rocket engineers whom the Army had spirited out of Germany during the last days of the Third Reich. In a memorandum dated April 29, von Braun told the vice president that "we do have a good chance of beating the Soviets to a manned laboratory in space," but "we have a sporting chance of sending a three-man crew around the moon ahead of the Soviets," and "we have an excellent chance of beating the Soviets to the first landing of a crew on the moon."

Von Braun judged that a lunar landing offered the U.S. the best opportunity to surpass the Soviets because "a performance jump by a factor of 10 over their present rockets is necessary to accomplish this feat. While today we do not have such a rocket, it is unlikely that the Soviets have it." He suggested that "with an all-out crash effort, I think we could accomplish this objective in 1967/1968."

On May 8, 1961, Johnson presented Kennedy with a memorandum that reflected the results of his investigation. It was signed by James Webb, the NASA administrator, and Robert S. McNamara, the secretary of defense. Webb and McNamara recommended that the U.S. should set the objective of manned lunar exploration "before the end of this decade." They argued that "this nation needs to make a positive decision to pursue projects aimed at enhancing national prestige. Our attainments are a major element in the international competition between the Soviet system and our own." The two men cited lunar and planetary exploration as "part of the battle along the fluid front of the cold war."

Kennedy accepted these recommendations and presented them to a joint session of Congress on May 25. The president said, "I believe we should go to the moon. . . . No single space project in this period will be more exciting, or more impressive to mankind. . . . While we cannot guarantee that we shall one day be first, we can guarantee that any failure to make this effort will find us last." Kennedy vowed that Americans would set foot on the moon "before this decade is out."

The president's call to action struck a responsive chord in the U.S. populace. There was little public or political debate over the wisdom of the lunar commitment in the weeks following Kennedy's speech. Within months Congress increased NASA's budget by 89 percent; another 101 percent increase came the next year. Between 1961 and 1963 NASA's payroll swelled from 16,500 people to more than 28,000, and the number of contractors working on the space program grew from less than 60,000 to more than 200,000.

During the first year after Kennedy's announcement, a fierce technical debate erupted that threatened to delay progress in getting to the moon. The dispute centered on the most efficient strategy for sending people to the lunar surface and back to the earth. One possibility was to use several rockets to launch pieces of a lunar spacecraft separately into earth orbit, where they would be assembled and directed on to the moon. Jerome Wiesner, the president's science adviser, and some elements within NASA initially inclined toward this "earth orbit rendezvous" plan. McNamara was also intrigued by the potential military applications of earth-orbiting missions.

As they examined how best to meet Kennedy's goal of getting to the moon before the end of 1969, a growing number of engineers within NASA favored another approach, called lunar orbit rendezvous. In this scheme, the entire *Apollo* spacecraft would be sent into space in a single launch and would fly directly into orbit around the moon; a small landing craft would detach from the main spaceship and ferry the astronauts from lunar orbit to the moon's surface and then back to the mother ship, which would then return to earth.

Lunar orbit rendezvous dramatically lowered the overall weight of the *Apollo* spacecraft. Consequently, the Apollo mission could be carried out using a single Saturn V rocket. After fending off Wiesner's objections, NASA officials approved lunar orbit rendezvous, realizing that it offered the greatest likelihood of reaching the lunar surface according to Kennedy's schedule. By the end of 1962 the U.S. was well on its way to the moon. Not so the Soviet Union.

Until a few years ago, the Soviets officially claimed that the U.S. was the sole participant in the race to the moon. The very existence of the Soviet lunar program was a tightly held secret. As a result of *glasnost* and the collapse of the U.S.S.R., that situation has significantly changed. Several crucial players in the space program of the 1960s (most notably Vasily P. Mishin, who headed the Soviet human spaceflight effort from 1966 to 1974) have finally been allowed to place their recollections of the period in the public record. On August 18, 1989, the Soviet newspaper *Izvestia* printed a lengthy and unprecedentedly frank account of the nation's unsuccessful assault on the moon. And an increasing number of photographs and engineering descriptions of Soviet lunar hardware have become available to Western analysts and space observers. A recent study by Christian Lardier, a French space researcher, has been particularly valuable in bringing such information to light. The result is a much clearer picture of just how extensive the Soviet lunar program was.

In June 1961, at his first summit meeting with Soviet premier Nikita S. Khrushchev, Kennedy twice raised the possibility that the U.S. and the U.S.S.R. might travel to the moon together. Khrushchev was unresponsive, at least in part because Kennedy's lunar-landing announcement had caught the Soviet Union by surprise. The Soviet leadership was so confident in the country's space prowess that it had not anticipated that the U.S. might actually try to compete in that arena.

More than three years of political debate dragged on before the Kremlin decided, and then only tentatively, that the Soviet Union should also have a lunar-landing program. During that time, powerful and entrenched leaders of the Soviet design bureaus (industrial organizations in which the Soviet technical capabilities for space resided) struggled for priority and for resources related to possible lunar missions. Those conflicts presented a roadblock to establishing a single, coordinated plan of action for reaching the moon.

Sergei P. Korolev, the top space engineer, headed one of the design bureaus. He was, in many ways, the Russian equivalent of Wernher von Braun. Korolev had both designed the rocket used for all Soviet space launches to that point and had managed the programs responsible for developing most of the payloads lofted by those rockets. He was also an energetic and enthusiastic proponent of space travel. Such secrecy surrounded his work that Korolev was identified only as the "Chief Designer"; his name was not publicly revealed until after his death.

Unfortunately for the Soviet space effort, in the early 1960s Korolev became embroiled in a personal and organizational conflict with Valentin P. Glushko, the head of the Gas

Dynamics Laboratory and the primary designer of Soviet rocket engines. Disputes between the two dated to the 1930s, when Glushko was one of those whose testimony helped to send Korolev to a forced-labor camp. The two men clashed over the concept of the rocket engines for the next generation of Soviet space launchers. Korolev wanted to use high-energy liquid hydrogen as a fuel (the choice the U.S. made for the upper stages of Saturn V). Glushko was only interested in designing an engine fueled by storable but highly toxic hypergolic compounds, such as hydrazine and nitrogen tetraoxide, that ignited on contact.

The dispute grew so bitter that Glushko refused to work with Korolev in the creation of a new rocket. Instead Glushko allied his laboratory with another design bureau, headed by Vladimir N. Chelomei, to compete for the lunar assignment. Chelomei's group had developed military missiles but had no experience with rockets for outer space. On the other hand, one of Chelomei's deputies was Khrushchev's son, Sergei. That family link offered a great advantage in a system where such personal connections were often all-important. Chelomei had ambitions to expand his bureau's works into what had been Korolev's turf.

On major technical issues such as space exploration, the Soviet leadership relied on recommendations from the Soviet Academy of Sciences. Mstislav V. Keldysh, the president of the academy, was given the task of advising the government on the technical merits of competing proposals for future efforts in space. Keldysh and his associates took the path of least political resistance and did not fully support either Korolev or his competitors until after Khrushchev was removed from power.

From late 1961 on, Chelomei's design bureau devoted most of its attention not to landing on the moon but to sending cosmonauts on a flight around the moon without even going into lunar orbit. This mission was to use a UR-500 rocket (later known as Proton), derived from one of Chelomei's failed designs for an intercontinental ballistic missile (ICBM). Chelomei also promoted an overly ambitious plan for a reusable rocket airplane that could reach the moon and even the other planets.

In August 1964 the Chelomei design bureau received Kremlin approval to build both a spacecraft and the UR-500 rocket to send cosmonauts on a circumlunar mission by October 1967, the 50th anniversary of the Bolshevik Revolution. But Chelomei's apparent victory over Korolev was short-lived. The Politburo removed Khrushchev from power in October 1964.

The post-Khrushchev leadership quickly discovered that little progress had been made by the organization that had been receiving the lion's share of funding related to possible lunar missions. The Chelomei design bureau soon fell from favor, and its contract for the circumlunar program was canceled.

Korolev, meanwhile, had not been entirely shut out of the Soviet space program. After his successful efforts in using a converted ICBM to carry out the initial Soviet forays into space, he had been thinking about the design of a new heavy-lift space launcher, which he had designated N-1. In mid-1962 the Keldysh commission authorized the development of a version of the N-1 that could launch 75 tons into earth orbit, but the commission did not approve Korolev's plan to utilize the N-1 for a lunar mission structured around earth orbit rendezvous.

The N-1 rocket was supposed to be ready for flight testing by 1965. Because he did not have access to the expertise of Glushko's Gas Dynamics Laboratory, Korolev had to find an alternative source of rocket engines. He turned to the design bureau led by Nikolai D.

Kuznetsov, which had previously worked on airplane engines. Kuznetsov's group had to begin its work on space propulsion systems basically from scratch. In the limited time available, Kuznetsov was able to develop only a conventionally fueled motor of rather little power. To achieve sufficient lifting power for a lunar mission, the N-1 ultimately needed 30 such engines in its first stage. (The American Saturn V had just five first-stage engines.)

After the fall of Khrushchev, the Soviet space program changed direction. Probably because it no longer feared angering Khrushchev, by December 1964 the Keldysh commission finally gave preliminary approval to a Korolev plan for placing cosmonauts on the moon. Korolev's revised lunar mission utilized a redesigned, more powerful N-1 rocket and the same lunar orbital rendezvous approach adopted for the Apollo mission. In May 1965 the Soviet government created the Ministry of General Machine Building to oversee the nation's space program; the ministry gave Korolev's lunar mission its highest priority. The official plan called for a first landing attempt in 1968, in the hope that the U.S.S.R. could still beat the U.S. to the moon.

Just as the Soviet effort was gaining momentum, disaster struck. In January 1966 Korolev died unexpectedly during simple surgery, robbing the Soviet space effort of its most effective and charismatic leader. Korolev's successor, Vasily Mishin, had neither Korolev's political standing nor his ability to lead. Continuing struggles with various government ministries and other design bureaus slowed progress. Chelomei continued to push an alternative lunar-landing scheme. To make matters worse, the revised N-1 launcher proved insufficiently powerful, so still more time was lost in another redesign.

Not until November 1966 did the Keldysh commission give a final go-ahead to the lunar-landing project. A joint government-party decree supporting the project was issued the following February, but still the Soviet government allocated only limited resources to it. By then the date for an initial lunar-landing attempt had slipped into the second half of 1969.

The U.S. was well aware of the Soviet decision to proceed with the N-1 but for several years remained unsure of the kind of mission for which it would be used. In 1964 U.S. intelligence satellites observed the construction of a launchpad for a large new booster and recorded the building of a second such pad in 1967. In a March 1967 national intelligence estimate (declassified in 1992), the Central Intelligence Agency suggested that "depending on their view of the Apollo timetable, the Soviets may feel that there is some prospect of their getting to the moon first, and they may press their program in the hopes of being able to do so."

After 10 successful launches of the two-man *Gemini* spacecraft during 1965 and 1966, NASA seemed well prepared to move on to Apollo test flights leading to a lunar landing in 1968. Then, on January 27, 1967, the program received a tragic setback. An electrical fire broke out in the Apollo 204 spacecraft (later renamed *Apollo 1*) during a countdown rehearsal on the launchpad. All three crewmen perished. Although critics lashed out at NASA, the agency never faltered. With limited congressional and White House intervention, NASA swiftly took the investigation into its own hands and identified and fixed the problems that had caused the fire. By the end of 1967 the space agency had set a new schedule for Apollo that called for an initial attempt at a landing by mid-1969, approximately the same target date as that of the Soviet program.

The U.S. and U.S.S.R. were also locked into a second contest: to see which country could first reach the vicinity of the moon. After the end of the Khrushchev era, the new Soviet leadership of Leonid I. Brezhnev and Alexei N. Kosygin asked Korolev to design a circumlunar mission similar to that of the now canceled Chelomei project. The Soviets still hoped to carry out such a flight in October 1967. After nearly a year of often acrimonious negotiations, Korolev and Chelomei in September 1965 agreed on a plan that would use the Chelomei UR-500 booster, supplemented by a Korolev upper stage being developed for the N-1 rocket and a two-cosmonaut version of the new *Soyuz* spacecraft being designed by the Korolev bureau.

Although the first few test flights of the UR-500 booster in 1966 were successful, there were a series of serious problems with subsequent launches. In addition, the first flight of the *Soyuz* spacecraft in April 1967 had a landing failure that killed the cosmonaut on board. Those setbacks made an October 1967 flight around the moon impossible. Even so, tests during 1967 and 1968 led to the successful Zond 5 mission of September 1968, in which UR-500 launched a modified *Soyuz* spacecraft carrying living organisms, including several turtles, on a course that took it around the moon and then safely back to the earth. The flight of a Soviet cosmonaut around the moon seemed imminent.

At the time of the Zond 5 mission, the U.S. had no officially scheduled flight to the lunar vicinity until well into 1969. The reality was rather different, however. By mid-1968 development of the redesigned *Apollo* command-and-service module, which would carry astronauts into orbit around the moon and back to the earth, was on schedule for a first orbital test flight in October. But the separate lunar landing module, intended to place astronauts on the moon's surface, was months behind schedule. It seemed unlikely that the lunar module would be ready for an earth orbital test until February or March 1969.

George M. Low, deputy director of NASA's Manned Spacecraft Center in Houston, recognized that the delay in testing the lunar module presented a real possibility that the U.S. might not meet the end-of-the-decade deadline originally set by Kennedy. On August 9, 1968, Low therefore made a bold proposal: he suggested inserting an additional flight into the *Apollo* launch schedule, one in which a Saturn V would send the command-and-service module carrying a three-man crew into orbit around the moon.

Such a mission obviously carried substantial risks. It meant sending astronauts to the vicinity of the moon much earlier than had been planned, and it would be only the second flight of the *Apollo* spacecraft since its redesign after the 1967 fire. Moreover, the Saturn V had been launched only twice, and the second launch had uncovered several major problems. But Low's strategy would allow NASA to gain the experience of managing a mission at lunar distance many months earlier than had been planned. The additional flight would greatly increase the probability of meeting the Apollo schedule. It would also improve the likelihood that the U.S. would reach the vicinity of the moon before the U.S.S.R. did.

Low's plan gained rapid acceptance within NASA, encountering only temporary resistance from NASA administrator Webb and George Mueller, the head of NASA's Manned Spaceflight Program. In a little over a week the agency revised its entire Apollo schedule, creating a new mission just four months before it would lift off. The dramatic nature of that flight remained secret until after the October Apollo 7 mission, in which the command-and-service module performed flawlessly. On November 11, NASA's leaders formally sanctioned the Apollo 8 flight to the moon.

The Soviets, meanwhile, were struggling to keep up. In October 1968 a redesigned *Soyuz* spacecraft carrying one cosmonaut was successfully tested in earth orbit. The Zond 6 mission, which one month later sent a similar but unmanned spacecraft around the moon, did not fare so well. The spacecraft depressurized on reentry. If it had carried a crew, they would have died.

Nevertheless, the Soviets made preparations for launching a circumlunar Zond flight carrying two cosmonauts in early December. Both Mishin and the crew agreed to take the substantial risks involved, because by then they knew that the U.S. intended to send humans into orbit around the moon later that month. This launch presented the Soviets with perhaps their final opportunity to beat the Americans to the moon, but they did not take advantage of that chance. Just days before the scheduled takeoff, the Soviet leadership canceled the mission, presumably because they judged it too perilous.

During the final weeks of training for their mission, the *Apollo* crew members were well aware of when a Soviet circumlunar mission could be launched. In a conversation with one of us (Logsdon), Mission Commander Frank Borman recalls breathing a sigh of relief as the last possible date passed, and he realized that his own flight to the moon had not been preempted.

Apollo 8 entered lunar orbit on Christmas Eve, 1968, all but ending the race to the moon. Furthermore, its accomplishments opened the way for the historic Apollo 11 mission seven months later, when Neil Armstrong planted the American flag in the lunar soil.

After the triumphs of Apollo 8 and Apollo 11, the Soviet lunar program faded into oblivion. But the Soviets did not give up on the moon immediately. Two more, unmanned Zond missions flew around the moon, one in 1969 and one in 1970. Shortly thereafter the Soviet leadership canceled the circumlunar program as it became clear that it had been totally overshadowed by Apollo.

The Soviet lunar-landing program suffered a more ironic fate. The first attempt to launch the N-1, in February 1969, failed one minute into flight. The second launch attempt on July 3, just 13 days before Apollo 11 lifted off for the moon, ended in an explosion on the pad that destroyed much of the booster's ground facilities and halted the Soviet lunar-landing program for two years. N-1 launches in July 1971 and November 1972 also failed.

If they could not be first, the Korolev design bureau leaders reasoned, they could still be best. Led by Mishin, they reorganized the program around the concept of extended stays on the moon that would be longer than the brief visits made by the crews of the six Apollo missions. By early 1974 Mishin believed that he and his associates had identified the sources of earlier problems and were on the brink of success. But in May 1974, Mishin was replaced as head of the design bureau by Glushko, the man who more than a decade earlier had fought with Korolev over the choice of the N-1 propulsion system.

In one of his first acts, Glushko terminated the N-1 program and destroyed the 10 remaining N-1 boosters. Mishin argued that at least the two N-1s almost ready for launch should be tested, but to no avail. Rather than continue with the lunar program to which it had devoted substantial resources for more than a decade, Glushko and his superiors chose the almost pathological response of destroying most of the evidence of its existence. The Soviet human spaceflight program from the early 1970s on has concentrated entirely on long-duration flights in earth orbit.

Once astronauts had established an American presence on the moon, the U.S. lunar program also soon wound down. The sixth and last Apollo landing mission left the moon in

December 1972. By then the lunar effort had clearly met the goals that Kennedy had set out in 1961.

Was the race to the moon worth winning? In our judgment, that question can be answered only in light of the circumstances under which the competition occurred. The moon race was a cold war undertaking that should be evaluated primarily in foreign policy terms. On those grounds, it was an important victory. The Apollo program undoubtedly aided America's global quest for political and military leadership during the 1960s. The lunar landing constituted a persuasive demonstration of national will and technological capability for the U.S.

Likewise, the failure of the Soviet lunar program was more than a public relations defeat. In 1961, as the race to the moon began, many people in the U.S. (and around the world) thought Soviet centralized planning and management systems would allow the nation to pursue vigorously its long-range goals in space. The dissipation of the Soviet Union's lead in space during the 1960s tarnished the image of socialist competence and diminished Soviet standing in world affairs.

Throughout his brief presidency, Kennedy was ambivalent about the competitive aspects of the space race. In his inaugural address, he suggested to the Soviet Union that "we should explore the stars together." Shortly after being sworn in, he asked NASA and the state department to draw up proposals for enhanced U.S.-U.S.S.R. space cooperation. Those proposals arrived at the White House on the day of Gagarin's initial orbital flight, an event that convinced Kennedy that the U.S. had to assume leadership in space. Yet on September 20, 1963, in an address to the General Assembly of the United Nations, he still asked, "Why should man's first flight to the moon be a matter of national competition?"

Kennedy's dream of cooperation between the two space superpowers is at last on the verge of becoming a reality. On December 15, 1993, Vice President Al Gore and NASA administrator Daniel S. Goldin signed agreements with their Russian counterparts for a series of joint space activities. That collaboration will culminate in an international space station, which will be built around U.S. and Russian capabilities but will include contributions from Europe, Japan and Canada. The station will begin operation soon after the turn of the century.

For 30 years, cold war rivalry was the lifeblood of both U.S. and Soviet programs of human spaceflight. If the adventure of space exploration is to continue into the 21st century, it will almost surely depend instead on widespread cooperation. The space station may serve as the harbinger of a new kind of foreign policy, one that brings the nations of the world together in the peaceful conquest of space.

SIC TRANSIT TRANSISTOR

Robert Friedel

INTRODUCTION

The modern electronic digital computer would not be possible without the transistor. The first in a family of what are known as semiconductors, the transistor uses the properties of certain solids to allow electric current to flow in one direction only, thus replicating the function of earlier vacuum tubes for switching and amplification in various electronics applications. As with many other technologies, the basic principles of the transistor are simple, but a great deal of expensive and difficult research and development was needed before this device and its successors found their way into profitable commercial use.

When reading this article by Robert Friedel, it is useful to consider whether or not the vacuum tube had reached its technological limits by 1947–1948, when the transistor emerged from the work of a team of engineers and scientists at Bell Labs. It may well be that the vacuum tube, despite its shortcomings in regard to power requirements and heat generation, still had much going for it. The vacuum tube was powerful and rugged, as evidenced by its wartime use in radar and the proximity fuze, and even after the introduction of the transistor, it continued to dominate electronics for another decade. In fact, audiophiles in the 1990s prefer stereo units operating on vacuum tubes to those using solid-state technology, and most televisions continue to rely on picture tubes rather than other forms of display.

The point is that by 1947 the vacuum tube was far from obsolescent, let alone obsolete. So, what drove Bardeen, Brattain, and Shockley at Bell Labs to begin work on the transistor, even though they knew that the vacuum tube was meeting all present and anticipated electronics requirements? Did they perceive from basic scientific information that vacuum-tube technology would at some future point fail; that is, that a technological revolution would soon take place? Or was the transistor simply more of an evolutionary technology "naturally" flowing from the vacuum tube as the Bell Labs people pursued more efficient and faster means of carrying out switching operations in telephone exchanges? Friedel does not really answer these questions. On one hand, he refers to the transistor as central to a revolutionary change in electronics, while on the other he views it as a transitional device that only points the way to the integrated circuits and microprocessors that made possible the real electronics revolution of the 1970s and early 1980s.

On the greeting-card racks this past Christmas could be seen a minor technological mir-acle—a Christmas card that upon opening showed a small yellow light that glowed while the card played a tinny but recognizable version of "Jingle Bells." The yellow light was the latest addition to a novelty that made its first appearance a couple of years ago—the elec-tronic greeting card. The thing that is most notable about this minor miracle is just how ordinary it seems, how easily it is shrugged off by a public that accepts it as simply another application of microelectronics, perhaps to join the ranks of Pong (the early video game), talking scales, and wristwatches that incorporate calculators and thermometers.

Most of those picking up the singing Christmas card have at least a vague idea of how it works. There is, of course, a battery-powered "chip"—an integrated circuit, combining hun-dreds or thousands of electronic functions on a fingernail-sized slice of crystal. This device, at the heart of modern electronics technology, from guided missiles to computers to pocket cal-culators, is the result of the harnessing of a class of substances called semiconductors.

Our mastery of these materials began in earnest almost forty years ago, with the inven-tion of the transistor. This most people realize; less well understood is the real role of the transistor in the microelectronics revolution. As some saw at its introduction, in 1948, the transistor brought to electronics new capabilities, presenting to engineers challenges and opportunities hitherto unknown and pointing ahead to a "solid-state" technology that would have a very different look and feel from vacuum-tube electronics. Yet the transistor as it first appeared and as it was applied over the first decade of its existence, was also the final stage in an older technical tradition, an electronics conceived and built around circuits of individual components. In hindsight, it is now possible to appreciate the single, discrete transistor as a truly transitional technology. It was distinctively different from older ways of doing things, but it was not fully a part of the revolution to come.

In the years after World War II, few scientists were looking for a revolution in electron-ics. The war had seen the flourishing of radio and related technologies beyond anything that could have been imagined before the conflict began. While there were indeed wartime tech-nical and scientific achievements that were more spectacular—the atomic bomb, for instance—to many observers it was electronics that gave the Allies the real technical margin of victory. Radar, sonar, field-communications systems, and the proximity fuze were recog-nized by soldiers and civilians alike as technical accomplishments of the first order, the cre-ations of engineers and physicists intent on demonstrating how advanced technology could make the critical difference in the war effort.

Many people were also aware of the creation of another new device, the electronic digi-tal computer, which saw limited wartime use but promised to open up whole new realms of technical possibilities. The years after the war were expected to see the consolidation of the great technical strides that had been taken under military pressure and the application of these new capabilities to areas that would improve civilian life. The world eagerly awaited the war-delayed spread of television and FM radio, and industry was hungry to see what the new electronics could do in the massive conversion to a consumer economy. No fundamen-tal technical change was sought or anticipated; everyone would be busy making the best use of the still bright, new technologies of the day.

Only a few years after the war's end, however, there began the most profound technical revolution since the beginning of electronics itself at the turn of the century. At the end of 1947, three physicists working at the Bell Telephone Laboratories in Murray Hill, New

Jersey, learned how to make a piece of semiconductor crystal behave like a vacuum-tube amplifier. The story of John Bardeen, Walter Brattain, William Shockley, and the invention of the transistor is a well-known tale of the successful application of science in an industrial setting, a research program that earned the investigators the Nobel Prize for physics and the Bell System its most valuable patent since the one Alexander Graham Bell took out for the telephone in 1876.

Not so well known is just how the transistor came to have the revolutionary impact it did. It was one thing to bring together advanced scientific knowledge and sophisticated technical insight to create a new component that worked on novel principles and in distinctly different ways from older ones. It was quite another to make that component a useful—not to say profoundly important—part of the technological world. Doing so presented a challenge to the engineers and designers who were the shapers of that world, a challenge that initially went unrecognized and unappreciated by people who were comfortable and confident with the established technical order of things. It took close to a decade from the time of the transistor's invention at Murray Hill to the point where the new technology began to have a real impact on modern life—and began to lead to other, more far-reaching inventions.

The source of the electronics engineers' confidence at war's end was mastery of the vacuum tube. The history of the electronic vacuum tube began in 1883 with Thomas Edison's observation of the passage of an electric current from the hot, glowing filament of one of his incandescent lamps, across the high vacuum of the bulb, to an extra electrode introduced into the bulb's glass envelope. Edison thought this effect might be somehow useful but couldn't think of a good application and so did nothing more with it. An Englishman, John Ambrose Fleming, figured out two decades later that this was just the kind of device needed by the infant technology of radio.

Since the Edison-effect current will flow only in one direction, from the filament (or cathode) to the other electrode (or anode) but not the reverse, Fleming called his invention a valve. It was useful for radio because the response of the valve to a radiowave signal, which is a kind of alternating current, was a direct current (hence the valve is also called a rectifier). Fleming's valve gave the radio pioneers a reliable and sensitive detector of signals and thus began displacing the "cat's-whisker" detector—a semiconductor crystal, ironically—that had been depended on up to then.

The real possibilities of vacuum-tube technology, however, were revealed by the American Lee de Forest in 1906. De Forest discovered that if he placed a third electrode between the cathode and the anode and allowed the radio signal to determine the voltage in this element (called the grid), the vacuum tube could be used as a powerful amplifier of the signal. De Forest called his invention an audion, but it became more generally known as a triode (just as the valve was referred to as a diode). The subsequent history of radio, and indeed of all electronics technology, for the next four decades involved the design of still more complex tubes—tetrodes, pentodes, hexodes, and even higher "odes"—and more complex circuits to make the best use of them. The "odes" were shortly joined by the "trons," such as the pliotron (a very-high-vacuum triode), the ignitron (for very-high-power applications), and the magnetron (for the generation of very-high-frequency signals).

When, in 1933, the electronics industry sought to show off its wonders at the Chicago World's Fair, one of the features of the display was a giant vacuum tube designed to explain the basic phenomenon to fairgoers. Other exhibits showed off some of the literally hundreds of different tubes that were used for a great variety of purposes, from ever-improving radio receivers to machine controls, phonograph amplifiers, short-wave radio sets, and even "electric eyes." Despite the Great Depression, the 1930s saw the vigorous expansion of electronics from the already impressive displays of Chicago in 1933 to the truly spectacular show put on at New York's World's Fair in 1939, where fully electronic television began regular broadcasting to the American public for the first time.

The coming of war in the 1940s, therefore, found the American electronics engineers well equipped to make important contributions to the nation's defense. Physicists and engineers at the MIT Radiation Laboratory devised tubes that made radar a reliable and widely applicable tool. Researchers at the Applied Physics Laboratory outside Baltimore built another, less famous but also strategically vital device, the proximity fuze. This consisted of a radar unit reduced in size to fit into an antiaircraft or artillery shell and set to detonate the shell at the desired distance from its target. It required the design of vacuum tubes that were both rugged enough to withstand being fired from a gun and small enough to fit into a circuit placed in the head of a five-inch shell. Engineers thus began speaking of "ruggedization" and "miniaturization" as new and important design challenges.

These challenges redirected the attention of some to the possible uses of semiconductors. Ever since the vacuum tube had replaced the cat's whisker, there had been only limited interest in these materials. Semiconductors, as the name implies, do not conduct electric currents as well as common metallic conductors (like copper, silver, or aluminum) but they perform better than true insulators (like glass, rubber, or most plastics). The contact between a semiconductor and a conductor can be designed so that current will pass easily in only one direction—acting as a rectifier. Before the war, numerous applications were found for rectifiers made of the semiconductor materials copper oxide and selenium. Ruggedization and miniaturization compelled many engineers to pay closer attention to these materials, but there was little theory to guide the applications of any of the semiconductors, and further uses would require more knowledge about how they really behaved.

Even before the war, and again during it, some electronics engineers asked if a semiconductor crystal couldn't be made to act like a triode amplifier as well as a diode rectifier. Isolated efforts showed that this was not, in fact, easily done. Besides, the ever-increasing power and versatility of vacuum tubes made the question of a semiconductor amplifier seem relatively unimportant. But tubes had their limitations, and as more applications were explored, these limitations became increasingly apparent. In high-frequency applications, tube designers often ran into severe difficulties in combining power, signal response, and reliability. When long-term reliability was necessary, as in telephone networks or undersea cables, tubes fell short of what was needed. And when thousands of tubes were used together, as in the new giant digital computers, the problems of keeping such large numbers of heat-producing devices going caused numerous headaches. Considerations such as these were at work at Bell Labs when plans were made for the research that led to the transistor.

Even in the 1930s, some engineers had perceived the limitations of the mechanical switching technology that was at the heart of the telephone network. People like Mervin Kelly, Bell's vice-president for research, saw that electronic switching, with its instantaneous response to signals, held out a possible answer. The roadblock was in the nightmare of depending on huge banks of hot vacuum tubes, each liable to break down after a few months of constant use. As Kelly saw it, a solid-state switching device, requiring no power at all most of the time and capable of responding immediately to an incoming signal, was not only desirable, it was becoming necessary if the telephone system was not to drown in its own complexity and size.

So, with the war winding to a close in the summer of 1945, a research group in solid-state physics was organized at Bell Labs. From the summer of 1945 until the end of 1947, the solid-state physics team under William Shockley performed experiments on silicon and germanium crystals, aided by the superior materials-handling capabilities of Bell chemists and metallurgists. The primary goal of their experiments was a semiconductor amplifier, a replacement for the vacuum triode. The transistor effect was first observed in December of 1947, and the people at Bell knew instantly that they had an important invention on their hands. It was so important, in fact, that they didn't allow word to get out for six months; patent documents were drawn up and further experiments were pursued to make sure that the investigators knew just how their device worked.

On June 30, 1948, an elaborate public announcement and demonstration was staged in New York City, complete with a giant model of the point-contact transistor and a radio and a television with the new devices substituted for tubes. The public response was muted—*The New York Times,* for example, ran the story on page 46, at the end of its "News of Radio" column. Perhaps it was the sheer simplicity of the device that deceived onlookers. The *Times* described it as consisting "solely of two fine wires that run down to a pinhead of solid semi-conductive material soldered to a metal base." The first transistor, housed in a metal cylinder a little less than an inch long and a quarter-inch across, was not much smaller than some of the miniature tubes that had been made for the military.

Nonetheless, some people were impressed, even if they could only dimly perceive the implications. The popular magazine *Radio-Craft,* for example, featured the Bell announcement in an article headlined ECLIPSE OF THE RADIO TUBE: "The implications of this development, once it emerges from the laboratory and is placed in commercial channels, are staggering." This comment was evoked less by the transistor's size than by its most conspicuous other feature, its low power requirement. "No longer will it be necessary to supply power—whether it be by batteries—or filament heating transformers—to heat an electron-emitting cathode to incandescence." Since all vacuum tubes begin with the Edison effect, they must be "lit" like light bulbs and thus require considerable power. The transistor required far less power and would not burn out, so it promised a reliability and longevity that tube designers could only dream about.

But the new point-contact transistor was in fact a very frustrating device. For a component that was supposed to be based on sound understanding of physical theory, it instead behaved more like the whimsical devices jury-rigged by amateurs in the first decades of radio. The first transistors were "noisy," easy to overload, restricted in their frequency responses, and easily damaged or contaminated. Transistor makers had great difficulty producing what they wanted. Some spoke of the "wishing in" effect, where the tester of a finished device was reduced to simply hoping it would work right. And there was the "friendly" effect—the tendency of a transistor to acknowledge on a testing oscilloscope a simple wave of the hand in its direction. At first only 20 percent of the transistors made were workable. One engineer was quoted later as saying, "The transistor in 1949 didn't seem like anything very revolutionary to me. It just seemed like another one of those crummy jobs that required one hell of a lot of overtime and a lot of guff from my wife."

To complicate things further, the transistor might do the same sorts of things a tube could do, but it didn't do them in the same way. This meant that circuit designers—the engineers responsible for turning components into workable tools and instruments—would have to reconfigure their often very complex circuits to accommodate the transistor's special characteristics. For many, it hardly seemed worth it. But others made enormous efforts to get the transistor working and out into the world of applications.

Besides the Bell System itself, the most important impetus to transistor development was provided by the U.S. military. The value of miniature electronics had been clear to some military men at least since the 1930s, when the Army Signal Corps made the first walkie-talkies. By the beginning of World War II, the corps had produced the Handie-Talkie, a six-pound one-piece radio that was essential to field communications. Experience with this device, however, highlighted the limitations of vacuum-tube technology. Under rugged battlefield conditions, especially in extreme heat and cold, the instruments were prone to rapid breakdown. Small as they might be, the virtues of even greater reductions in size were apparent to anyone who had used them in the field, and the problems of heavy, quickly exhausted batteries were a constant annoyance.

The Signal Corps thus expressed interest in transistors right away and even started manufacturing them on a very small scale as early as 1949. Other branches of the military quickly followed, and a number of the first applications of the transistor were in experimental military devices, particularly computerlike instruments. The military services pressed Bell to speed up development and to begin quantity production, and by 1953 they were providing half the funding for Bell's transistor research and underwriting the costs of manufacturing facilities.

With this kind of encouragement, the researchers at Bell Labs were able to make considerable improvements in transistor technology. The most important of these was the making of the first junction transistor in 1951. Relying on the theoretical work of William Shockley and very sophisticated crystal-growing techniques developed by Gordon Teal and others, the junction transistor utilized the internal properties of semiconductors rather than the surface effects that the point-contact device depended on. In the long run this was a much more reliable technology, and it provided the fundamental basis for all subsequent transistor development. While the making of junction transistors was initially extremely difficult, the result was a true marvel, even smaller than the original transistors, using even less power, and behaving as well as the best vacuum tubes in terms of noise or interference. Soon after the announcement of the junction transistor, Bell began making arrangements to license companies that wished to exploit the new technology, holding seminars and training sessions for outside engineers, and compiling what was known about transistors into fat volumes of technical papers.

By 1953 Bell and the military had finally begun to make use of the transistor, but there was still no commercial, publicly available application. The transistor still meant nothing to the public at large. This changed suddenly that year, not in a way that affected a large number of people, but in a way that a relatively small number were very grateful for. In December 1952 the Sonotone Corporation announced that it was offering a hearing aid for sale in which a transistor replaced one of the three vacuum tubes. The device wasn't any smaller than earlier models, but the transistor saved on battery costs. This opened the floodgates to exploitation of the new technology by dozens of hearing-aid manufacturers, and within months there were all-transistor hearing aids that promised to rapidly transform a technology that had been growing steadily but slowly since the 1930s.

As manufacturers redesigned circuits and found other miniature components to fit into them, hearing aids shrank radically. Just as important, however, was the savings in batteries. Despite the fact that transistors cost about five times what comparable tubes did, it was estimated that a hearing-aid user saved the difference in reduced battery costs in only one year. It is no wonder that the transistor took the hearing-aid industry by storm. In that first year, 1953, transistors were found in three-quarters of all hearing aids; by 1954, fully 97 percent of all instruments used only transistors. At the same time, hearing-aid sales increased 50 percent in one year (from 225,000 to 335,000). The transistor was showing a capacity for transforming older technologies that only the most prescient could have foreseen.

When the Regency radio made its appearance in time for Christmas of 1954, this first all-transistor radio was an instant success at $49.95. Other radios quickly followed, and the "transistorization" of consumer electronics was under way. Still, the early transistor radio was largely a novelty, only slowly displacing older, more familiar instruments. Much more important was the application of the transistor to digital computers. The first truly electronic programmable digital computer, the ENIAC, had been completed in February 1946. It contained 17,468 tubes, took up 3,000 cubic feet of space, consumed 174 kilowatts, and weighed 30 tons. Many engineers saw from the beginning the great promise that the transistor held out for computer technology, but it was not until 1955 that IBM began marketing its first transistorized machine (the 7090). Size was reduced, the air conditioning that the tubes required was gone, and power consumption was reduced 95 percent. It was obvious to all that the marriage of the transistor and the digital computer would be an important and fruitful one.

Still, in 1955 the transistor remained a minor element in the larger scheme of things. Total transistor production up to that time totaled less than four million units (over about seven years). That many vacuum tubes were being made in the United States every two working days. And as exciting as the computer might be, it represented a tiny market—only 150 computer systems were sold in the United States that year. Over the next few years, however, transistor production and use expanded rapidly. As more companies entered the business, fabrication techniques were improved, and engineers continued to design circuits that used semiconductor devices.

Nevertheless, the microelectronics revolution might have remained a quiet and limited affair but for two great events, one within the industry, the other a dramatic intrusion from the outside world. On October 4, 1957, the Soviet Union put *Sputnik I* into orbit around the Earth, ushering in an era of tense and vigorous competition for the mastery of space technology. The already considerable interest of the U.S. government in microelectronics now reached a fever pitch.

That same year, a small group of physicists and engineers, former employees of the transistor pioneer William Shockley, set up their own shop and laboratory in a warehouse in Mountain View, California, at the northern end of the Santa Clara valley. At the head of this new enterprise, called Fairchild Semiconductor, was the twenty-nine-year-old Robert Noyce. Within a couple of years Noyce and his colleagues had put together the elements of a new semiconductor technology that would shape the future in ways that the transistor itself never could have done.

In 1958 Fairchild's Jean Hoerni invented the planar technique for making transistors. Building on processes developed at Bell and General Electric, the planar technique allowed for simplification and refinement of transistor manufacture beyond anything yet possible. It consisted of making transistors by creating layers of silicon and silicon dioxide on a thinly sliced "wafer" of silicon crystal. This layering allowed careful control of the electronic properties of the fabricated material and also produced a quantity of very small, flat transistors in one sequence of operations. Much more important, however, the process led Robert Noyce to another, much more fundamental invention, the integrated circuit.

Noyce was neither the first to conceive of putting an entire electronic circuit on a single piece of semiconductor material nor was he the first to accomplish the feat. The idea had been around for some years, and in the summer of 1958 Jack Kilby, an engineer at Texas Instruments in Dallas, built the first true integrated circuit, a simple circuit on a piece of germanium. Kilby's device was a piece of very creative engineering, but it depended on putting together the circuit components by hand. Noyce's great contribution was to show how the planar process allowed construction of circuits on single pieces of silicon by the same mechanical and chemical procedures formerly used to make individual transistors. Noyce's process, which he described in early 1959 and demonstrated a few months later, allowed for the design and manufacture of circuits so small and so complex that the elements could not even be seen by the unaided eye. Indeed, in Noyce's circuits, the transistors were reduced to little dots under a microscope. Finally the microelectronics revolution had revealed its true form.

No one in 1948 could have predicted what that form would be. Indeed, even in 1962, when integrated circuits first came to market, the extraordinary nature of the changes to which they would lead was only dimly perceived by a few. The integrated circuit overcame what some engineers referred to as the "tyranny of numbers." By the late 1950s, large computers had as many as two hundred thousand separate components, and even with transistors the construction and testing of such large machines was becoming an engineering nightmare. Still larger computers, with millions of components, were envisioned, especially by military and space planners. The integrated circuit, with its ability to combine hundreds and later even thousands of elements into a single unit, made such complex machines possible. Just as importantly, however, it made them cheap. By the end of the 1960s, computer memory chips that could handle a thousand bits of information were available.

In 1971 the first microprocessor was introduced on the market by Intel Corporation. Sometimes called a "computer on a chip," the microprocessor demonstrated that sufficiently complicated integrated circuits could be mass-produced and could bring large, sophisticated computers down to such a tiny size and small cost that they could be inserted into every area of life. The home computer, the modern automobile's instrumentation, the digital watch, the bank's electronic teller machine, and even the electronic greeting card all testify to the power and pervasiveness of the integrated circuit's triumph over size and complexity.

The appearance of the integrated circuit little more than ten years after the announcement of the transistor's invention marked the onset of the next stage in the evolution of electronics, a stage that a quarter-century later has still not run its course. The transistor as a discrete device, as a replacement for the vacuum tube, is still important, but in a more profound sense, the transistor was a transitional technology. It showed engineers and others the way beyond the tube, even though the truly revolutionary paths of electronics in the late twentieth century were to be blazed by other, far more complex inventions.

27

THE REVOLUTION

Joel Shurkin

INTRODUCTION

This selection, part of a chapter from Joel Shurkin's book, *Engines of the Mind,* continues with the theme of revolutionary change in electronics technology. In this case, Shurkin focuses on the emergence of the microcomputer, more commonly known as the personal computer, or PC. Now ubiquitous and an essential tool of the engineer and historian alike, the personal computer grew out of the relentless curiosity of talented young programmers and engineers. Ed Roberts, of Micro Instrumentation Telemetry Systems in Albuquerque, New Mexico, developed the Altair 8800 in 1974 as a kit for electronics buffs. Stephen Wozniak and Steven Jobs built their first Apple the following year, selling fifty of the machines to a small electronics shop in Palo Alto, California.

As important as the hardware was the software that went along with the PC. The Apple II of 1977, a visually attractive and "user- friendly" machine, would most likely have been a commercial failure had it not been for the development of a "killer application," VisiCalc, a spreadsheet program that was an instant success with accountants. IBM's PC carved out a major segment of the market in large part because of the power and flexibility of its operating program, MS/DOS, introduced by Bill Gates and Paul Allen, the founders of industry giant Microsoft.

The personal computer is a good example of the democratization of technology in the United States. Before the PC, computers were all large, expensive "mainframes," understood and operated by a select group of administrators and technicians. Access was only via dedicated terminals in a few laboratories, business offices, and classrooms. Users had to reserve and rent time on these machines and keep their fingers crossed that they would return the processed data on schedule and without any serious "glitches." The revolution in personal computers may not have been so much their miniaturization and reduction in cost as it was in their ready availability and ease of use.

The PC revolution came from small companies and young people, not from the leading computer corporation, IBM, and its many experienced engineers. As Shurkin says, IBM never understood the concept of "distributed computing," even after 1981 when the company introduced its highly successful PC. What does this tell us about the relationship between innovation and the culture of large corporations? Why is it so hard for big, "satis-fied" companies to direct their resources toward new ideas and products? Is it their inherent conservatism or lack of creativity, or is it something even more fundamental having to do with the dynamics of innovation itself?

The innovations came from new, small companies. Larger, more established firms either could not generate and nurture the kind of creativity that led to the advances, or couldn't market the discoveries they did make, and fell by the wayside. Many of America's best-known electronics companies did just that. Philco, GE, RCA, Emerson, to name just some of many that disappeared, were swallowed up by conglomerates or abandoned the business.

Key employees (physicists, engineers, programmers) would leave their old jobs and start their own companies. Those firms would flourish, become more conservative, and spin off more employees. It became a way of life; for a while the average engineer in Silicon Valley changed jobs every eighteen months, and several bars up and down the valley became meat markets where the recruiters and the recruited met for tortilla chips, margaritas, and career changes. Changing jobs sometimes became as easy as turning in the wrong driveway and knocking on the door. The big companies left behind, including Texas Instruments, spent their declining years suing for patent infringement.

Founding companies itself became great sport. Some men founded three or four. Eugene Amdahl had no problem with his newest company competing against Amdahl Computer, a company named after him, his first-born. Failure lacked the stigma it had in other environments. Make a good try, fail, try again. No problem. The capital was just sitting there waiting for good ideas.

Fairchild Semiconductor was the first to feel the pain of change. Robert Noyce and Andrew Grove left in 1968 to found their own company, Intel. Fairchild was gradually absorbed by a French company and vaporized. Intel devoted itself to making the newest kinds of ICs, random access memory (RAM) chips, which shrank the size of computers even further. That wasn't the real miracle.

Question: If you could put thousands of bits of information on a silicon chip, in essence reduce all those memory tubes UNIVAC stacked in room-sized cabinets, why couldn't you also reduce the "brains" of the computer, better known as the processor, into a chip as well? The chip would act as both logic board and traffic cop to the flow of data. On large machines that was called the Central Processing Unit or CPU.

Ted Hoff, a Stanford graduate student working at Intel, did it just a few steps ahead of TI, getting all that circuitry into one chip. Intel called it a "computer on a chip." When it was connected to the memory chips and input and output devices, that is exactly what it was. The new devices are more properly known as microprocessors.

With that, the computer age was born. With more sophisticated microprocessors, the computers went from room size to table size to hand held. Intel's first microprocessor was called the 4004 because it could handle four bits (ons or offs) of information at a time. It was soon replaced by the 8008, with double the capacity. Each piece of usable informa-tion—the computer equivalent of a letter or number—was eight bits (or a "byte") and the 8008 could handle a byte at a time.

At this point the corporations and the universities gave way to the people.

The first person perhaps to smell the change was an MIT graduate and former IBM employee named Kenneth Olsen. In 1957, he and Harlan Anderson founded the Digital Equipment Corporation (DEC) with $70,000 in venture capital from Georges Doriot.[1] Olsen and Anderson moved into an old woolen mill in Maynard, Massachusetts, after the two men had cleaned the place out, which included scrubbing the bathrooms. They hired a number of engineers, mostly from IBM, and turned them into salaried (not commissioned) salesmen.

Olsen believed in two things fervently: that computers ought to be easy to operate (fun if possible) and that they ought to be smaller and cheaper than the machines IBM and the dwarfs were selling. His first computer, the PDP-1, sold for $120,000. In 1965 DEC produced the PDP-8, the first computer to use integrated circuits. It was an astounding success. Because of its size (it could fit in your average closet), Olsen called it a minicomputer.

The PDP-8 was important for several reasons. First, its success induced dozens of other companies to produce their own and the competition pushed the technology even further, which meant smaller, more powerful machines. An entire industry was created. Many of these companies were located on Route 128 outside Boston and for a decade Route 128 was the pot at the end of the rainbow.

Second, the machine was a perfect product. IBM had nothing like it and didn't understand the market. When the PDP-8 came out, only very large or very rich companies had computers, the hulking mainframes that IBM and its competitors sold. At universities, anyone wanting to use a computer, whether a physics lab or the economics department, had to find a way to work off the mainframe. Power struggles broke out between the data processing administrators and the faculty. The mainframe operators fought any attempt at independence in the labs partly because they philosophically believed in centralized computing and partly because decentralized computing eroded their power base. College campuses are very political places. On the other hand, faculty members across the country pushed the computer companies, especially IBM, to produce machines they could afford, computers that would fit in their labs. They wanted to do their own computing on their own time in their own way. IBM, getting rich with mainframes ($4 billion in profits a year), fought on the side of centralized computing, refusing to provide a product to fit the demand and supporting the data processing executives in the political wars. Because of IBM's reputation and clout, they rarely lost. The result was twofold: when DEC produced its first minis, university labs (and medium-sized companies) sucked them in as fast as DEC and its competitors could make them, usually using government grants and almost always going around the data processing administrators. Additionally, an animus toward IBM and its products grew and lasted for almost a generation on college campuses, particularly at engineering schools. When IBM finally saw the light and the need to accommodate decentralization, it was too late: where their salesmen were welcomed as old friends in the Fortune 500 companies, they were almost physically ejected from college labs and departments.

Third, the DEC experience was the first unmistakable harbinger that the world was changing. They knew it and prospered along Route 128, and they knew it and would prosper by the next stage in the Santa Clara Valley. The one place they did not know it was

---

1. When Doriot sold his share in 1972, it was worth $350 million.

Armonk, New York, at IBM's headquarters. Perhaps they were doing too well to pay attention; by the time IBM was finally hit by the changes, it was accumulating the largest profits in the history of capitalism. Nonetheless, through a combination of blindness, inertia, and blazing stupidity, IBM would make a series of tactical blunders almost unprecedented in American business. From a position of unassailed dominance—the company everyone envied and admired for its competence and profits—they would be brought to their knees by a kid from Seattle and put to shame by two young geniuses in Cupertino, California.

The drive was toward powerful computers small enough to fit on the desktop, giving *each individual* the computing power Eckert and Mauchly once dreamed of for large institutions. They would shrink even further and gain in power with no end in sight. Bill Gates in Seattle knew that; Steve Jobs and Steve Wozniak in Cupertino knew that. John Opel, then chairman of IBM in Armonk, appeared to have no clue what they were talking about.

You didn't even have to be in the computer industry to know it. An editor for *Popular Electronics*, Leslie Solomon, was urging the hobbyists who read his magazine to build machines that gave individuals power. The challenge was taken up in Albuquerque, New Mexico, by Ed Roberts, who cofounded a company called Micro Instrumentation Telemetry Systems (MITS), selling radio transmitters for model planes and kits for electronic calculators. The latter wasn't terribly successful; Texas Instruments could make and sell calculators for much less and by 1974 MITS was hanging by its thumbs. Roberts decided to follow the wisdom of Solomon.

Intel was selling its 8080 microprocessor for $360 a chip. Roberts talked them down to $75 each. He had in mind a computer kit that could be put together by a knowledgeable tinkerer and could be priced under $500. Solomon's twelve-year-old daughter came up with a name for the machine, Altair, after the star.[2]

After his first model apparently got lost in the mail, Roberts flew to New York and in desperation he and Solomon photographed a fake machine for the cover of *Popular Electronics*. Then he flew back to Albuquerque and actually built one. The magazine advertised the Altair for $397.

Absolute hell broke loose. Checks by the thousands poured into MITS and the staff spent most of its time opening envelopes and making deposits. Roberts and Solomon apparently had tapped an explosive—and apparently unsuspected—market. Although they were providing kits, not complete computers, MITS couldn't build the kits fast enough. The popularity was odd because you really couldn't do anything with an Altair. Programming meant throwing switches one after the other, and if you made a mistake you had to start over. Readouts consisted of blinking lights. It served absolutely no useful purpose; there was nothing Altair could do that you couldn't do faster and easier another way. It was the principle of the thing.

Two young men in Massachusetts, however, had an idea. Paul Allen and William Gates III were part of a growing group of kids fascinated by computers. While students at a Seattle high school, they broke into Control Data's Cybernet system (something CD said couldn't be done) and crashed it by typing fourteen characters. They were just "hacking around," they said. They simply were bewitched by the machinery and the intellectual challenge. They became hackers.

---

2. She was watching "Star Trek" at the time and Altair was where the *Enterprise* was going that week.

Gates, the son of a prominent lawyer, was doing his pre-law at Harvard and Allen was working for Honeywell in Massachusetts, when Solomon's *Popular Electronics* edition with Altair came out. The goddess of history watched smiling while Allen and Gates looked at the magazine and knew immediately what the Altair was good for. They began work on a version of the computer language BASIC which could be stored on paper tape and loaded into the Altair. With BASIC it would be possible to program an Altair to do actual—if stupidly simple—computing. The Altair only had a capacity of 2,000 characters. They wrote "Roberts" on the letterhead of a company they had formed as kids that no longer existed, claiming to have a BASIC that ran on all 8080 microprocessors, which wasn't true. Allen had programmed a DEC PDP-10 to act like an 8080 (a chip they had never seen) to work in an Altair (a computer they hadn't seen either). Understandably skeptical, Roberts invited them to Albuquerque. Gates stayed behind to further test the program and sent Allen off with a copy.

Allen arrived to find that MITS's offices were stacked between a laundromat and a massage parlor. After stalling for a day to hear if Gates had found any bugs, Allen fed the tape into an "advanced" (6k) Altair. The machine burped and printed out the word READY on the Teletype machine connection. Of such stuff are revolutions made. Allen was twenty-two, Gates twenty and looked sixteen.

Gates knew enough law to know he needed a legal entity to negotiate with Roberts, so he and Allen formed Micro-Soft in July 1975 to develop software for desktop computers, the first company of its kind in the world.[3] Micro-Soft licensed Roberts to sell their version of BASIC, while retaining ownership of the language, the model for software contracts today.

Meanwhile, MITS was going downhill; Roberts was no businessman. The kits he could produce were unreliable. He finally sold the company.

Gates and Allen began thinking of other horizons, finally hiring other programmers and a secretary and moving to an office of their own in downtown Albuquerque. Gates quit Harvard before graduation, to the consternation of his parents. He and Allen began selling their BASIC to other manufacturers, including Tandy, which had just launched its Radio Shack TRS-80 machines, and the Canadian firm Commodore.

In March 1975 a group of San Francisco Bay "hackers" formed the Homebrew Computer Club in a garage in Menlo Park, just north of the Stanford campus. Many of them were engineers; many were refugees of the counterculture of the 1960s, generally from Stanford or Berkeley. They too were hackers. All they had to work with were Altairs and Altair clones. Meetings consisted of demonstrations of gadgets and discussions of problems. Nonetheless, by the third meeting the garage was too small and the club moved to a Victorian house.

Stephen G. Wozniak ("The Woz" forevermore) was a Homebrew member, a superb engineer, and another college dropout. Woz joined up with Steven Jobs, sharing his love for computers and for what were kindly called pranks. Following the lead of the legendary "Captain Crunch" (John Draper), Jobs and The Woz developed "blue boxes" designed to fool pay telephones into giving them free long-distance calls. Jobs then was working for Nolan Bushnell, the developer of the first computer game, Pong, at Atari; Woz was a programmer at Hewlett-Packard.

---

3. The hyphen was dropped quickly.

Woz had once built an improved Altair, which he called the Cream Soda Computer and thought he could do better yet. He took a new eight-bit microprocessor called the 6502, then selling for $20, and built a machine that could run BASIC. For no reason he ever could remember, he called it an Apple. Jobs was impressed. He sold his Volkswagen bus and Wozniak sold his two scientific calculators to raise capital and the two men went into business. Homebrew member Paul Terrell ordered fifty for his new Palo Alto computer shop. Moving into an apartment, Jobs and Wozniak founded the Apple Computer Corporation.

Still not satisfied with their machine, Woz and Jobs made modifications that leaped way ahead of anything on the market, adding a keyboard, a color screen, and built-in BASIC. The new machine was called the Apple II. In a few years, Apple became what was then the fastest-growing company in American history. The Apple II became the people's machine.

Because Jobs and Woz bought Gates's BASIC, teenagers still fighting acne could sit in the basement of their suburban homes writing software and becoming richer than their parents. Writers wrote word processing software. Scientists wrote analysis programs. Teachers fell in love with the Apple II and moved the machine into the classrooms, frequently writing their own software as they went along. Everybody wrote games. Apple IIs began showing up at homes and offices, and the complexity of the software grew geometrically. They moved from toy to usefulness in a matter of a few years.

A Harvard MBA student, Dan Bricklin, developed an accounting system that transferred the accountant's worksheet onto the computer screen. Making a change in one cell in the worksheet automatically updated other pertinent cells, and because it was a computer, not a human, it never made arithmetic mistakes. He and his friends formed a company called Software Arts and signed an agreement with Dan Fylstra of Personal Software, Inc., to market the program Bricklin called VisiCalc.

Fylstra's first big customer was Apple. VisiCalc was so good—it actually did a better job and worked faster than the best accountant could with paper and pencil—people bought Apple IIs just to use VisiCalc; indeed, by September 1980, Apple estimated that one-fifth of its Apple II sales were driven by VisiCalc. The software eventually was written for other machines.

Companies rose and fell. Fortunes were made in months. In less than ten years after MITS's Altair, the microcomputer business became a $100 billion industry. Microsoft had grown into one of the largest software applications houses.

Programs were divided into applications and operating systems. Operating systems were the basic programs that turned a piece of metal, glass, and silicon into a computer. Applications were programs that ran on that computer, the ones that did the actual work for the user, such as VisiCalc. All the programs were written in one of several layers of language. In July 1977, Microsoft began selling versions of several languages, FORTRAN and COBOL. Because of the complexity of those languages, they were sold mostly for computers that ran an operating system called CP/M (Control Program for Microcomputer), written and sold by a small company in Monterey, California, called Digital Research, owned by Gary Kildall, another Seattle native.

CP/M could run on any computer using the 8080 microprocessor or its clones. It was tiny—3,000 lines of code—and could let applications do anything within the memory capabilities of the computer, a brilliant feat. Kildall made $60,000 the first year he was in business, and by the late 1970s CP/M was the dominant force, the so-called industry standard, in microcomputers.

In 1978, Microsoft was making more than $1 million a year and doubling sales. The firm had thirteen employees in its Albuquerque office. Allen thought they were in something of a geographic backwater and ought to move. Silicon Valley, where most of the customers were, seemed the obvious choice, but Allen wanted to go home to Seattle. He also thought Silicon Valley was too unsettled to be nurturing to stable businesses, what with engineers and programmers skipping from company to company. Gates was too busy to care. In the summer of 1978, Microsoft moved back to Washington, taking most of its employees with it.

In 1979, Microsoft's sales hit $2.5 million, with a million copies of BASIC out in the hands of paying customers. With the help of a high school student, Allen developed a card that would fit into Apple IIs that would let those machines, which then dominated the market, use CP/M and the newest BASIC. Microsoft sold 100,000 of them, making Apple the largest user of the operating system.

At that point, the giant stirred. Back in Armonk, somebody noticed that kids out west were making an awful lot of money with the cute little computers and thought it would be nice if their company got a piece of the action. IBMers, as they are called, didn't believe the machines would ever be major threats—nothing worked better than their mainframes—but a buck is a buck.

They naturally formed a committee. First they tried to buy Apple but Jobs and Wozniak wouldn't sell. So IBM decided to go it alone. The plan was to do as little actual development as possible. They would try to buy what they needed and "kludge" together a computer. Now, if you were thinking of getting into the microcomputer business, the two people you had to talk to were Bill Gates and Gary Kildall—Gates for the language to write your applications on, Kildall for the operating system to hang it on. An IBM executive named Jack Sams, one of the legions of middle-level executives that made IBM run, visited Seattle. Nothing definite is going on, he told Gates, who had borrowed a suit for the occasion, just want to talk about microcomputers in case IBM ever, well, you know. . . . Sams described a machine much less powerful than the one IBM wanted to build just to see what Gates said. Gates said it wasn't powerful enough. Thanks, Sams said, we may get back to you. Then again, we may not. He left.

After a couple of weeks of silence, Sams called again for another meeting. He said he was going to bring his legal team to talk to Gates's legal team, and a technical team to talk to Gates's technical team. Gates didn't have a legal team and he was the technical team, so he brought along four other employees so he wouldn't be outnumbered. Sams arrived with a lawyer and someone from "corporate practices" who was essentially a spy for upper management to report what the middle manager was doing and to keep the middle manager from saying things he ought not to say. Gates thought this was a wacky way to do business. Legal papers called non-disclosure agreements were signed to preserve the secrecy of the meeting.

By this time IBM was fighting a federal antitrust suit that was soaking up time and resources. Lawyers began dominating the company and almost nothing was done of any consequence without first clearing it with them. One of the mistakes IBM would make in the subsequent years was forgetting that you hire lawyers to give advice, not make decisions. Considering the antitrust suit, however, this mistake was understandable. What wasn't understandable was why anyone would agree to the legal restrictions IBM placed on anyone doing business with it. IBM had a horrible record of treating contractors poorly, raising some to heights of wealth they never dreamed of, then walking out when it suited Big Blue's purposes. The legal papers Gates was asked to sign essentially gave away the right to sue IBM, even when IBM deserved to be sued. Gates, however, was intrigued by the possibility of working with the world's largest computer company and agreed. He was right for the wrong reasons.

Microsoft and IBM agreed that Microsoft would consult on an IBM microcomputer. Sams asked about an operating system. Gates told them to talk to Kildall. He and Kildall had an informal agreement that Microsoft wouldn't do any operating systems and Digital Research wouldn't do languages.

IBMers flew to Monterey to see Kildall, but Kildall was off flying his new glider and had no intention of cutting short his flight to meet with the easterners. His CP/M was raking in money and, as the industry standard, would do so for years, he felt. IBM could wait. So the IBM contingent had to deal with his lawyer-wife, who took one look at their non-disclosure agreements and threw the visitors out. She was wrong for all the right reasons.

IBM had one weakness even its executives admitted to: it couldn't write software. It was a combination of not having the best programmers (you had much more freedom and might make much more money working elsewhere), the fact that their software didn't have to be brilliant (you want to use our computers, use our software), and a culture in which nothing was done without hordes of people flying all over the world, going to meetings, showing charts, and writing memoranda in lieu of actual work. Everything was done by consensus; individuality was discouraged as not being in "the IBM way." Writing great software is a highly individual process, requiring genius, daring, peace, patience, and courage. The IBM management was wise enough to know this. Sams called Gates and told him to get an operating system or the deal was off. Reluctantly, Gates agreed, knowing it would violate his agreement with Kildall, but it was Kildall's fault. Gates found a small Seattle company that had a rudimentary system called QDOS, for Quick and Dirty Operating System, and bought the rights for $175,000. It became the basis for MS-DOS.

IBM announced its first microcomputer on August 12, 1981, priced from $1,565 to $6,000, depending on the configuration. It was built around an Intel 8088, a 16-bit processor, and marked the beginning of a crucial relationship between the two companies. It could run VisiCalc or word processing and could link with data bases. The machine appeared in stores two months later and to the amazement of Armonk and everyone else was a gigantic hit. IBM also made a crucial decision that would rattle down its corporate history for a generation: the machine had open architecture, which meant that other companies could easily produce peripheral appliances or software that would work on the machine. The director of the product, Don Estridge,[4] pledged to provide anyone who asked the complete specifications. It ran Gates's MS-DOS, which was on the open market. That decision led to the dominance of the IBM-PC as a standard and ironically to the downfall of IBM.

---

4. Estridge, one of IBM's most brilliant managers, was killed in an airline crash in Dallas. Had he not, the history of IBM might have been different. As soon as he died, the bureaucracy in Armonk took control of his program and IBM's fall was unavoidable.

Kildall took one look at what Gates had done and saw considerable similarities between CP/M and Gates's operating system. Most programs that ran on CP/M also ran on MS-DOS because several functions were deliberately copied from CP/M so that software would be compatible. Since his wife had refused to sign IBM's nefarious non-disclosure agreement, Kildall had not given away his right to sue—and did just that. IBM truthfully claimed it had no idea there were similarities in the code and made Kildall a very reasonable offer: if he dropped his suit they would agree to offer the 16-bit version of CP/M as well as MS-DOS to its customers when it was ready. Kildall accepted.

Kildall, who had already made one terrible mistake, now destroyed himself: He decided that CP/M would remain the industry standard and that he could price the operating system at any level he wished, say four times what Gates was charging for MS-DOS ($240 versus $60). It was CP/M, after all, and people would pay the price. He was wrong. By the time IBM could offer CP/M, Microsoft had established itself as the operating system for the IBM-PC. The difference in price—plus a six-month delay in the product—ended any chance of Kildall's recovering. Kildall and his company quickly disappeared, the victim of a *hubris* worthy of a Sophocles hero.[5] Within a few years the IBM-PC and Gates's operating system dominated the industry, helped by another financial program, Lotus's 1,2,3.

One problem with Estridge's open architecture policy was that other companies could buy the Intel chip, produce clones of the IBM machine, and often sell them cheaper than could Big Blue. Soon IBM found itself with the standard and a rapidly shrinking market share. Nonetheless for a time IBM, Microsoft, and Intel dominated the microcomputer industry.

The paradigm had one more shift, and that came from Jobs back at Apple. Jobs had to do something; the Apple II had been surpassed both technologically and in market changes. He was wise enough to understand that Apple had become a very large company and had all the symptoms of a coagulating bureaucracy. He took a group of programmers and designers out of the main office, set them up over a fast-food restaurant in Cupertino flying a skull and crossbones flag. He kept them totally isolated from the corporate structure. Their orders were to produce a computer dramatically unlike anything on the market. Their first design, Lisa (allegedly named after Jobs's illegitimate daughter), was an incredible 32-bit machine that used graphic icons instead of words and had an operating system controlled by a mouse that swooped around a metaphoric desktop. Lisa was awesomely slow, and writing software for it was mind-bending, but it begat the Macintosh in 1984.

Jobs insisted on several things for the Mac: it would be closed architecture so that no one could clone it; it would be easy to assemble (you cannot plug in peripherals incorrectly because the cables only fit in the right receptacles); and it carried the visual metaphor, now known as GUI or graphical user interface, to the point where users didn't have to know a thing about computers and never had to type a command or write a program. Operating the machine was largely intuitive. Where MS-DOS was verbal, the Mac operating system was visual. Where it took days to assemble and then teach someone to use an MS-DOS machine,

---

5. Kildall died in 1994. His family and friends insisted that he never looked back at his failure, never read stories about Bill Gates, and never wondered whether he, not Gates, would have become the richest man in America. The author does not believe a single word.

you could set up and be using a Mac in two hours. Because graphics can be easily incorporated into the operation, Macs essentially invented the desktop publishing industry and revolutionized publishing. By the end of the decade even IBM was using Macs for its publications. Software for the first Macs came from Gates.

Although Jobs's computer was several generations ahead of anything IBM and its cloners could produce, and developed a cult of "true believers," it never took a large enough market share to threaten IBM financially. IBM was still too powerful in the corporate culture. Yet the Mac heralded the future in a way IBM couldn't understand.

IBM never philosophically embraced what is called "distributed computing." As late as 1992, they were still designing micros that worked best when connected to a mainframe, which they touted as a virtue. Silicon Valley thought that hilarious. IBM could not compete on price with the clone-makers and quickly lost what technological edge they had. Computers became smaller, finally going to laptop to notebook size to hand-held, but rarely because of anything IBM did. The company was mired in bureaucracy, surrounded by legal and security concerns that would have sent Gilbert & Sullivan into paroxysms of laughter, was lawyer-ridden and disabled by a culture of meetings, overhead charts, and consensus. The differences were most apparent when IBM and Gates got together to write an operating system. Gates would put a few dozen people to work in one building and turn them loose. IBM had to use hundreds, perhaps thousands, spread out all over the world to keep all their division managers happy, shell surround them with security people and lawyers. Programmers spent more time on airplanes and going to meetings than writing software. IBM even forced Microsoft through distracting security procedures.

The difference was largely generational. Silicon Valley (and Seattle) were hackers, products of the counterculture, partial to jeans and Birkenstock sandals, Friday afternoon beer bashes, all-night work orgies, and standing around in Fry's electronics store in Cupertino discussing processing speed, Star Trek, metaphors, and personal freedom. They played rock music in their labs, often smoked dope, and frequently burned out by the time they were thirty-five, wealthy enough to buy a place somewhere and start over when they recovered. IBM essentially was run by white-shirted salesmen and bureaucrats who couldn't be fired and were sure of a pleasant retirement when their risk-free careers were over.

Most important, however, was a philosophical chasm: only when it began losing gigantic sums of money did IBM understand where computing was going. The mainframe became the modern dinosaur, well on its way to extinction, and IBM came too late to understanding that. All of IBM's chairmen had come up through the oceans of in-house management, and all accepted the common wisdom of centralized computing through the mainframe. The chasm in understanding between those men and Gates, Jobs, and the engineers in Silicon Valley, who understood the power of distributed computing, was vast and daunting: while IBM was working from the big to the small—reluctantly shrinking mainframes—Gates and Jobs were working up, gleefully taking small computers and making them more powerful. IBM was trying to make desktop computers that made using mainframes more efficient; Gates and Jobs wanted workers free from what they considered the tyranny of mainframe computers and their administrators. Every time Gates negotiated another deal with IBM— and he spent a decade battling with them—he had two unassailable advantages: besides being the smartest person in the room, he knew something the others in the room did not—he knew the future. He never lost. Even the formerly successful manufacturers of minicomputers, such as Control Data and Digital, underestimated the paradigm and Route 128 became a ghost town.

Desktop computers became workstations, and by 1990 the workstations were as powerful as the minicomputers on the desktop, and the minicomputers, with architectures such as parallel processing (more than one microprocessor, sometimes thousands, working simultaneously), could outperform some mainframes. Designers also were seeing how small they could make the box; by 1995 they were producing computers so small that the size of the keys, which had to be struck surely by an adult human finger, were determining how small computers could be made, not the electronics.

By 1991, it all collapsed; a company that once bragged that it never laid off any employee let go 140,000. Entire towns surrounding IBM facilities were almost financially destroyed as tax dollars dried up and thousands of residents found themselves out of work. Hardest hit were the middle-aged, middle-level managers, people who generally could not find jobs elsewhere. IBM stock lost $75 billion in value, about the gross national product of Sweden.

After a succession of failures in the board room, IBM eventually hired from outside the company and outside the industry for the first time, taking a manager from RJR-Nabisco as its CEO. As of this writing, Louis V. Gerstner, Jr., had restored the grand old company to profitability, but it was only a ghost of itself, shed of half its employees and $5.6 billion in costs. As a final insult, IBM, like a fading aristocrat with an estate it could no longer afford, began auctioning its extensive collection of American art, first collected by Tom Watson, Sr., to improve the "human spirit."

The winners were the shock wave riders. Other companies that missed the shift, such as Wang, which produced a splendid word processor that did nothing else, or those that didn't play the currents right, such as Kaypro, came and went.

Even the riders had their problems. Jobs, unable to run the company himself, hired John Scully from Pepsi-Cola. It was not clear if Scully knew anything about computers beyond turning them on. The result was turmoil; Apple lurched from one technological path to another, executive turnovers came every six months (one of those was Wozniak, who couldn't stand Scully or the direction he was taking the company), reorganizations raged once a year. Apple, which became one of the worst managed companies in the valley, still has not recovered several years after Scully was fired. Further, Jobs had insisted on closed architecture that meant—unlike what was true for IBM—no one could clone an Apple, but also that no one else was pushing the technology, and the Mac lost its technological advantages while Scully chased after chimera.[6] In 1994, Apple agreed to permit clones but it may be too late.

Apple did win the philosophical war. Every year the software that ran IBM compatibles looked more like Macintosh. Gates, wise as usual, knew that Mac's technology was superior in most ways, and Microsoft devised a program called Windows that essentially sat in front of MS-DOS and pretended it worked like a Macintosh. It was much slower, not nearly as good—Mac enthusiasts dubbed it "Windoze"—but it was better than dealing with MS-DOS. Windows sold so many copies that it turned Gates, still the largest Microsoft

---

6. Jobs left to form his own company, Next, which produced a machine that dazzled users and an operating system far ahead of anything else on the market. It was a total failure. Microsoft had already won the operating system war. Scully was finally forced out but Apple has never recovered.

stockholder, into the richest man in America.[7] Soon even laptops came with mouses, and the metaphors that began with the Macintosh[8] would become the dominant way of operating a computer as the machines became easier to use.

Eventually, both Apple and IBM would call a truce. Both companies joined with Motorola, the manufacturer of Apple's microprocessor, to produce a new processor for both companies' machines. Apple's PowerMacs have been successful; IBM's computers are just coming out at this writing. For Apple, it is a last ditch effort to remain a player in the computer business; for IBM it means freedom from Microsoft and Intel.

After years of battling with Gates over operating systems, IBM finally went on to try its own and free itself of Gates's domination. It took much too long, and by the time it came out in 1994, OS/2 was probably too little and much too late. IBM finally learned how to let people write good software. IBM returned to profitability, and, to demonstrate it was a new company after all these years, pulled off a hostile takeover of Lotus apparently hoping to add its software and programming skills. Skeptics remain.

In June 1995, IBM licensed Apple's Macintosh OS to run on its PowerPC machines, along with OS/2, an acknowledgment it could not fight Microsoft alone. After spending a decade denigrating the Mac and doing everything possible to kill it off, they surrendered.

Things that go around do come around. Microsoft and Intel run the computer industry with 70 percent of the worldwide market, but even they can see the perils of flying high. Intel has been threatened by competitors who won law suits enabling them to produce clones of their most popular chips. Other competitors are beginning to dog them with advanced technologies.

Microsoft, which had control of 85 percent of the operating systems in personal computers, was hit by its very own antitrust suit, essentially for acting like the IBM of old. By controlling both the operating systems and the applications for computers, others in the industry charged the company had acquired too much power. If you wanted to write software for Windows, you had to deal with Microsoft, which meant that company knew what its own competitors were planning. The company adopted another page from the old IBM playbook with a practice known as "vaporware." If you see a competitor is going to produce something truly wizard, you promise your customers that you are working on something better even when in fact you have nothing even close that will be ready on time. IBM did that for years to keep mainframe customers from jumping to competitors. Microsoft did it with the latest version of Windows to keep potential buyers from jumping to Power Macs and OS/2.

Windows 95 finally came out in August of 1995, with Gates spending hundreds of millions of dollars on promotional stunts, including flashing the Windows logo on the Empire State Building and buying out the entire press run of the *Sunday Times* of London for advertising. A sycophantic media covered the event as the Second Coming. In fact, Windows 95 was merely an upgrade of an existing program and essentially turned Intel machines into imitations of slow, two-year-old Macintoshes. It also lagged behind OS/2 in pure power. Gates will probably make billions.

---

7. Paul Allen retired in 1983.
8. The metaphor and GUI were actually developed by Xerox's Palo Alto Research Center (PARC), one of the legion of firms with first-class research laboratories that proved completely incapable of marketing the results of that research. IBM is another. Jobs adopted what he saw at PARC for the Lisa.

Microsoft was similar to the old IBM in other ways as well: it could get away with second-rate products because, as writer Steven Levy puts it, they owned both the railroad tracks and the trains. Microsoft's software rarely led, followed others' advances only with reluctance. If someone had a product that was too good, Gates bought the company.

The Clinton Justice Department settled the Microsoft suit in 1994, but a federal judge, listening to the howls of protest from Microsoft's competitors, rejected the settlement. In June 1995, a federal appeals court overturned the judge's decision, and to the dismay of Microsoft's competitors the settlement was upheld. Justice Department pressure that blocked Microsoft's purchase of Intuit—the seller of the most popular personal finance program—held, however, and the companies dropped merger plans. Competitors of Microsoft also feared that the company was trying to muscle into the lucrative Internet service, software that would allow users access to the world-wide computer network. At issue was the plan for Microsoft to set up its own computer network and build access programs into Windows 95. That would directly compete against services such as America Online and CompuServe. The Justice Department was less concerned and also in June 1995 said it was not pursuing anti-trust action.

Nonetheless, the paradigm shifted, the revolution was in full steam, and the world changed. Computing had become totally decentralized. Everyone had the power on their desk or at home. The priesthood of the mainframe's information managers was dead. The people had won.

28

THE ATOMIC AGE AT 50

INTRODUCTION

On August 6, 1945, an American B-29 nicknamed *Enola Gay* dropped an atomic bomb on the Japanese city of Hiroshima. The results were devastating. In a fraction of a second, an explosion equivalent to 20,000 tons of TNT destroyed the heart of the metropolis, killing tens of thousands of people instantly and leaving tens of thousands more critically injured and dying. As if one nuclear weapon were not enough, a second atomic bomb devastated most of the city of Nagasaki on August 9, killing another 60,000 to 70,000 people. Five days later, Japan surrendered and World War II came to an end.

More than fifty years later, the atomic bomb and its use against Japan remains one of the most controversial subjects in modern history. On one side are those who consider the bombings completely justified within the context of the war. Had the bomb not been used, the United States would have had to mount a massive and costly invasion of the Japanese mainland. Not only might this offensive have prolonged the war well into 1946, but it could have resulted in as many as 1 million American casualties. How could any political or military leader in all conscience justify ordering hundreds of thousands of Americans to their deaths, knowing all the time that the nation had a weapon that might end the conflict virtually overnight? On the other side are those who argue that the Japanese in August 1945 were already defeated and that another few weeks of bombardment with conventional high explosives, combined with the shock of the Soviet Union entering the war in the Pacific, would have brought surrender without either an invasion or the use of the bomb. We would then be free of the guilt of killing hundreds of thousands of innocent people with a murderous new weapon.

The following articles are among those that appeared in 1995 in a special issue of *Technology Review*. They examine some of the vexing questions surrounding the development and use of the atomic bomb and the broader implications of nuclear weapons in the post-World War II era. Of considerable interest to students of the history of technology is that nuclear weapons in particular and atomic energy in general represent science-based technology, stemming from theoretical studies of nuclear physics earlier in the century. Many of the people who worked on the Manhattan Project that developed the atomic bomb were physicists. They understood only too well the enormity of the weapon and recognized their unique responsibility as its creators; some of them felt the moral obligation to go on record during and after the war in opposition to its use against civilian targets without warning.

This leaves all of us with a fascinating question—in what ways, if at all, are scientists and engineers accountable for their actions? If atomic scientists carry the guilt of Hiroshima and Nagasaki, then why not the aeronautical engineers at Boeing who designed and built the B-29 heavy bomber? Or, conversely, are scientists and engineers only the messengers, and that the truly guilty are the political and military leaders in Washington who made the decision to use the weapons against the two Japanese cities? Or, is no one guilty?

Of all twentieth-century technologies, the atomic bomb may be the least understood but may have had the most influence on our lives. At the level of popular culture, countless movies, books, and television shows since the late 1940s revolved around the theme of nuclear weapons, which historian Spencer Weart refers to as a "symbol for the worst of modernity." Of more significance, perhaps, nuclear weapons may have prevented a disastrous World War III fought between the superpowers with conventional weapons. If Alex Roland is to be believed, the atomic bomb actually saved hundreds of millions of lives. Finally, there is the lingering threat of accident and terrorism that surrounds nuclear weapons and the tons of highly toxic plutonium used in their manufacture. Even if the major powers exercise restraint in the use of these terrible weapons, will those with less to lose do the same? Physicist Theodore B. Taylor, who worked on the Manhattan Project and later nuclear weapons programs, thinks not, concluding that the only sane thing to do is to eliminate all nuclear weapons and the deadly materials used to make them. The answers to these questions are not simple, but they are important enough to warrant our most profound consideration.

This August 6 and 9 mark the fiftieth anniversary of an awesome pair of events—the dropping of atomic bombs by the United States on the Japanese cities of Hiroshima and Nagasaki. The second and third such devices ever built—the first was successfully tested by Manhattan Project scientists in New Mexico just three weeks before—they were the only atomic weapons ever actually used in war, and they provided a dramatic finish to the ordeal of World War II.

Although these devices abruptly ended one era, they simultaneously ushered in another —this one seemingly without end—humankind in sudden and irreversible possession of the most potent technological force ever seen on earth. For most of the past 50 years such knowledge has been used to drive a veritable "population explosion" of nuclear weapons, all of them far more sophisticated and destructive than their relatively modest but nevertheless city-destroying ancestors of 1945, a tide that has only lately begun to recede.

The "golden anniversary" of Hiroshima and Nagasaki thus begs for reflection, analysis, and the formulation of lessons learned and policy recommendations, not only regarding the events at Hiroshima and Nagasaki themselves but the nuclear arms race they helped precipitate, its wider ramifications, and prospects for its future.

WHAT SCIENTISTS KNEW AND WHEN THEY KNEW IT

Ronald Takaki

Scientists of the Manhattan Project recently claimed they were surprised to learn from an article by nuclear physicist Arjun Makhijani that Japan had always been the target of the weapon they developed. Had they known this "back then," some of them suggested in a *New York Times* report of April 18, 1995, the nuclear effort might have been "slowed" or "crippled." Physicist Hans A. Bethe was quoted as saying, "Most of us considered the Nazis the main enemy."

But history invariably turns out to be more nuanced than its participants will admit. Contrary to the recollection of some Manhattan Project veterans, the bomb scientists knew in May 1945—three months before the explosion at Alamogordo—that Japan was the target. In fact, as a member of the Target Committee, Los Alamos Laboratory director J. Robert Oppenheimer recommended on May 11 that the bomb be used against Japan.

When the scientists learned that plans for an atomic attack on Japan were under way, many of them did indeed organize to stop the bombing—but it was beyond their power to cripple the weapon's development. Leo Szilard of the Chicago Metallurgical Laboratory decided that he and his fellow atomic scientists should forthrightly declare their moral opposition to the use of the atomic bomb—a weapon of mass and indiscriminate killing of civilians—against Japan. Szilard drafted a petition to Truman. It exhorted, among other things, "that you exercise your power as Commander-in-Chief, to rule that the United States shall not resort to the use of atomic bombs in this war unless the terms which will be imposed upon Japan have been made public in detail and Japan knowing these terms has refused to surrender. . . ."

Szilard admitted to his fellow scientists that the petition would be futile. "However small the chance might be that our petition may influence the course of events," he wrote to a colleague on July 4, "I personally feel that it would be a matter of importance if a large number of scientists who have worked in this field went clearly and unmistakably on record as to their opposition on moral grounds to the use of these bombs in the present phase of the war." In other letters, he argued that "from a point of view of the standing of the scientists in the eyes of the general public one or two years from now it is a good thing that a minority of scientists should have gone on record in favor of giving greater weight to moral arguments and should have exercised their right given to them by the Constitution to petition the President."

Szilard's petition prompted the Manhattan Project leaders to poll the atomic scientists in July, asking them whether and how the weapon should be used against Japan. The options presented were:

1. Use the weapons in the manner that is from the military point of view most effective in bringing about prompt Japanese surrender at minimum cost to our armed forces.
2. Give a military demonstration in Japan, to be followed by a renewed opportunity for surrender before full use of the weapon is employed.
3. Give an experimental demonstration in this country, with representatives of Japan present, followed by a new opportunity for surrender before full use of the weapons is employed.

4. Withhold military use of the weapons, but make [a] public experimental demonstration of their effectiveness.
5. Maintain as secret as possible all development of our new weapons, and refrain
   from using them in this war.

Only 15 percent voted for number 1, while 46 percent voted for number 2, 26 percent
for number 3, 11 percent for number 4, and 2 percent for number 5. Thus 85 percent of the
scientists voted against the way the bomb would actually be employed at Hiroshima and
Nagasaki—the surprise "full use" of the bomb.

On July 13, 1945, the poll's results were transmitted to Arthur H. Compton, project
leader of the Chicago Metallurgical Laboratory. Three days later, the first atomic bomb was
exploded at Alamogordo. On July 24, in a memo to Colonel K. D. Nichols, who worked
under the Manhattan Project's director, General Leslie Groves, Compton forwarded Szilard's "A Petition Addressed to the President of the United States," dated July 17. Sixty-
seven scientists had signed.

General Groves received the petition on July 25 but held onto it until August 1, when he
finally forwarded it to Secretary of War Henry L. Stimson. Stimson was at the Big Three
meeting in Potsdam, Germany, and did not see the petition until his return later that month.

By then it was too late. Hiroshima had happened. On August 6, Szilard wrote to his close
friend and future wife, Trude Weiss: "I suppose you have seen today's newspapers. Using
atomic bombs against Japan is one of the greatest blunders of history. Both from a practical
point of view on a 10-years scale and from the point of view of our moral position. I went
out of my way (and very much so) in order to prevent it, but, as today's papers show, without success. It is very difficult to see what wise course of action is possible from here on."

While Oppenheimer, unlike Szilard, supported the deployment of the bomb in combat
against Japan, he nevertheless felt an agonizing uncertainty about the unleashing of this
"shatterer of worlds." On August 6, 1945, he received a phone call from Groves. The general said that the bomb had gone off with a "tremendous bang," and that he was glad he
had appointed Oppenheimer director of Los Alamos. In fact, Groves said, that move had
been "one of the wisest things" he had ever done. "Well," Oppenheimer replied, "I have my
doubts, General Groves." After the atomic bomb was dropped on Hiroshima, the physicist
reported having "terrible moral scruples" about the killing of 70,000 people.

On October 16, when Oppenheimer stepped down as director of the lab, the entire Los
Alamos community gathered to honor him; General Groves presented him with the secretary of war's Certificate of Appreciation. But Oppenheimer did not share the euphoria of the
moment, and even lent a somberness to the event. In a short speech he wondered how future
generations would remember the Manhattan Project: "If atomic bombs are to be added as
new weapons to the arsenals of a warring world, or to the arsenals of nations preparing for
war, then the time will come when mankind will curse the names of Los Alamos and
Hiroshima."

The bombing of Hiroshima marked a crossing to a new level of international violence, the
horror of which was not lost on atomic scientists like Szilard and even Oppenheimer. They
could have pleaded scientific neutrality, claiming that they were merely the technical creators
of the bomb, not the military and political decision makers. They could have tried to avoid
moral responsibility. But they found themselves murmuring, as did the butler Stevens in

Kazuo Ishiguro's *Remains of the Day,* upon realizing he had failed to confront the great ethical issues of World War II: "Really—one has to ask oneself—what dignity is there in that?"

THE BOMB IN POP CULTURE

Bryan C. Taylor

Although the bomb has been an enduring feature of postwar culture, most Americans have never encountered it directly. Nuclear weapons are manufactured and deployed under the strictest secrecy. They are controlled by experts using technical language and complex reasoning. And the sheer anxiety that such weapons inspire inhibits most citizens from even wanting to learn about them.

But even if we have not deliberately sought information on the bomb, we have not stopped thinking about it, and popular culture reflects that. Television programs, mass-marketed fiction, and Hollywood films have repeatedly focused on nuclear weapons. In fact, argues the philosopher Jacques Derrida, it could not have been any other way. Because full-scale nuclear war has not happened, and could not be recorded if it did, stories of the bomb are mostly all that we have—symbols without a "real" referent (we keep hoping). Looking back on these cultural artifacts, we can see the shock, fantasy, regret, denial, and resolve of society as it has struggled with the possibility of nuclear destruction.

That struggle has been going on longer than most Americans might think: extensive storytelling actually anticipated the development of nuclear weapons. Historian Spencer Weart has detailed how early twentieth-century audiences incorporated the discovery of radioactivity into the pre-existing cultural myth of alchemy. Americans were fascinated and horrified by the way in which matter could, through its own destruction, be converted into this strange kind of energy, and they harbored similar feelings toward the scientific elites who possessed such powerful, forbidden secrets. While popular writers of the period conjured utopian visions of inexpensive and unlimited power generated by nuclear fission, entrepreneurs exploited the primordial association between energy rays and sexuality, marketing radioactive tonics for fatigue, baldness, and impotence. But underneath this enthusiasm lay fear. H. G. Wells imagined global nuclear war in his 1914 novel *The World Set Free,* and apocalyptic visionaries of all stripes quickly took up nuclear energy as a potential cause of The End.

The 1945 atomic bombings only heightened the conflict, creating an outburst of both jubilation and anxiety. The bomb decisively concluded a long and bitter war, but according to Weart, it also disrupted "the delicate balance by which people in normal times manage to live with the knowledge of their mortality." It was not simply the scale of damage at Hiroshima and Nagasaki that produced this dread; indeed, as defenders of the bomb argued, the firebombings of Dresden and Tokyo produced a greater level of devastation. Rather, what disturbed people was the frightening efficiency of destruction inherent in nuclear-weapons technology—the ability to wipe out whole cities in an instant. As philosophers and religious leaders debated the implications of nuclear weapons—and as defense analysts both predicted their development by other governments and acknowledged the impossibility of defending against them—the nation shuddered.

Eruptions of Fear

The mass media quickly moved to assist Americans in assimilating the bomb, and nuclear technology in general, as a necessary, positive, and "natural" presence. The propagandistic tone of what emerged suggests that government interests had an influence as well. William Laurence of the *New York Times,* for example, described nuclear weapons and test explosions in mythical and supernatural terms—as awesome, "titanic" forces from "the heavens" reflecting "the power of the Almighty"; such descriptions deflected questions about human responsibility that might have leaped out at readers if the writing had been more matter of fact. Curious moviegoers were treated to a spate of melodramatic, pseudo-documentary reenactments of the top-secret Manhattan Project, including *The Beginning or the End,* which featured a young scientist who resolves his moral doubts about working on the bomb through patriotic rationalizations.

As historian Paul Boyer has argued, the campaign to normalize nuclear weapons was not entirely successful, however. The decade between 1953 and 1963 saw an outpouring of works that were anything but reassuring. Writers and filmmakers not wholly preoccupied with reaching a mass audience recovered their artistic voices to evoke the existential dread of postnuclear contamination, as reflected in the novel *On the Beach* and the film of the same name. Popular culture also carried nuclear-psychological freight. Susan Sontag has observed that the "radiated monster" films of this period, such as *The Beast from 20,000 Fathoms,* reflected the public's anxiety about the biological effects of ionizing radiation, the monsters functioning as symbols of a mutated postnuclear humanity. Ironically, these films often showed the monsters created by radiation finally being defeated with nuclear weapons. It was as if the symbolic eruptions of nuclear fear could be disciplined only by the technology that had caused them in the first place.

The surge of nightmarish images declined temporarily after the 1963 signing of the atmospheric test-ban treaty. Antinuclear sentiment, like nuclear testing itself, went underground—only to resurface in the early 1980s in reaction to renewed Cold War tensions during Ronald Reagan's first term. Literature such as Jonathan Schell's *The Fate of the Earth,* television dramas such as *The Day After,* and films such as *Testament* aimed to frighten people into opposing the arms race by depicting a desperate, bleak, and violent postnuclear landscape.

Yet not all pop-culture genres appeared to dread the prospect of such a world. Macho pulp-fiction series like *The Survivalist* portrayed bands of hard men roaming the same landscape and recovering the Cold War, armed combat, and primitive heterosexuality from the ashes of feminism and the liberal welfare state. This fantastic denial of postnuclear realities, argue critics such as William Chaloupka, Robert Mielke, and James William Gibson, reflected the insecurity of the American male warrior—whose traditional battlefield heroism had been supplanted by nuclear weapons.

Still other kinds of works have arrived on the scene since 1989, when the apparent end of the Cold War confused both American foreign policy and popular culture. An emerging impulse toward seeing nuclear history in new ways was displayed in the 1989 film *Fat Man and Little Boy,* which showed Manhattan Project officials at odds with the nuclear scientists in their employ, suppressing ethical dissent among them to produce a weapon whose military effect was redundant. At the same time, ambivalence about the possibility of national security without nuclear weapons was manifested in the 1989 film *The Package,* in which renegade U.S. and Soviet military officers conspire to prevent the signing of an arms-control treaty because they are certain that it will lead to conventional warfare between their nations.

In more recent years, films and novels with scenarios based on destabilized post-Cold War politics have become popular. These newly fashionable thrillers center on the theft of nuclear materials and weapons by various ethnic, nationalist, and separatist groups. The result is either nuclear terrorism and blackmail, as in Steven Seagal's *Under Siege* and Tom Clancy's *Ops Center,* or an accidental or unauthorized use of nuclear might that threatens the fragile post-Cold War peace, as in *Crimson Tide.*

As the post-Cold War world evolves, spawning new concerns, we can count on nuclear popular culture to evolve with it, mirroring those concerns in works that feel both timely and familiar, stocked with predictably heroic characters and well-worn plot devices. If we have made peace with nuclear weapons, it is an uneasy peace at best. The bomb is, in Weart's words, "a symbol for the worst of modernity," and for just that reason it will continue to form a screen onto which we project our assorted and everchanging conflicts.

KEEP THE BOMB

Alex Roland

A Marine Corps major in the late 1970s decorated the door of his office at the Pentagon with a poster trumpeting "Ban the Bomb!" Barely visible at the bottom margin was the riposte: "Make the World Safe for Conventional War."

The poster was intended to be funny. Its premise, however, is not. With the world's major military powers paralyzed in a nuclear balance of terror, conventional war between them—the large-scale, mechanized, resource-intensive campaigning made familiar by the two world wars—has become unthinkable, lest it escalate into nuclear war. The result has been a far more peaceful world over the last 50 years than the one that surely would have existed without nuclear weapons. They have done more good than harm in the world.

Those of us who lived through the Cold War are not accustomed to thinking of nuclear weapons in these terms. Especially in the 1950s, when the insanity of the Cold War was at its peak, just the opposite seemed likely. Atmospheric testing of nuclear weapons poisoned the air. Khrushchev threatened to bury us. In response, we prepared to bury ourselves in bomb shelters. The besetting question about nuclear war was not if, but when.

And the danger was real. At the climax of the Cold War, during the Cuban Missile Crisis of 1962, the superpowers came closer than ever before or since to unleashing their nuclear arsenals.

To those who formed their opinions about nuclear weapons during this early and dangerous era, nuclear weapons seemed likely to kill more people than any other technology in human history. Happily, such a cataclysm has never occurred. Instead, consider how many deaths have been *prevented* by nuclear weapons. An ever-growing body of evidence suggests that the number of people whose lives have been saved by nuclear weapons reaches into the hundreds of millions.

Through most of human history, death in war has been constant, horrible, and scant. Harvard sociologist Pitirim Sorokin estimated that war casualties in the Roman empire ranged from .07 percent to .36 percent of the empire's population. By comparison, the Soviet Union lost an estimated 14 percent of its population in World War II.

The reason that ancient warfare did not wipe out more people was not human kindness but limited technology. Killing was simply a labor-intensive enterprise. Virtually all deaths in combat came from sword stroke, spear thrust, or the discharge of some muscle-powered missile. Fights to the death were the exception rather than the rule. Armies losing ground in an engagement would more often flee than fight; victors seldom had the energy or the will to hunt them down. Even in naval warfare, where the sinking of a ship held out promise of mass casualties, most battles were decided by boarding, hand-to-hand combat, and the capture of prisoners. Humans were surely bloody in tooth and claw, but their reach was limited.

Two revolutions broke through this ceiling. The invention of gunpowder in the late Middle Ages allowed soldiers and sailors to kill their enemies at greater distance and in greater numbers. In her book *World Military and Social Expenditures,* Ruth Sivard, former chief of the economics division of the U.S. Arms Control and Disarmament Agency, has compared global war casualties over the past five centuries. Her research shows that with the aid of gunpowder, worldwide deaths in warfare quadrupled from an estimated 1.5 million during the sixteenth century to 6.2 million during the seventeenth.

Worse still, the Industrial Revolution mechanized warfare, further expanding its reach. Vast quantities of weapons could now be produced to supply armies of unprecedented size. Inventions such as the steamboat, railroad, and telegraph allowed those armies to be transported around the globe, resupplied for indefinite campaigns, and directed from afar in their grisly business. According to Sivard, global deaths caused by war increased from 6.4 million during the eighteenth century to 20 million in the nineteenth.

And the power to kill has continued to grow exponentially. The twentieth century has the grim distinction of being the most deadly in human history, with approximately 103 million war-related deaths so far. The first half of the century and the world wars that scarred it may be seen as the culmination of the gunpowder and industrial revolutions.

But after the mid-century mark, things change. According to Sivard's calculations, 84 percent of the casualties from war in this century occurred before 1950. Moreover, the ratio of casualties to world population is now decreasing. By the latter measure, the rate of war-related deaths in the second half of the twentieth century is one-tenth that in the first half, lower than in the second half of the nineteenth century, and almost as low as in the first half of the nineteenth century.

The world has not been this safe since 1850. And the peace holds. The so-called proxy wars, in which the superpowers armed and aided the protagonists—Korea, Vietnam, Angola—have subsided. Certainly conventional armed conflict has persisted in the form of the Falklands War, the Iran-Iraq War, the Gulf War, and the war in Bosnia, but these remain localized conflicts with relatively limited casualties. It is hard to imagine an approaching cataclysm on the trajectory set up by the Napoleonic Wars, our Civil War, and the two world wars.

Had there been conventional war in the second half of the twentieth century on the scale seen in the first half, we could have expected more war deaths than occurred throughout recorded history up to the twentieth century—and more than piled up in the two world wars combined. Extrapolating from Sivard's figures, we can reasonably project that another world war, say in the decade of the 1980s, could have killed 250 million people—5 percent of the world population—even if the combatants used only conventional weapons.

Since Sivard calculates that some 17 million people died in war between 1949 and 1990, we might conclude that more than 230 million people have been spared from the trajectory of death laid out by the Industrial Revolution and the world wars. Those people lived because of nuclear weapons.

With the advent of nuclear weapons, humans finally succeeded in devising an instrument of war so terrible that other means had to be found to settle political conflicts. Surely there has been no lack of conflict. Surely man's inhumanity to man is still a potent force in world affairs. Surely the United Nations and other institutions of collective security have proven ineffective. Yet the fear of conflict in many cases has become more powerful than the forces of conflict themselves.

Throughout the seventeenth, eighteenth, and nineteenth centuries, visionaries as disparate as John Donne and Robert Fulton hoped that cannons, ships, and other artifacts of humanity's triumph over nature would make war too horrible to pursue. But only in the desert of New Mexico, in the summer of 1945, did the scientists and engineers of the Manhattan Project finally realize that goal. J. Robert Oppenheimer looked at the result of their labors and feared, "Now I have become death." For the victims of Hiroshima and Nagasaki, his fears proved true enough. But the legacy of that bomb has been life for hundreds of millions of people.

What reason is there to think that, in the absence of these terrible weapons, there would have been conventional war on such a massive scale? At no time in human history have two major powers, divided by ideology and ambition and united by proximity and conflicting interests, resisted the temptation to settle their differences on the battlefield. The rhetoric of the Cold War, and the huge conventional military forces amassed by both sides, give every reason to suspect that without nuclear weapons there would have been a World War III by now. Perhaps it would have come during one of the Berlin crises, or the Korean or Vietnam wars, or one of the countless other confrontations between East and West. But come it would have.

Still, it may be argued, the success of nuclear weapons in preventing World War III is hardly grounds for believing that these horrendous instruments have not posed—and do not still pose—a threat to humanity that entirely outweighs the fragile peace they have so far forced upon us. What about proliferation? What about the possibility of terrorists brandishing these weapons on the world stage? What about the argument of Admiral Noel Gaylor (a cold warrior turned peace activist) that these weapons, like all others in human history, will be used eventually—and with results that will obliterate the transient gains of the last 40 years?

Predictions of the imminent use of nuclear weapons have been made since 1946, and all have proven false. The darkest forecasts accompanied China's acquisition of nuclear weapons in the 1960s. But Mao and his successors have been true to their promise to use nuclear weapons only to ensure that China would not be attacked. Indeed, unlike the other major powers, China does not rattle the nuclear sabre.

Six to twelve nations now possess nuclear weapons, and the technology is within the reach of many more states and even some terrorist groups. Yet none has used them; most have foregone even developing them. The record grows stronger every year.

And what if nuclear weapons were to be used again? What if, for example, India and Pakistan—widely regarded as having nuclear weapons or the capacity to acquire them—

drove each other, *in extremis,* to push the button? The casualties would surely be horrendous, but they would amount to only a fraction of the number that would have been killed by now without nuclear weapons.

The argument made here is not new. Historian Bruce Mazlish made a similar case in the 1960s; so have political scientists Kenneth Waltz and John Mearsheimer. But all of them wrote during the Cold War, too close to the event for their ideas to win broad acceptance.

Now the Cold War is over. What it has wrought may finally be viewed without the passions bred by fear. The great bloodletting engendered by the Industrial Revolution has peaked. We need to acknowledge this blessing and preserve the relative peace that it has brought—even if the price of peace is to live in apprehension, even dread, of our own capabilities for destruction.

Keep the bomb. Save the world from conventional war.

A BAN ON NUCLEAR TECHNOLOGIES

Theodore B. Taylor

For an instant after the Nagasaki bomb was detonated, an amount of energy equivalent to 20 million kilograms of dynamite resided in a sphere of plutonium no bigger than a baseball and weighing about 6 kilograms. Today, more than 400 nuclear power plants operating in 30 countries automatically produce, as part of the fission process, about 70,000 kilograms of plutonium annually. The world's inventory of plutonium produced in nuclear reactors now totals about 1 million kilograms, nearly five times the amount produced for the world's nuclear weapons. This so-called reactor-grade plutonium can be used for making a wide variety of nuclear weapons, as well as for making relatively crude, easily transportable nuclear explosives that could be used by terrorists.

To be used in nuclear weapons, the plutonium must first be chemically separated from the other materials in the spent reactor fuel, but the technology for doing this has been widely accessible for decades. Although most nonmilitary plutonium is contained within stored spent uranium fuel awaiting decisions in some 30 countries about how to dispose of it, roughly 200,000 kilograms of plutonium has already been separated because some nations expect eventually to use it as a component of reactor fuel.

Most of the world's nuclear power plants require low-enrichment uranium—composed of only 3 or 4 percent of the isotope U-235, rather than the highly enriched material used in weapons. But the enrichment plants that produce low-enrichment uranium can also be used to increase enrichment to nuclear-weapon grade. There are many different possible technical approaches to uranium enrichment and this technology is also proliferating rapidly.

Through their bomb programs, nuclear-weapon states have accumulated more than 1 million kilograms of highly enriched uranium (HEU). While this material has only rarely been used in nuclear power plants, large quantities have been diverted to R&D purposes. The world's inventory of nonmilitary HEU is now about 20,000 kilograms—enough for more than 2,000 nuclear warheads. Possession of bomb quantities of this material is by no means restricted to the announced nuclear-weapon states.

The time and resources needed to make the transition from latent to active production of nuclear weapons can be very small. Secret design and testing of non-nuclear components of nuclear warheads can allow a nation, or possibly a terrorist group, to build deliverable nuclear weapons in months, or even days, after acquiring a few kilograms or more of the key nuclear-weapon materials.

Combatants can also turn nuclear power facilities into nuclear weapons that release huge quantities of radioactive materials by bombing them or through sabotage. Bombing operating nuclear power plants or a facility for storing high-level radioactive waste from many reactors may represent the extreme upper limit of death and environmental chaos from violence initiated by small numbers of people.

I am convinced that the connection between nuclear weapons and nuclear power is so strong that all technologies for releasing energy from fission chain reactions should be rapidly phased out and then globally banned. I would also end further attempts to develop power plants based on nuclear fusion, since they could be used or modified to make neutrons very cheaply, which can then be used to produce cheap plutonium.

I do not propose to ban basic nuclear research or medical use of radioactive materials, provided such uses do not require materials that can sustain an explosive nuclear chain reaction. All radioisotopes that satisfy this condition could be provided by particle accelerators kept under close international scrutiny to ensure that they are not used to produce nuclear-weapon materials.

The major focus of global nuclear abolition, then, would be to ban any undisclosed possession or production of plutonium or enriched uranium. Stockpiles of these materials could be kept under international safeguards—awaiting final, irretrievable disposal—to prevent diversion, theft, sabotage, or accidents.

If nuclear power is phased out within a decade or two, how can the world make up for this loss of energy? The environmental consequences of continuing to rely on fossil fuels as the world's main source of commercial energy are unresolved, including continued controversy about climatic instabilities enhanced by large releases of carbon dioxide. Fortunately, two attractive options for shifting global energy use away from fossil and nuclear fuels already exist: reducing demand by using energy much more efficiently, and shifting to locally appropriate, renewable forms of energy derived, directly or indirectly, from sunlight.

Efforts to conserve energy in buildings, industries, and transport vehicles are proving cost-effective even on relatively short time scales. Other technologies that show great promise in the near term, to name only a few, include wind power, algal ponds for converting sunlight to plant fuels, and pumped hydroelectric power to help meet energy demand at times of the day or year when levels of incident sunlight for solar electric cells are relatively low. Meanwhile, research is thriving on techniques for harnessing the sun to split water molecules to make hydrogen. The hydrogen can be used directly as a fuel or to increase production of other fuels such as methanol from biomass. Skeptics may ask whether communities can spare the space required to move to a solar-energy world. But at an overall average efficiency of 15 percent for converting incident solar radiation to some form of primary energy, less than 0.4 percent of the world's land area could supply present total energy demand.

The benefits of intensive, cooperative, worldwide action in response to these opportunities could be universal, huge, and prompt. Humankind now has the chance, perhaps for only a brief period, to reject the cosmic energy first released massively 50 years ago—energy that can much more easily be used to destroy than to build—and embrace the energy from our sun, which has, for a very long time, sustained all life on earth.

REVISITING SOLAR POWER'S PAST

Charles Smith

INTRODUCTION

In response to two oil embargoes imposed by OPEC (the Organization of Petroleum Exporting Countries) and the subsequent energy crisis of the 1970s, western nations began seriously to explore so-called alternative energy sources and innovative power technologies. Among these were synthetic fuels, biofuels, hydrogen, oil shale, and a wide array of technologies designed to harness the power of wind, water, and sun. Many commentators at the time discerned what they thought was a turning point in American history. Rather than exploiting a seemingly endless supply of fossil fuels, Americans would now, out of necessity, be forced to turn to renewable energy sources. The results would be beneficial in two ways: the nation would gain complete energy independence and be insulated from the economic consequences of international political unrest; and the country would at long last be firmly committed to cleaner, more environmentally friendly energy technologies. It appeared to be a "win-win" situation.

It turned out to be very different. The opening of new petroleum reserves and dissension among its membership weakened the power of OPEC, and the price of oil plummeted in the 1980s. Most alternative energy technologies became prohibitively expensive and commercially infeasible. Regulatory agencies, if not openly hostile to alternative energy technologies, lacked the support of the nation's political leadership and failed to develop imaginative programs intended to deal with long-range energy requirements. As long as gasoline and fuel oil were plentiful and cheap, Americans generally lost interest in seeking ways to reduce the nation's growing dependence on petroleum imports.

Usually thought of as exotic and totally impractical outside of a few specialized applications, solar power has, for nearly a century, been one of the most highly touted alternative energy technologies. First introduced in the 1860s by engineers who worried that the West would run out of coal, solar power matured to the point that by 1914, most of its technical problems had been overcome. It appeared only to be a matter of time before the commercial development of solar power brought its costs down and allowed it to compete with fossil fuels as a major source of energy. But World War I intervened, and after the war vast new sources of petroleum in the Middle East rendered solar power totally uneconomical.

Readers need to ask themselves why this technology failed. Was it due to shortcomings in the technology itself, or were external, nontechnical factors to blame? The answer may be surprising, for there was nothing inherently wrong with the technology. Solar power works. Its failure, instead, has everything to do with influences beyond technology, among them political and regulatory forces and public attitudes toward energy and the environment. Unless solar power and other alternative energy technologies enjoy widespread popular understanding and support, it appears nothing short of war or a comparable national emergency is likely to turn us away from burning greater and greater quantities of coal and oil.

Many of us assume that the nation's first serious push to develop renewable fuels was spawned while angry Americans waited in gas lines during the "energy crisis" of the 1970s. Held hostage by the OPEC oil embargo, the country suddenly seemed receptive to warnings from scientists, environmentalists, and even a few politicians to end its overreliance on finite coal and oil reserves or face severe economic distress and political upheaval. But efforts to design and construct devices for supplying renewable energy actually began some 100 years before that turbulent time—ironically, at the very height of the Industrial Revolution, which was largely founded on the promise of seemingly inexhaustible supplies of fossil fuels. Contrary to the prevailing opinion of the day, a number of engineers questioned the practice of an industrial economy based on nonrenewable energy and worried about what the world's nations would do after exhausting the fuel supply.

More important, many of these visionaries did not just provide futuristic rhetoric but actively explored almost all the renewable energy options familiar today. In the end, most decided to focus on solar power, reasoning that the potential rewards outweighed the technical barriers. In less than 50 years, these pioneers developed an impressive array of innovative techniques for capturing solar radiation and using it to produce the steam that powered the machines of that era. In fact, just before World War I, they had outlined all of the solar thermal conversion methods now being considered. Unfortunately, despite their technical successes and innovative designs, their work was largely forgotten for the next 50 years in the rush to develop fossil fuels for an energy-hungry world.

Now, a century later, history is repeating itself. After following the same path as the early inventors—in some cases reinventing the same techniques—contemporary solar engineers have arrived at the same conclusion: solar power is not only possible but eminently practical, not to mention more environmentally friendly. Alas, once again, just as the technology has proven itself from a practical standpoint, public support for further development and implementation is eroding, and solar power could yet again be eclipsed by conventional energy technologies.

THE FIRST SOLAR MOTOR

The earliest known record of the direct conversion of solar radiation into mechanical power belongs to Auguste Mouchout, a mathematics instructor at the Lycée de Tours. Mouchout began his solar work in 1860 after expressing grave concerns about his country's dependence on coal. "It would be prudent and wise not to fall asleep regarding this quasi-security," he wrote. "Eventually industry will no longer find in Europe the resources to satisfy its prodigious expansion. Coal will undoubtedly be used up. What will industry do then?" By the following year he was granted the first patent for a motor running on solar power and continued to improve his design until about 1880. During this period the inventor laid the foundation for our modern understanding of converting solar radiation into mechanical steam power.

Mouchout's initial experiments involved a glass-enclosed iron cauldron: incoming solar radiation passed through the glass cover, and the trapped rays transmitted heat to the water. While this simple arrangement boiled water, it was of little practical value because the quantities and pressures of steam it produced were minimal. However, Mouchout soon discovered that by adding a reflector to concentrate additional radiation onto the cauldron, he could generate more steam. In late 1865, he succeeded in using his apparatus to operate a small, conventional steam engine.

By the following summer, Mouchout displayed his solar motor to Emperor Napoleon III in Paris. The monarch, favorably impressed, offered financial assistance for developing an industrial solar motor for France. With the newly acquired funds, Mouchout enlarged his invention's capacity, refined the reflector, redesigning it as a truncated cone, like a dish with slanted sides, to more accurately focus the sun's rays on the boiler. Mouchout also constructed a tracking mechanism that enabled the entire machine to follow the sun's altitude and azimuth, providing uninterrupted solar reception.

After six years of work, Mouchout exhibited his new machine in the library courtyard of his Tours home in 1872, amazing spectators. One reporter described the reflector as an inverted "mammoth lamp shade . . . coated on the inside with very thin silver leaf" and the boiler sitting in the middle as an "enormous thimble" made of blackened copper and "covered with a glass bell."

Anxious to put his invention to work, he connected the apparatus to a steam engine that powered a water pump. On what was deemed "an exceptionally hot day," the solar motor produced one-half horsepower. Mouchout reported the results and findings to the French Academy of Science. The government, eager to exploit the new invention to its fullest potential, decided that the most suitable venue for the new machine would be the tropical climes of the French protectorate of Algeria, a region blessed with almost constant sunshine and entirely dependent on coal, a prohibitively expensive commodity in the African region.

Mouchout was quickly deployed to Algeria with ample funding to construct a large solar steam engine. He first decided to enlarge his invention's capacity yet again to 100 liters (70 for water and 30 for steam) and employ a multi-tubed boiler instead of the single cauldron. The boiler tubes had a better surface-area-to-water ratio, yielding more pressure and improved engine performance.

In 1878, Mouchout exhibited the redesigned invention at the Paris Exposition. Perhaps to impress the audience or, more likely, his government backers, he coupled the steam engine to a refrigeration device. The steam from the solar motor, after being routed through a condenser, rapidly cooled the inside of a separate insulated compartment. He explained the result: "In spite of the seeming paradox of the statement, [it was] possible to utilize the rays of the sun to make ice." Mouchout was awarded a medal for his accomplishments.

By 1881 the French Ministry of Public Works, intrigued by Mouchout's machine, appointed two commissioners to assess its cost efficiency. But after some 900 observations at Montpelier, a city in southern France, and Constantine, Algeria, the government deemed the device a technical success but a practical failure. One reason was that France had recently improved its system for transporting coal and developed a better relationship with England, on which it was dependent for that commodity. The price of coal had thus dropped, rendering the need for alternatives less attractive. Unable to procure further financial assistance, Mouchout returned to his academic pursuits.

THE TOWER OF POWER

During the height of Mouchout's experimentation, William Adams, the deputy registrar for the English Crown in Bombay, India, wrote an award-winning book entitled *Solar Heat: A Substitute for Fuel in Tropical Countries*. Adams noted that he was intrigued with Mouchout's solar steam engine after reading an account of the Tours demonstration, but that the invention was impractical, since "it would be impossible to construct [a disc-shaped reflector] of much greater dimensions" to generate more than Mouchout's one-half horsepower. The problem, he felt, was that the polished metal reflector would tarnish too easily, and would be too costly to build and too unwieldy to efficiently track the sun.

Fortunately for the infant solar discipline, the English registrar did not spend all his time finding faults in the French inventor's efforts, but offered some creative solutions. For example, Adams was convinced that a reflector of flat silvered mirrors arranged in a semicircle would be cheaper to construct and easier to maintain. His plan was to build a large rack of many small mirrors and adjust each one to reflect sunlight in a specific direction. To track the sun's movement, the entire rack could be rolled around a semicircular track, projecting the concentrated radiation onto a stationary boiler. The rack could be attended by a laborer and would have to be moved only "three or four times during the day," Adams noted, or more frequently to improve performance.

Confident of his innovative arrangement, Adams began construction in late 1878. By gradually adding 17-by-10-inch flat mirrors and measuring the rising temperatures, he calculated that to generate the 1,200°F necessary to produce steam pressures high enough to operate conventional engines, the reflector would require 72 mirrors. To demonstrate the power of the concentrated radiation, Adams placed a piece of wood in the focus of the mirrored panes where, he noted, "it ignited immediately." He then arranged the collectors around a boiler, retaining Mouchout's enclosed cauldron configuration, and connected it to a 2.5-horsepower steam engine that operated during daylight hours "for a fortnight in the compound of [his] bungalow."

Eager to display his invention, Adams notified newspapers and invited his important friends—including the Army's commander in chief, a colonel from the Royal Engineers, the secretary of public works, various justices, and principal mill owners—to a demonstration. Adams wrote that all were impressed, even the local engineers who, while doubtful that solar power could compete directly with coal and wood, thought it could be a practical supplemental energy source.

Adams's experimentation ended soon after the demonstration, though, perhaps because he had achieved his goal of proving the feasibility of his basic design, but more likely because, as some say, he lacked sufficient entrepreneurial drive. Even so, his legacy of producing a powerful and versatile way to harness and convert solar heat survives. Engineers today know this design as the Power Tower concept, which is one of the best configurations for large scale, centralized solar plants. In fact, most of the modern tower-type solar plants follow Adams's basic configuration: flat or slightly curved mirrors that remain stationary or travel on a semicircular track and either reflect light upward to a boiler in a receiver tower or downward to a boiler at ground level, thereby generating steam to drive an accompanying heat engine.

COLLECTION WITHOUT REFLECTION

Even with Mouchout's abandonment and the apparent disenchantment of England's sole participant, Europe continued to advance the practical application of solar heat, as the torch returned to France and engineer Charles Tellier. Considered by many the father of refrigeration, Tellier actually began his work in refrigeration as a result of his solar experimentation, which led to the design of the first nonconcentrating, or nonreflecting, solar motor.

In 1885, Tellier installed a solar collector on his roof similar to the flat-plate collectors placed atop many homes today for heating domestic water. The collector was composed of ten plates, each consisting of two iron sheets riveted together to form a watertight seal, and connected by tubes to form a single unit. Instead of filling the plates with water to produce steam, Tellier chose ammonia as a working fluid because of its significantly lower boiling point. After solar exposure, the containers emitted enough pressurized ammonia gas to power a water pump he had placed in his well at the rate of some 300 gallons per hour during daylight. Tellier considered his solar water pump practical for anyone with a south-facing roof. He also thought that simply adding plates, thereby increasing the size of the system, would make industrial applications possible.

By 1889 Tellier had increased the efficiency of the collectors by enclosing the top with glass and insulating the bottom. He published the results in *The Elevation of Water with the Solar Atmosphere,* which included details on his intentions to use the sun to manufacture ice. Like his countryman Mouchout, Tellier envisioned that the large expanses of the African plains could become industrially and agriculturally productive through the implementation of solar power.

In *The Peaceful Conquest of West Africa,* Tellier argued that a consistent and readily available supply of energy would be required to power the machinery of industry before the French holdings in Africa could be properly developed. He also pointed out that even though the price of coal had fallen since Mouchout's experiments, fuel continued to be a significant expense in French operations in Africa. He therefore concluded that the construction costs of his low-temperature, nonconcentrating solar motor were low enough to justify its implementation. He also noted that his machine was far less costly than Mouchout's device, with its dish-shaped reflector and complicated tracking mechanism.

Yet despite this potential, Tellier evidently decided to pursue his refrigeration interests instead, and do so without the aid of solar heat. Most likely the profits from conventionally operated refrigerators proved irresistible. Also, much of the demand for the new cooling technology now stemmed from the desire to transport beef to Europe from North and South

America. The rolling motion of the ships combined with space limitations precluded the use of solar power altogether. And as Tellier redirected his focus, France saw the last major development of solar mechanical power on her soil until well into the twentieth century. Most experimentation in the fledgling discipline crossed the Atlantic to that new bastion of mechanical ingenuity, the United States.

THE PARABOLIC TROUGH

Though Swedish by birth, John Ericsson was one of the most influential and controversial U.S. engineers of the nineteenth century. While he spent his most productive years designing machines of war—his most celebrated accomplishment was the Civil War battleship the *Monitor*—he dedicated the last 20 years of his life largely to more peaceful pursuits such as solar power. This work was inspired by a fear shared by virtually all of his fellow solar inventors that coal supplies would someday end. In 1868 he wrote, "A couple of thousand years dropped in the ocean of time will completely exhaust the coal fields of Europe, unless, in the meantime, the heat of the sun be employed."

Thus by 1870 Ericsson had developed what he claimed to be the first solar-powered steam engine, dismissing Mouchout's machine as "a mere toy." In truth, Ericsson's first designs greatly resembled Mouchout's devices, employing a conical, dish-shaped reflector that concentrated solar radiation onto a boiler and a tracking mechanism that kept the reflector directed toward the sun.

Though unjustified in claiming his design original, Ericsson soon did invent a novel method for collecting solar rays—the parabolic trough. Unlike a true parabola, which focuses solar radiation onto a single, relatively small area, or focal point, like a satellite television dish, a parabolic trough is more akin to an oil drum cut in half lengthwise that focuses solar rays in a line across the open side of the reflector.

This type of reflector offered many advantages over its circular (dish-shaped) counterparts: it was comparatively simple, less expensive to construct, and, unlike a circular reflector, had only to track the sun in a single direction (up and down, if lying horizontal, or east to west if standing on end), thus eliminating the need for complex tracking machinery. The downside was that the device's temperatures and efficiencies were not as high as with a dish-shaped reflector, since the configuration spread radiation over a wider area—a line rather than a point. Still, when Ericsson constructed a single linear boiler (essentially a pipe), placed it in the focus of the trough, positioned the new arrangement toward the sun, and connected it to a conventional steam engine, he claimed the machine ran successfully, though he declined to provide power ratings.

The new collection system became popular with later experimenters and eventually became a standard for modern plants. In fact, the largest solar systems in the last decade have opted for Ericsson's parabolic trough reflector because it strikes a good engineering compromise between efficiency and ease of operation.

For the next decade, Ericsson continued to refine his invention, trying lighter materials for the reflector and simplifying its construction. By 1888, he was so confident of his design's practical performance that he planned to mass-produce and supply the apparatus to the "owners of the sunburnt lands on the Pacific coast" for agricultural irrigation.

Unfortunately for the struggling discipline, Ericsson died the following year. And because he was a suspicious and, some said, paranoid man who kept his designs to himself until he filed patent applications, the detailed plans for his improved sun motor died with him. Nevertheless, the search for a practical solar motor was not abandoned. In fact, the experimentation and development of large-scale solar technology was just beginning.

THE FIRST COMMERCIAL VENTURE

Boston resident Aubrey Eneas began his solar motor experimentation in 1892, formed the first solar power company (The Solar Motor Co.) in 1900, and continued his work until 1905. One of his first efforts resulted in a reflector much like Ericsson's early parabolic trough. But Eneas found that it could not attain sufficiently high temperatures, and, unable to unlock his predecessor's secrets, decided to scrap the concept altogether and return to Mouchout's truncated-cone reflector. Unfortunately, while Mouchout's approach resulted in higher temperatures, Eneas was still dissatisfied with the machine's performance. His solution was to make the bottom of the reflector's truncated cone-shaped dish larger by designing its sides to be more upright to focus radiation onto a boiler that was 50 percent larger.

Finally satisfied with the results, he decided to advertise his design by exhibiting it in sunny Pasadena, Calif., at Edwin Cawston's ostrich farm, a popular tourist attraction. The monstrous machine did not fail to attract attention. Its reflector, which spanned 33 feet in diameter, contained 1,788 individual mirrors. And its boiler, which was about 13 feet in length and a foot wide, held 100 gallons of water. After exposure to the sun, Eneas's device boiled the water and transferred steam through a flexible pipe to an engine that pumped 1,400 gallons of water per minute from a well onto the arid California landscape.

Not everyone grasped the concept. In fact, one man thought the solar machine had something to do with the incubation of ostrich eggs. But Eneas's marketing savvy eventually paid off. Despite the occasional misconceptions, thousands who visited the farm left convinced that the sun machine would soon be a fixture in the sunny Southwest. Moreover, many regional newspapers and popular-science journals sent reporters to the farm to cover the spectacle. To Frank Millard, a reporter for the brand new magazine *World's Work,* the potential of solar motors placed in quantity across the land inspired futuristic visions of a region "where oranges may be growing, lemons yellowing, and grapes purpling, under the glare of the sun which, while it ripens the fruits it will also water and nourish them." He also predicted that the potential for this novel machine was not limited to irrigation: "If the sun motor will pump water, it will also grind grain and saw lumber and run electric cars."

The future, like the machine itself, looked bright and shiny. In 1903 Eneas, ready to market his solar motor, moved his Boston-based company to Los Angeles, closer to potential customers. By early the following year he had sold his first complete system for $2,160 to Dr. A. J. Chandler of Mesa, Arizona. Unfortunately, after less than a week, the rigging supporting the heavy boiler weakened during a windstorm and collapsed, sending it tumbling into the reflector and damaging the machine beyond repair.

But Eneas, accustomed to setbacks, decided to push onward and constructed another solar pump near Tempe, Arizona. Seven long months later, in the fall of 1904, John May, a rancher in Wilcox, Arizona, bought another machine for $2,500. Unfortunately, shortly afterward, it was destroyed by a hailstorm. This second weather-related incident all but proved that the massive parabolic reflector was too susceptible to the turbulent climactic conditions of the desert southwest. And unable to survive on such measly sales, the company soon folded.

Though the machine did not become a fixture as Eneas had hoped, the inventor contributed a great deal of scientific and technical data about solar heat conversion and initiated more than his share of public exposure. Despite his business failure, the lure of limitless fuel was strong, and while Eneas and the Solar Motor Company were suspending their operations, another solar pioneer was just beginning his.

MOONLIGHT OPERATION

Henry E. Willsie began his solar motor construction a year before Eneas's company folded. In his opinion, the lessons of Mouchout, Adams, Ericsson, and Eneas proved the cost inefficiency of high-temperature, concentrating machines. He was convinced that a nonreflective, lower-temperature collection system similar to Tellier's invention was the best method for directly utilizing solar heat. The inventor also felt that a solar motor would never be practical unless it could operate around the clock. Thus thermal storage, a practice that lent itself to low-temperature operation, was the focus of his experimentation.

To store the sun's energy, Willsie built large flat-plate collectors that heated hundreds of gallons of water, which he kept warm all night in a huge insulated basin. He then submerged a series of tubes or vaporizing pipes, inside the base to serve as boilers. When the acting medium—Willsie preferred sulfur dioxide to Tellier's ammonia—passed through the pipes and transformed into a high-pressure vapor, which passed to the engine, operated it, and exhausted into a condensing tube, where it cooled, returned to a liquid state, and was reused.

In 1904, confident that his design would produce continuous power, he built two plants, a 6-horsepower facility in St. Louis, Missouri, and a 15-horsepower operation in Needles, California. And after several power trials, Willsie decided to test the storage capacity of the larger system. After darkness had fallen, he opened a valve that "allowed the solar-heated water to flow over the exchanger pipes and thus start up the engine." Willsie had created the first solar device that could operate at night using the heat gathered during the day. He also announced that the 15-horsepower machine was the most powerful arrangement constructed up to that time. Beside offering a way to provide continuous solar power production, Willsie also furnished detailed cost comparisons to justify his efforts: the solar plant exacted a two-year payback period, he claimed, an exceptional value even when compared with today's standards for alternative energy technology.

Originally, like Ericsson and Eneas before him, Willsie planned to market his device for desert irrigation. In both his later patents Willsie wrote that the invention was "designed for furnishing power for electric light and power, refrigerating and ice making, for milling and pumping at mines, and for other purposes where large amounts of power are required."

Willsie determined all that was left to do was to offer his futurist invention for sale. Unfortunately, no buyers emerged. Despite the favorable long-term cost analysis, potential customers were suspicious of the machine's durability, deterred by the high ratio of machine size to power output, and fearful of the initial investment cost of Willsie's ingenious solar power plant. His company, like others before it, disintegrated.

A CERTAIN TECHNICAL MATURITY

Despite solar power's dismal commercial failures, some proponents continued to believe that if they could find the right combination of solar technologies, the vision of a free and unlimited power source would come. Frank Shuman was one who shared that dream. But unlike most dreamers, Shuman did not have his head in the clouds. In fact, his hardheaded approach to business and his persistent search for practical solar power led him and his colleagues to construct the largest and most cost-effective machine prior to the space age. Shuman's first effort in 1906 was similar to Willsie's hot-plate collector design except that it employed ether as a working fluid instead of sulfur dioxide. The machine performed poorly, however, because even at respectable pressures, the steam—or more accurately, the vapor—exerted comparatively little force to drive a motor because of its low specific gravity.

Shuman knew he needed more heat to produce steam, but felt that using complicated reflectors and tracking devices would be too costly and prone to mechanical failure. He decided that rather than trying to generate more heat, the answer was to better conserve the heat already being absorbed.

In 1910, to improve the collector's insulation properties, Shuman enclosed the absorption plates not with a single sheet of glass but with dual panes separated by a one-inch air space. He also replaced the boiler pipes with a thin, flat metal container similar to Tellier's original greenhouse design. The apparatus could now consistently boil water rather than ether. Unfortunately, however, the pressure was still insufficient to drive industrial-size steam engines, which were designed to operate under pressures produced by hotter-burning coal or wood.

After determining that the cost of building a larger absorber would be prohibitive, Shuman reluctantly conceded that the additional heat would have to be provided through some form of concentration. He thus devised a low-cost reflector stringing together two rows of ordinary mirrors to double the amount of radiation intercepted. And in 1911, after forming the Sun Power Co., he constructed the largest solar conversion system ever built. In fact, the new plant, located near his home in Talcony, Pennsylvania, intercepted more than 10,000 square feet of solar radiation. The new arrangement increased the amount of steam produced, but still did not provide the pressure he expected.

Not easily defeated, Shuman figured that if he couldn't raise the pressure of the steam to run a conventional steam engine, he would have to redesign the engine to operate at lower pressures. So he teamed up with E. P. Haines, an engineer who suggested that more precise milling, closer tolerances in the moving components, and lighter-weight materials would do the trick. Haines was right. When the reworked engine was connected to the solar collectors, it developed 33 horsepower and drove a water pump that gushed 3,000 gallons per minute onto the Talcony soil.

Shuman calculated that the Talcony plant cost $200 per horsepower compared with the $80 of a conventionally operated coal system—a respectable figure, he pointed out, considering that the additional investment would be recouped in a few years because the fuel was free. Moreover, the fact that this figure was not initially competitive with coal or oil-fired engines in the industrial Northeast did not concern him because, like the French entrepreneurs before him, he was planning to ship the machine to the vast sunburnt regions in North Africa.

To buy property and move the machine there, new investors were solicited from England and the Sun Power Co. Ltd. was created. But with the additional financial support came stipulations. Shuman was required to let British physicist C. V. Boys review the workings of the machine and suggest possible improvements. In fact, the physicist recommended a radical change. Instead of flat mirrors reflecting the sun onto a flat-plate configuration, Boys thought that a parabolic trough focusing on a glass-encased tube would perform much better. Shuman's technical consultant A. S. E. Ackermann agreed, but added that to be effective, the trough would need to track the sun continuously. Shuman felt that his conception of a simple system was rapidly disintegrating.

Fortunately, when the machine was completed just outside of Cairo, Egypt, in 1912, Shuman's fears that the increased complexity would render the device impractical proved unfounded. The Cairo plant outperformed the Talcony model by a large margin—the machine produced 33 percent more steam and generated more than 55 horsepower—which more than offset the higher costs. Sun Power Co.'s solar pumping station offered an excellent value of $150 per horsepower, significantly reducing the payback period for solar-driven irrigation in the region. It looked as if solar mechanical power had finally developed the technical sophistication it needed to compete with coal and oil.

Unfortunately, the beginning was also the end. Two months after the final Cairo trials, Archduke Ferdinand was assassinated in the Balkans, igniting the Great War. The fighting quickly spread to Europe's colonial holdings, and the upper regions of Africa were soon engulfed. Shuman's solar irrigation plant was destroyed, the engineers associated with the project returned to their respective countries to perform war-related tasks, and Frank Shuman died before the armistice was signed.

Whether or not Shuman's device would have initiated the commercial success that solar power desperately needed, we will never know. However, the Sun Power Co. can boast a certain technical maturity by effectively synthesizing the ideas of its predecessors from the previous 50 years. The company used an absorber (though in linear form) of Tellier and Willsie, a reflector similar to Ericsson's, simple tracking mechanisms first used by Mouchout and later employed by Eneas, and combined them to operate an engine specially designed to run with solar-generated steam. In effect, Shuman and his colleagues set the standard for many of the most popular modern solar systems 50 to 60 years before the fact.

THE MOST RATIONAL SOURCE

The aforementioned solar pioneers were only the most notable inventors involved in the development of solar thermal power from 1860 to 1914. Many others contributed to the more than 50 patents and the scores of books and articles on the subject. With all this sophistication, why couldn't solar mechanical technology blossom into a viable industry? Why did the discipline take a 50-year dive before again gaining a measure of popular interest and technical attention?

First, despite the rapid advances in solar mechanical technology, the industry's future was rendered problematic by a revolution in the use and transport of fossil fuel. Oil and coal companies had established a massive infrastructure, stable markets, and ample supplies. Also, besides trying to perfect the technology, solar pioneers had the difficult task of convincing skeptics to see solar energy as something more than a curiosity. Visionary rhetoric without readily tangible results was not well received by a population accustomed to immediate gratification. Improving and adapting existing power technology, deemed less risky and more controlled, seemed to make far more sense.

Finally, the ability to implement radically new hardware requires either massive commitment or the failure of existing technology to get the job done. Solar mechanical power production in the late nineteenth and early twentieth centuries did not meet either criterion. Despite warnings from noted scientists and engineers, alternatives to what seemed like an inexhaustible fuel supply did not fit into the U.S. agenda. Unfortunately, in many ways, these antiquated sentiments remain with us today.

During the 1970s, while the OPEC nations exercised their economic power and as the environmental and "no-nuke" movements gained momentum, Americans plotted an industrial coup whose slogans were energy efficiency and renewable resources. Consequently, mechanical solar power—along with its space-age, electricity-producing sibling photovoltaics, as well as other renewable sources such as wind power—underwent a revival. And during the next two decades, solar engineers tried myriad techniques to satisfy society's need for power.

They discovered that dish-shaped reflectors akin to Mouchout's and Eneas's designs were the most efficient but also the most expensive and difficult to maintain. Low-temperature, nonconcentrating systems like Willsie's and Tellier's, though simple and less sensitive to climatic conditions, were among the least powerful and therefore suited only to small, specific tasks. Stationary reflectors like those used in Adams's device, now called Power Tower systems, offered a better solution but were still pricey and damage prone.

By the mid-1980s, contemporary solar engineers, like their industrial-revolution counterparts Ericsson and Shuman, determined that for sunny areas, tracking parabolic troughs were the best compromise because they exhibited superior cost-to-power ratios in most locations. Such efforts led engineers at the Los Angeles-based Luz Co. to construct an 80-megawatt electric power plant using parabolic trough collectors to drive steam-powered turbines. The company had already used similar designs to build nine other solar electric generation facilities, providing a total of 275 megawatts of power. In the process, Luz engineers steadily lowered the initial costs by optimizing construction techniques and taking advantage of economies of buying material in bulk to build ever-larger plants until the price dropped from 24 to 12 cents per kilowatt hour. The next, even larger plant—a 300-megawatt facility—scheduled for completion last year, promised to provide 6 to 7 cents per kilowatt hour, near the price of electricity produced by coal, oil, or nuclear technology.

Once again, as with Shuman and his team, the gap was closing. But once again these facilities would not be built. Luz, producer of more than 95 percent of the world's solar-based electricity, filed for bankruptcy in 1991. According to Newton Becker, Luz's chairman of the board, and other investors, the demise of the already meager tax credits, declining fossil fuel prices, and the bleak prospects for future assistance from both federal and state governments drove investors to withdraw from the project. As Becker concluded, "The failure of the world's largest solar electric company was not due to technological or business judgment failures but rather to failures of government regulatory bodies to recognize the economic and environmental benefits of solar thermal generating plants."

Other solar projects met with similar financial failure. For example, two plants that employed the Power Tower concept, Edison's 10-megawatt plant in Daggett, California, and a 30-megawatt facility built in Jordan performed well despite operating on a much smaller scale and without Luz's advantages of heavy initial capital investment and a lengthy trial-and-error process to improve efficiency. Still they were assessed as too costly to compete in the intense conventional fuel market.

Although some of our brightest engineers have produced some exemplary solar power designs during the last 25 years, their work reflects a disjointed solar energy policy. Had the findings of the early solar pioneers and the evolution of their machinery been more closely scrutinized, perhaps by Department of Energy officials or some other oversight committee, contemporary efforts might have focused on building a new infrastructure when social and political attitudes were more receptive to solar technology. Rather than rediscovering the technical merits of the various systems, we might have been better served by reviewing history, selecting a relatively small number of promising systems, and combining them with contemporary materials and construction techniques. Reinventing the wheel when only the direction of the cart seems suspect is certainly not the best way to reach one's destination.

While the best period to make our energy transition may have passed and though our energy future appears stable, the problems that initiated the energy crisis of the 1970s have not disappeared. Indeed, the instability of OPEC and the recent success in the Gulf War merely created an artificial sense of security about petroleum supplies.

While we should continue to develop clean, efficient petroleum and coal technology while our present supplies are plentiful, this approach should not dominate our efforts. Alternative, renewable energy technologies must eventually be implemented in tandem with their fossil-fuel counterparts. Not doing so would simply provide an excuse for maintaining the status quo and beg for economic disruption when reserves run low or political instability again erupts in oil-rich regions.

Toward that end, we must change the prevailing attitude that solar power is an infant field born out of the oil shocks and the environmental movement of the past 25 years. Such misconceptions lead many to assert that before solar power can become a viable alternative, the industry must first pay its dues with a fair share of technological evolution.

Solar technology already boasts a century of R&D, requires no toxic fuel and relatively little maintenance, is inexhaustible, and, with adequate financial support, is capable of becoming directly competitive with conventional technologies in many locations. These attributes make solar energy one of the most promising sources for many current and future energy needs. As Frank Shuman declared more than 80 years ago, it is "the most rational source of power."

THE MARVELS OF MODERN MEDICINE:
A MIXED BLESSING

Derek Humphry and Ann Wickett

INTRODUCTION

No field of modern technology has produced more marvels than medicine. With the development of such "wonder drugs" as penicillin, streptomycin, and the polio vaccine, certain infectious diseases virtually have been wiped out. Lives have been sustained or saved by the invention of such new surgical techniques as the coronary bypass and the organ transplant, and life-threatening health problems have been kept in check by ingenious new devices like the kidney dialysis machine and the heart pacemaker. The electrocardiograph, CAT and PET scanners, and other diagnostic tools have made it possible to detect problems and abnormalities before they cause real trouble. Respirators and other sophisticated health care machines can sustain life when otherwise it would end.

Advances in medicine and health care have worked to keep us and our loved ones healthy and alive longer, but at the same time many of these advances have prolonged our suffering, raised the cost of health care to a phenomenally high level, made us more dependent on the medical profession and its institutions, and raised a host of legal, ethical, moral, and religious considerations.

One of the most basic and controversial issues brought on by new medical technology, as the following selection suggests, is the dividing line between life and death. Consider the case of any patient who has no consciousness of his being but who still has vegetative functions when connected to a respirator. Is this person dead or alive? What if the patient is "brain dead," in an irreversible coma? Or consider the case of a patient who is definitely conscious but who is suffering horribly from some presently incurable and increasingly debilitating disease like Alzheimer's, AIDS, or cancer? Is it wrong to put this person to death, to perform some form of "mercy killing," if the suffering person so chooses? These are only some of the dilemmas that we now face because of our advancing medical technology.

One of the most succinct commentaries on these dilemmas and on the "mixed blessings" of our modern medical technology in general is the following chapter from a 1986 book, *The Right to Die: Understanding Euthanasia,* by Derek Humphry and Ann Wickett. While reading the chapter, it should not be hard for the reader to figure out where the authors stand on many of the controversial issues. Do the authors' opinions match up with any of your own? Does what they have to say in any way change your mind about what medicine is doing to us?

It is incontrovertible that fear of dying in the cold clutches of modern technology has given a major boost to public acceptance of voluntary euthanasia. In the days when physicians and nurses practiced the "healing arts" without the benefits of modern medicine, euthanasia was rarely requested because death came naturally and at home. When aid-in-dying was appropriate, the privacy of the domestic bedroom shielded a doctor who deliberately oversedated.

Today's doctors might correctly be defined as "body technicians." As we tend to die in health care facilities, the treating physician is likely to be one of many caring for the patient. There may well be someone of an opposite ethical viewpoint, such as a pro-life nurse, who would report a deliberate overdose (as has been done), however much that action was requested and was administered out of compassion.*

As well, many patients are connected to alarm systems which report fluctuations in body functions. Resuscitation efforts are ceaseless, and when the hapless patient dies, it is to the accompaniment of buzzers and bells.

Public education about medical treatment is so thoroughly and explicitly reported in the media that today few people are unaware of what hospital care entails. The middle-aged and the elderly, who frequently visit dying parents and loved ones in the hospital, are particularly sensitized to the process of excessive, and not always desired, treatment. The phrase most often heard by euthanasia societies is: "I have a dreadful fear of being trapped and out of self-control like my mother/father was."

It's hardly surprising, then, that one writer concluded that euthanasia is a phenomenon "created or intensified by recent advances in medical science and technology."[1] While many medical advances in diagnosis and treatment have happily saved lives and reduced suffering, in other instances they have had appalling consequences. For many patients, suffering has been prolonged by lifesaving techniques often called "heroic." Yet what is heroic about the results? Medical critic Richard Taylor described an intensive care unit he had observed:

> Rows of physiological preparations (also known as human beings) lie surrounded by an astounding array of mechanical gadgetry. A tube or catheter of some description violates every natural orifice, and perforations in various parts of the body are made especially for the placement of others. Multi-colored fluid is pumped in, similar fluid drains out, respirators sigh, dialysers hum, monitors twitch, oxygen bubbles through humidifiers. The unfortunate hostages, mercifully unresponsive to their environment (either through natural causes or drugs), lie silent while their ritual desecration takes place.[2]

For lives saved by such aggressive technology, for lives whose usefulness is restored, unquestionably the pain and discomfort are worthwhile. But why should those people with

---

* This was the case with Dr. Vincent Montemarano, for example, who was charged with murdering a patient in 1973. In 1981 a nurse reported Drs. Barber and Nedjl, who were subsequently charged with murder and wrongful termination of life in California. In August 1985 a nurse called a patient abuse hotline when she became suspicious about a patient's sudden decline. Later, the physician, John Kraai, was charged with murder.

no chance of recovery be subjected to such treatment? When is it appropriate to refuse aggressive measures? When is it appropriate to withdraw such "heroic" efforts?

Before the twentieth century, little was written about the care of the dying. The absence of antibiotics, chemotherapeutic agents, and sophisticated medical procedures made illness more likely to be deadly than it is today. Certainly, death then was more swift. Yet in just a few decades, technological advances in medicine have dramatically transformed this situation. Infectious diseases, once life-threatening, have become reversible, while degenerative and chronic diseases have become the predominant causes of death.

By the 1950s, technological wizardry had come to the forefront with stunning results. In that decade, for example, an artificial breathing technique was developed for polio victims, as well as the cardiopulmonary bypass machine and coronary angiography. Such breakthroughs were considered miraculous by most people, both lay and medical. The 1960s saw even greater medical progress: Renal dialysis, organ transplants, cardiac valve prostheses, external cardiac massage, coronary care units, and nonsurgical life supports were all in use. Computerized axial tomography (CAT) scanners were developed in the 1970s.

A decade later, CAT's successor, the Nuclear Magnetic Resonance Imager, and the artificial heart made their way into medical use.[3] Such developments have influenced the care of the sick and dying and saved many lives. In cases in which they have not been able to prevent death, they have changed the manner in which it occurs—for better or, in some instances, worse.

Medical technology has been defined by the Office of Technological Assessment as: "The drugs, devices and medical surgical procedures used in medical care, and the organizational and supportive systems within which such care is provided."[4] This definition includes diagnostic therapies (e.g., the CAT scan), preventive measures such as polio vaccines, therapeutic treatments (chemotherapy), administrative aids (computers), and supportive or ancillary technologies like more effective hospital beds.

In fact, there is a kind of hierarchy of technologies, depending upon their relative effectiveness. Physician and writer Lewis Thomas categorized each of these by the degree of understanding medical science has of the disease process. His categories fit on a continuum, from having little understanding of the disease to having a complete understanding—and thus the ability to deal effectively with it. For instance, "high" technologies, such as antibiotics and vaccines, fall into the latter category. On the other hand, nontechnological procedures are generally regarded as supportive care or reassurance. In essence, they are not technology as such but a part of patient care, the kind that doctors give patients with intractable cancer—supportive therapies and other soothing techniques that help patients endure the course of their disease until they die.

"Halfway" technologies are efforts to compensate for the incapacitating effects of certain diseases whose course the physician is unable to do very much about. As Thomas explained, their purpose is to "make up for disease, or to postpone death."[5] Examples of halfway technologies are artificial organs, such as hemodialysis and the artificial heart, transplanted organs, and chemotherapy. Such measures are used when there is limited information about the ailment. The main objective is to ease discomfort and to keep the patient functioning, rather than to necessarily arrest the disease.

Yet it is the halfway technologies that are often the most debatable, since in some instances they lead to an undesired level of functioning. In the 1950s, for example, polio could be treated only with an iron lung. Fortunately, polio today is understood and controllable with a vaccine, an example of high technology. But questions remain, like those raised by Gertrude Morrow, a victim of polio in 1952. She must live her life as she has done for the last thirty-three years, dependent on a respirator and a motorized wheelchair. While she manages to lead an active life, she is sure that, should she suffer a heart attack or stroke, she does not want to be resuscitated. "Living a life more limited would be very difficult," she says.[6]

Still, Gertrude Morrow has adjusted fairly well to her life, depending on a halfway technology. Others are not as fortunate. A case in point is hemodialysis, which purifies blood passing through kidneys that no longer function properly. There are many advantages to this treatment, but patients are constantly reminded of their disease and their dependence on a machine. They often have physiological complaints. On top of that, they must adhere to a strict diet, treatments may be uncomfortable, and there is the inconvenience of the dialysis appointments—four hours, three times a week. For many, the treatment and discomfort are unendurable. As one patient said, when he ripped out the tubes and left the treatment room, "It's just not worth it." He was dead a week later.[7] Notably dialysis patients have a suicide rate seven times higher than the national average.[8]

Should these patients have a right to refuse treatment?

Peter Clinque, who won the right to halt his dialysis, was blind, incapacitated, and in pain as a result of kidney disease. Treatment did nothing to relieve his suffering, and he decided to halt it. However, his case was argued in court. The acting plaintiff was the hospital, which refused to abide by Clinque's wishes.

Deciding in favor of the defendant, Justice Arthur Spatt held that Mr. Clinque had the right to terminate his extraordinary means of life support, dialysis, because his decision was based on a desire to escape the "constant and severe pain caused by his multiple debilitating, irreversible and terminal conditions."[9] Clinque died within one hour of the ruling.

Certainly technology creates some problems, particularly for the terminally ill patient if the technological imperative takes precedence over the individual's values. By the 1950s, those techniques that had been developed to serve human interests, and which often did so brilliantly, began, in a moral sense, to override and even displace human priorities. Since then, though some therapies have eased pain and suffering, in other instances they have been used inappropriately and overzealously.

As David Thomasma of the Chicago Medical Center observed: "The direction of medicine toward life prolongation leads to an increasingly positivistic view of man as a biological functioning machine. . . . Our political system no longer preserves life in its fuller dimensions, but enhances only the biological quality of life."[10]

Such an attitude has often led to the overutilization of intensive care units. Initially these units were designed to treat trauma and some postoperative cases, not the hopelessly ill. Yet intensive care units are now full of the elderly, those with underlying untreatable diseases (such as cancer), and patients with loss of cerebral function.[11] Such people will not benefit from the high concentration of medical techniques available in these units, nor would many of them approve of the procedures—ones that limit their freedom and dignity—if they were capable of choosing.

Thomasma believes that the use of such artificial devices to prolong life will lead to a vision of man as a technological product.[12] If we depend on biological functioning, he argued, we may lose sight of those social aspects that are so important in living and interacting; we have come to perceive medicine as a powerful force that can control nature.

As one philosopher stated, such power over nature then becomes an abstraction and an ideal, with knowledge as the sole, manipulating instrument.[13] Death is regarded as a failure, and the terminally ill as embodiments of such failure.

In their zeal to fashion new and better technologies, many doctors have promoted measures that have unintended consequences. These efforts have provoked a certain backlash of disapproval, such as growing resistance to cardiopulmonary resuscitation (CPR)—a technique that has greatly increased survival from cardiac arrest, but has not yet found a way to deal with the brain damage resulting from diminished oxygen supply during the arrest.

Side effects from other techniques have been criticized. Researcher D. S. Kornfeld found that patients recovering from open-heart surgery were immobilized by catheters and tubes, and disturbed by the lights and sounds of monitoring machinery. As a result, they showed signs of sensory monotony and sleep deprivation.[14] Observing similar circumstances, one sociologist concluded: "The technological environments themselves have dehumanizing effects that may be counter to the intentions of the developer."[15]

The artificial heart has had similar drawbacks. After surgery, the recipient faces an existence radically different from what even the most sedentary person has known. Typically, he is constrained by a six-foot-long air hose which is attached to a 375-pound cart of equipment. Dr. William Parmley, chief of cardiology at the University of California, San Francisco, said: "If it were me, I don't think I'd be too excited about it, if it meant being tethered to an external air source."[16] An official at Humana Heart Institute said that the artificial heart "is not a success so far because it has substituted mechanical problems for disease."[17]

Is the risk worth the end result? Millions of Americans watched, horrified, as news flashes showed the mental and physical deterioration of heart-transplant recipient William Schroeder. Even Schroeder's wife expressed her doubts. "If he had anticipated the hardship," she said, "he might not have done it. Bill thought he'd either die or be better."[18] The article quoting her pointed out that Schroeder was "suspended in a twilight zone between life and death—a guinea pig in an unfinished experiment, a patient whose treatment had gone sour."

Such examples illustrate our society's infatuation with technology. Faith in the power of such solutions to medical problems gives rise to expectations of omnipotence—expectations shared, to some degree, by patients and doctors alike. We tend to be so awed at what medical progress can do that we often lose sight of the fact that there can be unbearable consequences. Technology is helpful, but its applications must be controlled. Observers in hospitals have sometimes noticed that technology is often being used because it is there, not because its use is justified by patient need.

How can this imbalance be explained? One author suggests: "Technological emphasis on medical care in the United States is not happenstance; rather, it is the natural extension of producers' and consumers' efforts to harness science and technology."[19]

Once this technology is harnessed without consideration given to the ethics of treatment, it has a tendency to be used excessively or inappropriately. Such overuse is prompted by physician's training—which places great value on scientific achievement—as well as by malpractice fears, methods of reimbursement, national priorities, and fear of death.

Consumer demands also promote the use of technology in medicine. The public's perceived needs or wants at times manipulated by the media, are not always realistic. More often than not, these wants are created by the desire to understand or control the unknown.

For instance, feared diseases such as AIDS or herpes create a need, sometimes excessive, for services and additional information. Ivan Illich, the philosopher and writer, feels the public fascination with high technology care and death in cases like this can be understood as a "deep-seated need for the engineering of miracles."[20]

In other words, technology offers the possibility of cure to patient and family, promising eternal hope. The yearning for highly specialized techniques and procedures turns into expectations which, however unreal, are then translated into demands. In turn, hospitals often bow to such pressures and acquire excess equipment and gadgetry to quell these consumer demands. And once the skilled procedures are secured, they must be utilized to meet the costs of use and maintenance.

The physician is subjected to similar pressures. Striving to live up to patient expectations, he often provides care beyond what is necessary and, in some cases, desired. This is particularly true with the terminally ill. There is no question that these patients will die, but more often than not, only after aggressive medical intervention. When the occasional therapeutic attempt is successful and there is, say, a miraculous remission, the physician and his team are heralded by their colleagues and the press, fueling the public's expectations even more—despite the fact that these cases reflect a tiny minority.

National priorities, too, influence the proliferation of new technologies through research and development grants. Again, the desire for never-ending cures accounts for much of the funding. As one observer noted: "The technological explosion of the late 1960s encouraged the myth that technology could rescue patients from the consequences of the major diseases affecting the population."[21]

As a result, the government has continued to invest more money in finding new and better cures. In 1983, for example, $6 billion was spent on health research alone. This is expected to increase to $10 billion in 1990.[22]

Dr. William Knaus, the director of intensive care research at George Washington University Medical Center, commenting on the funding, said: "We believe in the power of science to correct our problems, so we have invested a great deal of confidence and money in these life-support systems. The machines are useful, but not in making miracles."[23] Yet the belief that more is better predominates over the practical issues of assessing the use and application of these technologies in diagnosis and therapy.

How does all this affect the dying? While many life-support systems and techniques *are* beneficial, too often they are used simply because they are there, and because they reinforce the notion that death can be eluded indefinitely. Studies have shown that many terminal patients are isolated from others and receive less personal attention from the staff than recovering patients.[24] Insofar as the physician believes that "to care for" means "to cure," he is as helpless to act in the face of suffering as the terminal patient is. Thus, not only are many dying patients secluded, they are also overtreated—but by machines and therapies, rather than by personal contact. Any acknowledgment of death is avoided.

The physician's fear of death is also apparent in his reluctance to tell a terminal patient the truth about his illness, even though, according to the law of informed consent, he is supposed to. To compound the problem, many patients' families fail to discuss among themselves the appropriateness of a life-prolonging procedure because of the same fear.*

Too, skilled techniques and sophisticated therapies—all dubbed "lifesaving"—postpone decision-making. As one medical health writer noted, the use of such artificial life supports "demonstrates how the medical profession, by and large, has shrunk from coping with new dilemmas, and how inaction has allowed medical technology to dictate its actions."[25]

Thus the dying patient, if he is conscious, lies isolated, bewildered, betubed, and monitored not by human contact but by the marvels of scientific progress, the almighty life-support system.

In 1949, 50 percent of the population died in institutions—hospitals, medical centers, or nursing homes. In 1958, the figure was 61 percent. Two decades later, the number had risen 10 percent. Finally, in the 1980s, 80 percent of the chronically ill died in institutions.[26]

To the dying person in particular, hospitals tend to be intimidating and impersonal. Typically, the terminal patient is a captive to his lifelines—monitors, tubes, and other mechanical gadgets carrying life-sustaining nutrients and fluids. Privacy is limited as the medical staff, looking for any significant change, observe the patient. Family contact is often restricted by a rigid schedule for visiting hours. The ubiquitous machinery surrounding the patient resembles an intricate obstacle course, defying even minimal physical contact.[27] One woman who wanted to lie with her dying husband in his final moments dislodged an intravenous tube. She retreated, horrified. No one can experience a peaceful, dignified death in such an alienating atmosphere.

While the dying still cling to life, the question remains: At what point should the terminal patient refuse further treatment, insisting that enough is enough? Pope Pius XII's statement in 1957 differentiating ordinary from extraordinary means has been used as a benchmark by many people in deciding what is appropriate treatment. Catholic thinkers such as Gerald Kelly have struggled to define these terms more explicitly so that they can have meaning for a patient, especially one who is Catholic and wants to adhere to Church policy.

Kelly defines ordinary means as all medicines, treatments, and operations "which offer a reasonable hope of benefit for the patient and which can be obtained and used without excessive expense, pain or other inconvenience." Extraordinary measures, on the other hand, are those which "cannot be obtained or used without excessive expense, pain or other inconvenience, or which, if used, would not offer a reasonable hope of benefit."[28]

However, as admirable as these attempts to define different forms of treatment are, they are open to a great deal of interpretation. Clearly, what is painful, inconvenient, or expensive to one patient may not be to another. Also, what is ordinary treatment for one patient may be extraordinary for someone else. For instance, in the case of Claire Conroy in New Jersey, nasogastric nutrition was ruled by the court to be an extraordinary means of treatment and was discontinued. Not surprisingly, many people disagreed with the court's ruling, arguing that food and water are essential elements for life and are therefore part of ordinary care.

---

* The doctrine of informed consent establishes a dual responsibility for physicians: (1) a duty to disclose to the patient the nature and ramifications of available treatments, and (2) a duty to obtain the patient's consent to any treatment prior to its administration. Recent judicial decisions have established the responsibility of a physician to inform his patient adequately of treatment alternatives as an integral protection of the informed consent doctrine.

Thus the complexities of new and innovative techniques demonstrate how technology has confounded the issue of which treatments are suitable for which patients, especially for those who are dying. In many ways, there are no fixed guidelines to decide what is suitable. One can only ask: Who is to decide? And, as happened in the Conroy case, is litigation inevitable when the question can't be answered? Most people find the possibility of an attorney at every death-bed appalling.

Further confounding the options available for a hopelessly ill patient is when death can and should be declared. Many people in the early stages of a terminal illness fear, more than anything, being kept alive in a state that can only be described as vegetative. David Lygre, in *Life Manipulation,* illustrated how machines can keep a patient "hovering between life and death . . . even mask[ing] death." He went on to say:

"For as long as [the machines] circulate, oxygenate, and cleanse the patient's blood, his organs will continue many of their normal functions."[29] With the aid of such medical intervention, people can exist in a comatose state for years.

Although the point of death has been redefined in the last few decades, it has been confined to a strictly biological point of view, much to the horror of ethicists and others. There is more to a person than organs and brain-stem functioning. Even with the most recent proposal for a definition of death—the Uniform Determination of Death Act—personality, memory, and emotions are not considered relevant factors in deciding whether a person is technically dead and whether any quality of life remains or could remain.

To rely on technology to define the state of life and of death is to deny those parts of man that give his life substance. Medical decisions based solely on biological functions disregard the social and spiritual aspects of life which make it truly fulfilling and unique.

Why *are* hospitals so dependent on technology?

If there are drawbacks for the terminally ill, who may be overtreated to death, there are unmistakable advantages for the hospital, advantages that take precedence over more humane considerations.

Certainly, if a hospital prides itself on its sophisticated procedures and equipment, it will attract talented and superbly qualified physicians. It will also attract more patients, who respond to the reputation of the skilled medical staff. The word spreads. A first-rate staff and richly endowed resources ensure success, success that is often defined in terms of a bank statement.

Humana, Inc., illustrates this point. Administrators there were able to attract William DeVries, the prominent heart surgeon, to Louisville to perform artificial-heart operations. As the magazine *Business Week* observed, this, administrators felt, was the "shrewdest move to date . . . [which] has already paid off in spades."[30] As a result, they plan to capitalize on free publicity generated by the success of the artificial heart operations and to turn Humana into a "national brand of health care."[31] Chairman and chief executive David Jones was heard referring to patients as "customers"; he is said to be concentrating on the profits of artificial-heart implants, rather than weighing the relative benefits and harm generated by this new and startling technology.*

---

* On the September 25, 1985 radio show Morning Edition, Michael Harrington noted: "Medicine is developing more and more on the corporate model. There are merger discussions under way for profit hospitals and medical suppliers, which would create new entities yielding more than $5 billion a year in sales. Indeed, the Republic Health Corporation is now trying to figure out the costs and profitability of performing tonsillectomies or coronary bypasses. The poor, needless to say, are shunted over into the public sector."

Much of this philosophy, more fiscal than humanitarian, is camouflaged by the insistence that all such procedures are lifesaving and therefore to be applauded. In this respect, hospitals are categorically dedicated to the principle that they improve life since such procedures prolong it. Little mention is made of whether the patient approves of such procedures, if, indeed, he has a choice, or whether quality of life is enhanced in the process. As the director of Beth Israel Hospital in Boston said: "The hospital must be pro-life. When you see someone who looks as if he is dying, you don't question whether it is moral or ethical to save him, you just go."[32]

Such a one-dimensional attitude also means that fewer decisions have to be made. The assistant chief of medicine at Stanford Medical School in California commented that, even with the hopelessly ill, "It is much less complex and stressful to place such a patient on a breathing machine and send him to ICU [intensive care unit] than to decide that he has almost no chance to regain good quality of life and therefore should not be placed on extraordinary life support."[33]

A frequently mentioned example of patient abuse is cardiopulmonary resuscitation, which has saved the lives of many otherwise healthy patients but has prolonged the suffering of the terminally ill. The *New England Journal of Medicine* reported a study in which only 14 percent of all patients who were resuscitated lived to leave the hospital.[34] The procedure is violent; the family must stand by, aware that with someone who is hopelessly ill, CPR only ensures a more protracted deathbed. Yet a hospital could boast that it had revived and saved the lives of certain patients, without mentioning that those who left the hospital and returned to a meaningful existence were in an extremely small minority.

How can patients counter this?

In some hospitals, ethics committees serve as a sounding board for decision-making. The American Society of Law and Medicine describes these committees as: functioning to review treatment decisions on behalf of the patient; reviewing medical decisions having ethical implications; providing social, psychological, spiritual, or other counseling where necessary; establishing treatment and administrative guidelines; and providing education to the public about ethical questions in the health care field.[35]

However, the committees are purely advisory, and they are not intended to replace traditional methods of decision-making between doctor and patient. And as Leonard Glanz, from the Boston University School of Public Health and Medicine, warns: "We must be very careful [with ethics committees]. We don't want just another layer of bureaucratic decision-making to bog down our health care system more." Nor does he want ethics committees to diffuse the responsibility on sensitive issues, although he does foresee such committees as making real progress in teaching that "sometimes less treatment is better treatment."[36]

In some hospitals, to avoid overtreatment and CPR abuses, do-not-resuscitate orders are honored for those patients who would be otherwise hopelessly revived. For instance, the Minnesota Task Force on the Affordability of New Technology and Specialized Care defines DNR orders as an explicit policy that "preempts the emergency summoning of a resuscitation team if the patient suffers a cardiac arrest."[37] Such a policy is decided on by the attending staff—which weighs medical and ethical criteria, as well as the wishes of the patient and the patient's family. In short, a DNR decision is upheld when it is agreed that the patient's best interests would not be served.

The Critical Care Committee of Massachusetts General Hospital has gone even further, recommending a system of classification for treatment decisions. The system consists of a ranking of conditions from A to D, with category D explicitly addressed to those patients for whom resuscitation would be futile.

Class A: Maximal therapeutic effort without reservation.

Class B: Maximal therapeutic effort without reservation, but with daily evaluations because possibility of survival is questionable. This enables the physician to obtain further consultation and promotes communication between the doctor, the hospital staff, and the patient.

Class C: Selective limitation of therapeutic measures. At this time certain procedures may cease to be justifiable and then become contraindicated, i.e., resuscitation limiting full CPR; inappropriate admission to Intensive Care Unit. The patient must be given full general supportive care.

Class D: All therapy can be discontinued. Any measures which are indicated to insure maximum comfort to the patient may be continued or instituted. Turning off the life support systems is to be performed by the physician only after consultation with and concurrence of family members and hospital committees.[38]

This system emphasizes consensus among physician, patient, family, hospital staff, and hospital director.

However, problems do arise, especially when the patient's wishes are not specified beforehand. A Living Will has not been signed, for example, or the patient has not made his priorities clear to his family. To avoid this confusion, patients and the medical staff, whenever possible, should discuss in advance the treatment anticipated and how far it should be carried out.

Still, in spite of advances made in this area, many physicians resist the DNR order, no matter how explicit a patient has been. In many instances, "no code" instructions—do not resuscitate—are not prominently displayed on a patient's chart; when someone whose heart has stopped is brought into emergency, nurses work to revive the patient (something that is almost reflexive), before taking the time to read the chart.

As a kind of compromise, a measure called "slow code" (loosely defined as responding to a code slowly or not using every available lifesaving measure) is practiced in some hospitals. Here attempts are made to revive the patient, but only after a delay, usually long enough to ensure that the patient won't respond. In this way, the patient's wishes—or so the physicians can claim—have been honored, while the hospital is protected from possible litigation. However, as one nurse noted, resuscitation, even when delayed, is rarely done for the patient's benefit: "Resuscitation is more for the benefit of the living than helpful to the dead or dying patient. The family can say they tried everything, but [the loved one] was too far gone to bring him back, and the act of resuscitation makes the professional staff look efficient."[39]

Because of the lack of consistent standards, more accurate ways of assessing the patient's needs should be installed in all hospitals, using the kind of criteria adopted by Massachusetts General Hospital, for example. As well, ethics committees to back up such decision-making help secure the best and most fitting treatment.

Until that time, an absence of such measures—or compromise techniques such as slow codes—only ensures that many patients will be treated in ways they would not have wished. They will be resuscitated and subjected to an abundance of diagnostic and therapeutic procedures that are senseless, costly, and, ultimately, undignified. The patient lies, either comatose or with his mental and physical capacities severely diminished, a hostage to a system that too often believes that lives should be saved, whatever the cost.

Physicians collude in the pattern of overtreatment for a variety of reasons. Certainly, medical schools emphasize technological progress and sophisticated therapies, concentrating on attacking the disease without necessarily weighing the ethics of such treatment. After medical school, most doctors specialize. This means that, unlike the old-fashioned doctor-patient relationship in which patient and disease were treated as a whole, today the doctor tends to the specific area that interests him: the organ or body function that is his particular specialty.

The pattern is further compounded, the responsibility further diffused. Often, in the process of treating one patient, several physicians are called in, thus diluting decision-making as well as personal rapport. For instance, a patient suffering from breast cancer may first be diagnosed by her gynecologist. If she has surgery, which is likely, she will be treated subsequently by an oncology surgeon and an anesthesiologist, not to mention chemotherapy specialists, laboratory technicians, oncology nurses, a pharmacist, a social worker, and other health care workers. Coordinating information—not to mention crucial decisions that have to be made—is complicated even more. Responsibility for the patient is spread over a team of specialists, not all of whom have equal input about the patient's welfare. Nor do they necessarily have equal say or equal interest.

In many cases, the physician in charge continues to use his expertise to press for intensifying treatment, even when the patient is in the final throes of a fatal illness. The doctor justifies his efforts by claiming that such undertakings combat the disease and prolong the life of the patient, considered by many to be the sole objective. As Ivan Illich noted:

> Not only does the medicalization of terminal care ritualize macabre dreams and enlarge professional license for obscene endeavors; the escalation of terminal treatments removes from the physician all need to prove the technical effectiveness of those resources he commands. There are no limits to his power to demand more and more.[40]

Ultimately he can say he has done everything possible to help the patient. The family will thank him profusely, and the rest of the medical staff will nod approvingly.

In the process, the doctor has become little more than a body technician, isolating himself from the organism as a whole—the patient. As Illich said: "The doctor's refusal to recognize the point where he has ceased to be useful as a healer, and to withdraw when death shows on his patient's face, has made him into an agent of evasion or outright dissimulation."[41] And, sadly, the patient's inability to die on his own terms makes him pathetically dependent, painfully helpless.

If technology is a mixed blessing, then, it is because it has been developed and incorporated into hospital and medical practices at such a rapid rate that decisions on how to use it appropriately have lagged behind. Melissa Spears, a nurse, commented in an article in the *Washington Post:* "I think we have a real gap between our technology and our ethics."[42]

Typically, medical decisions have emphasized the mechanistic or quantifiable aspects of treatment, while corporate decisions—such as those arrived at by hospital boards—concentrate on cost effectiveness and population impact. Ethics committees and other countermeasures have been slow to arrive on the scene. By the end of 1985, only 30 percent of hospitals had ethics committees, according to an American Hospital Association survey.

Laurence Tancredi, associate professor of law and psychiatry at New York University, has suggested ways in which technology can be employed usefully but in more humane ways. Utmost in Tancredi's philosophy is the ability to assess the efficiency of a particular technology—say, accelerated chemotherapy—in direct relation to a patient's personal evaluation of how such a treatment will affect his or her quality of life.

Tancredi's factors include: the ability to return to baseline function, the degree of relief from expected symptoms, the requirements of treatment and how well the patient can adapt to them, the psychological effects of the procedure, the impact of such a treatment on the patient's self-image (e.g., loss of hair), the cost of the procedure, and finally, the quality of death.[43] Another law professor, John Robitscher, defining the latter, spoke of "a death that saves us from a meaningless prolongation of a painful existence or maintenance of some body process in the absence of consciousness and the hope of regaining consciousness."[44] The ultimate goal is to prolong a patient's life only when a sense of wholeness, of self-determination, and of freedom remains intact.

Such a sense of wholeness can be made clear only if a patient has indicated his wishes beforehand to his physician and family. Informed consent is crucial in giving the patient the power to signal to the medical team the extent to which he or she wants treatment—ordinary, extraordinary, or otherwise.

Even today, many people are unaware of the fact that everyone has the right to refuse treatment. If it is administered against a patient's will, the physician is guilty of technical battery, based on a patient's constitutional right of privacy. Tancredi has defined the goal of informed consent as to "shift, whenever possible, the decision-making power onto the patient, and to incorporate the patient's values in dealing with the social, psychological, economic, and medical issues involved in his or her treatment."[45]

Karen Ann Quinlan and Claire Conroy have become symbols of the fight against technological death. In both cases, they were unable to make medical decisions for themselves, but their "proxies" held that it was in the patients' best interest to have their life-support systems removed. As Associate Justice Sidney M. Schreiber said in the Conroy case: "A competent patient has the right to decline any medical treatment, including artificial feeding, and should retain that right when and if he becomes incompetent."[46]

Reviewing the matter, one journalist pointed out that "medical technology has its benefits, but it also has its limits, and it is [the court] that is measuring what those limits are."[47] Although such litigation has been costly and time-consuming—as well as painful for the plaintiffs' families—it has at least upheld what many ethicists and others have insisted on for so long: that we do indeed have the right to die. Once technology is inalienably linked to that right, as many recent court decisions have confirmed, innovative techniques and bold new medical procedures can be used ethically and humanely, and very much to the patient's advantage.

Medicine is not solely a technical profession. Neither are physicians simply monitors of electrolytes or brain-stem functions, or dispensers of drugs. They are healers of human beings. Assessing the place of technology at the patient's bedside, one writer concluded that it is useful only inasmuch as it helps people "feel the rich fabric of life." He went on to say: "We should respect a patient's decision to decline further treatment when life has become burdensome. . . . We must learn how to make death a decent and humane experience, not something bitterly contested to the last gasp."[48]

NOTES

1. Jerry Wilson, *Death by Decision: The Medical, Moral, Legal Dilemmas of Euthanasia* (Philadelphia: Westminster Press, 1975), 97.
2. Richard Taylor, *Medicine Out of Control: The Anatomy of a Malignant Technology* (Melbourne, Australia: Sun Books, 1979), 119.
3. H. David Banta et al., *Toward Rational Technology in Medicine* (New York: Springer Series on Health Care and Society, 1981), 28–9; Charles Sanders, "Technology in Hospitals," in *Medical Technology: The Culprit Behind Health Care Costs?* ed. Stuart Altman and Robert Blendon (USDHEW PHS 79–326,1997),62–6.
4. Banta, *Toward Rational Technology,* 5.
5. Lewis Thomas, "The Technology of Medicine," *New England Journal of Medicine,* December 9, 1971,1367.
6. B. D. Cohen, "Buying Time for the Terminally Ill," Newsday Special Reprint, April 15–April 19, 1984,16.
7. *Life,* January 14, 1972, 49.
8. Gina Bari Kolata, "Dialysis After Nearly a Decade," in *Medical Ethics: A Clinical Textbook and Reference for Health Care Professionals,* ed. Natalie Abrams and Michael Brucker (Cambridge, Mass.: MIT Press, 1983), 571.
9. *New York Times,* October 23, 1982.
10. David Thomasma, "The Goals of Medicine and Society," in *The Culture of Biomedicine,* ed. D. Heyward Brock (Newark, Del.: University of Delaware Press, 1984), 38.
11. Taylor, *Medicine Out of Control,* 120.
12. Thomasma, "The Goals of Medicine," 38.
13. Leon Kass, "The New Biology: What Price Relieving Man's Estate," *Science* 174 (November 19,1971):782.
14. D. S. Kornfeld, "The Hospital Environment: Its Impact on the Patient," *Advances in Psychosomatic Medicine* 8 (1972): 25–70.
15. David Ellison, *The Biomedical Fix: Human Dimensions of Bio-Medical Technologies* (Westport, Conn.: Greenwood Press, 1978), 17.
16. *San Francisco Chronicle,* August 15, 1982.
17. *Los Angeles Times,* May 15, 1985.
18. "A Moratorium on Heart Transplants," *Discover,* July 1985, 87.
19. Robert Derzon, "Influences of Reimbursement Policies on Technology," in *Critical Issues in Medical Technology,* ed. Barbara McNeil and Ernest Cravalho (Cambridge, Mass.: Auburn House, 1982),140.
20. Ivan Illich, *Medical Nemesis: The Exportation of Health* (New York: Bantam Books, 1976), 100.
21. Sanders, "Technology in Hospitals," 59.
22. Ross Arnett and Carol Cowell et al., "Health Spending Trends in the 1980's: Adjusting to Financial Incentives," *Health Care Financing Review* 6 (Spring 1985): 23.
23. "The Cost, Pain of Holding On," *Sacramento Bee,* June 24, 1984.
24. *E.g.,* Norman K. Brown, "The Preservation of Life," *Journal of the American Medical Association* 211 (January 5, 1970): 76–82; H. Feifel et al., "Physicians Consider Death," American Psychological Association, 75th Annual Convention 1967, 201–2.
25. Taylor, *Medicine Out of Control,* 2.
26. President's Commision for the Study of Ethical Problems in Medicine and Biomedical and Behavioral Research, *Deciding to Forego Life-Sustaining Treatment,* March 1982, 17–18.
27. See Joseph Fletcher, "The Patient's Right to Die."
28. Gerald Kelly, *Medico-Moral Problems* (St. Louis: Catholic Hospital Association, 1958), 129.

29. David G. Lygre, *Life Manipulation: From Test Tube Babies to Aging* (New York: Walker Company, 1979),108.
30. "Humana: Making the Most of Its Place in the Spotlight," *Business Week,* May 6, 1985, 69.
31. Ibid., 68.
32. Stein, *Making Medical Choices,* 217–18.
33. Thomas Raffin, "The Right to Live, The Right to Die," *Stanford Magazine,* Spring 1983, 26.
34. Susanna Bedell et al., "Surviving After Cardiopulmonary Resuscitation in the Hospital," *New England Journal of Medicine* 309 (September 8, 1983): 574.
35. President's Commission, 439–4 1.
36. *New York Times,* November 4, 1984.
37. Minnesota Coalition on Health Care Costs, *The Price of Life: Ethics and Economics,* December 1984, 12.
38. "Optimum Care for Hopelessly Ill Patients," in *Medical Ethics: A Clinical Textbook and Reference for Health Care Professionals,* ed. Natalie Abrams and Michael Brucker (Cambridge, Mass.: MIT Press, 1983), 314–15.
39. Richard Benton, *Death and Dying* (New York: Van Nostrand Reinhold, 1978), 241. Professional report by Mary Kathleen Chudleigh.
40. Illich, *Medical Nemesis,* 94.
41. Ibid., 97.
42. *Washington Post,* December 2, 1984.
43. Laurence Tancredi, "Social and Ethical Implications in Technology Assessment," *Critical Issues in Medical Technology,* 95–7.
44. John Robitscher. "The Problems in Prolongation of Life," in *Biomedical Ethics and the Law,* ed. James Humber.
45. Tancredi, "Social and Ethical Implications," 99.
46. *New York Times,* January 18, 1985.
47. Ibid.
48. Lygre, *Life Manipulation,* 111.

THE BRAIN OF A CELL

David Baltimore

INTRODUCTION

Biotechnology is the umbrella term used to encompass enterprises and research ranging from the processes associated with brewing beer to the high-tech world of manipulating DNA and genetically engineering new organisms. Like many twentieth-century technologies, biotechnology is strongly science-based, resting on fundamental discoveries in molecular biology in the 1940s and 1950s. The most important of these revelations was the identification of DNA as the carrier of genetic information within all living organisms and the determination by Robert D. Watson and Francis Crick in 1953 of DNA's basic molecular structure—the famous double helix. Watson and Crick drew on previous studies of genetics and biochemistry to assemble their model of DNA. But they also used judgment and intuition to match conjecture with mathematical analysis. It was, as David Baltimore asserts in this article, a "triumph of intelligence."

Once it was understood that the linear sequence of four chemicals known as nucleotides made up the code that controlled protein synthesis within the cell, the way was clear for analyzing that sequence, and, using specific enzymes, breaking the DNA molecule at key points and recombining it to rewrite the genetic code. It all sounds deceptively simple, but finding the right enzymes and "mapping" the DNA molecule, in addition to perfecting means of carrying the altered genes into the cell, took nearly two decades of research and development. Once that was completed, entrepreneurs almost immediately saw the potential of genetic engineering to produce new chemicals, drugs, and agricultural products.

This article raises philosophical and moral issues about biotechnology and its implications for manipulating living organisms. Restricted only to the genetic engineering of individual cells, biotechnology has generated little controversy. But the use of the technology to modify basic inheritable characteristics is another matter altogether, for it means we must make decisions about how much we want to alter or "improve" ourselves or our offspring. It will, naturally, be a great relief to parents to know that their unborn children are free of genetic defects, but what will it mean for society if parents of the future can make choices about specific mental and physical characteristics of their children? The real questions suggested by this article are not technological, but instead center on individual and community values for which there are no easy answers.

Biology, for all its mystery, is woven into the fabric of our daily lives. We cultivate plants and raise animals to eat; we burn wood to keep warm; we wear leather, cotton, or wool. Over the centuries, man has become increasingly adept at harnessing the biologic world, but before the 1950s our knowledge of how living things work was at best superficial. That has changed. One discovery stands out as the primary generator of our new understanding of biologic systems and our power to manipulate them: the 1953 elucidation of the structure of DNA by James D. Watson and Francis Crick.

No scientific discovery occurs in a vacuum. In biology, a concern with the underlying structure of living systems can be traced back for a century before Watson and Crick's seminal one-page paper. But nothing in pre-1950 biology prepared scientists for the revolution unleashed by the understanding of DNA's structure. To comprehend the importance of the discovery requires dissecting out two strains of research on living systems: the biochemical, or physiological, and the genetic.

The physiological approach to biology is a success story that started in the 19th century and continues today. It sees living organisms as factories and tries to achieve understanding by analyzing the machines themselves—what they are made of, how they work, how they are integrated. It seems the logical way to decipher the bewildering array of mechanisms that together allow the system to function.

The approach of genetics, on the other hand, is to ask about blueprints, not machines; about decisions, not mechanics; about information and history. In the factory analogy, genetics leaves the greasy machines and goes to the executive suite, where it analyzes the planners, the decision makers, the computers, the historic records. It is the business school approach rather than the engineering approach.

The factory whose structure preoccupies biology today is the cell. Biologists of the 19th century realized that living systems are designed as an array of individual, tiny units called cells. Twentieth-century biologists turned to analyzing events and structures inside the cells. Cells are incredibly complicated, and it was not immediately apparent how they were organized and integrated. Biologists needed to find the cell's brain.

The answer had begun to emerge from the first experiments in genetics in the 19th century. Gregor Mendel had noticed regularities of inheritance of color and structure in peas, and he postulated an underlying unit of inheritance now known as the gene. Later researchers realized that the genes were located on the stubby, sausage-like chromosomes found in the cell's nucleus, segregated from the rest of the cell. The brain of the cell had been found, but there was no way to penetrate its structure and organization.

For 50 years, the best and the brightest of biologists fought with this frustration by creating genetics, a science of extraordinary beauty and insight but one that dealt with virtual objects, units of heredity that were definable operationally but not mechanically. Thus, the early 1950s found us with the monumental intellectual construct of genetics and with increasingly detailed knowledge of cellular activity coming from physiologists and biochemists. But there was no understanding of the link between the executive suite and the factory floor. Watson and Crick provided that link.

Their approach, so predictable in retrospect, was to apply the power of biochemistry to analyze the stuff of genes. It was not obvious, however, of just what stuff the genes were made. In 1944, an experiment by Oswald Avery and his colleagues at the Rockefeller

Institute indicated that the chemical transmitter of genetic information was deoxyribonu-
cleic acid, or DNA, and a second experiment in 1952 by Alfred Hershey and Martha
Chase at the Cold Spring Harbor Laboratory drove home the conclusion. Watson and
Crick, therefore, had a good idea where to look. But the only microscope that could
resolve DNA's structure used X rays rather than light.

Studying molecular structure using X rays was a great specialty of British science. The
technique, known as X-ray crystallography, was first applied to salt in 1912 and was being
applied to large molecules in the 1930s. By the early 1950s, two investigators in London,
Rosalind Franklin and Maurice Wilkins, independently had achieved high-resolution pictures
of DNA. But X-ray pictures are not like pictures taken with light rays. Because there are no
lenses to focus X rays, mathematics takes the place of glass. And the mathematics needed to
see DNA involved calculating from models that were guesses about possible structure.

Watson and Crick, then, were working with imprecise information and ambiguous tools.
They combined insight, hunch, and analysis to build a model of DNA's structure that was
consistent with what the X-ray images did show. Their triumph was a personal one, a triumph of intelligence. What they discovered was that a double helix of two intertwined
strands would satisfy the constraints placed by the X-ray images. Although scientists argue
to this day about the detailed structure of DNA, Watson and Crick's model made such perfect sense that it was almost immediately accepted.

Genes, Watson and Crick found, are constructed of four chemical units arranged along
each of two complementary strands, and the units form a code of instructions necessary for
an organism's growth and reproduction. The enlightenment that followed the discovery is
astounding to contemplate. Watson and Crick's model revealed that genes store information
in a digital fashion; that the storage code has a four-letter alphabet; and that the mutually
complementary strands, the double helix, allow the genes to duplicate themselves accurately. A possible implication, later proven, was that the letters are strung out along a virtually endless "computer tape" so that, although genes seem to be discrete entities, they are
really just regions of the tape defined by encoded stop and start signals.

Today, the computer tape analogy for DNA is obvious. Computers use only a two-signal
code, but aside from that, DNA could easily be seen as the embodiment of principles first
realized in the late 1930s by Alan Turing and enshrined in the Turing machine, which
responds to signals encoded on a tape. Had biologists been steeped in information theory,
they might have conceived earlier that the thin molecular string pointed to by Oswald Avery
back in 1944 can function in a way exactly analogous to how information is stored in books
and computers.

Once the structure of DNA was found, the link between physiology and genetics was
soon made. The cell's brain had been found to be a tape reader scanning an array of information encoded as a linear sequence, that is ultimately translated into three-dimensional
proteins. The computer analogy for the cell's brain has an actual counterpart. The amount
of information stored in DNA is, of necessity, enormous, and methods developed during the
last 15 years allow molecular biologists to read large chunks of the DNA code at will. The
information is then put into a computer that, acting as a surrogate cell, helps us understand
the encoded information.

The ability to decipher the structure of DNA was only the beginning of the revolution of
modern biology. In the 20 years that followed Watson and Crick's discovery, scientists found

proteins that would duplicate DNA, that would cut DNA, and that would patch together DNA. The combined capabilities of these proteins turned an analytical science into a synthetic science. By 1974 it became apparent that the tools available would allow a molecular biologist to capture a gene from one animal and insert it into a set of genes in another species. Specifically, we found out how to take genes from humans and insert them into the genetic programs of bacteria, yeast, and viruses. The ability to manipulate these one-celled creatures and viruses could be used in two ways: as a molecular microscope with which to peer into the details of genes and as a factory able to synthesize the product encoded by genes. For basic scientists this meant an enormous increase in analytic power; for the more practically minded it meant the ability to make, in large quantities, proteins that had previously been available only in minute amounts.

Triumphs studded the next decade. Cancer genes were discovered, the immune system was unraveled, and large amounts of the antiviral protein interferon were produced, which may prove useful in treating cancer. These are just highlights; more is yet to come.

Nineteen eighty-four finds us just at the beginning of some of the dramatic advances that can be expected from molecular biology. Chances are good that even the greatest mystery of biology, the functioning of the human nervous system, will be unraveled in the next decades. We can also predict that many new pharmaceutical agents, many new methods of chemical production, and possibly new methods of energy generation and of micro-electronic circuitry can come from our knowledge of biological structure and function.

Not everyone is overjoyed by the prospect of harnessing living systems in the service of man. It represents the ultimate ascendance of man to the control of all elements of his surroundings, including other living organisms. Such power touches on deep philosophical as well as practical considerations. How far should we go in controlling our environment? How much do we know about the ultimate effects of our interventions? These questions require long, hard, and careful reflection. One aspect in particular, the power of modern biology to engineer the traits of human beings, has been widely discussed in recent years.

Although it is much more difficult to manipulate the genetics of a complicated multicellular creature than those of a one-celled microorganism, we could potentially manipulate our own genetic structure. For mice, at least, genetic manipulation is becoming routine. The techniques currently used for experimental investigation, however, are not necessarily appropriate for use in human beings.

To understand this point requires a distinction between two kinds of genetic engineering envisioned for people. Therapeutic, or somatic, genetic engineering involves genetic manipulations of cells that might cure inherited diseases but will not affect the genes that are passed on to future generations. Such therapy is possible and would be widely accepted as desirable, but it may be of limited usefulness. For instance, in the not-too-distant future it may be possible to modify blood cells so that inborn errors of heredity, such as sickle cell disease, can be reversed, but transplant techniques may make the procedure unnecessary.

By contrast, the second kind of genetic engineering, inheritable genetic modification or germ-line genetic engineering, involves changing the genes that are passed on from one generation to the next. This procedure might be contemplated to prevent a child from inheriting a genetic disease carried by its parents, but it raises serious questions about what genes are appropriately changed and whether we fully understand the implications of meddling with our own genetics.

Inheritable genetic modification is a hypothetical possibility, but from what we know about experimental systems, it is not today a feasible procedure. For a method to be feasible, it would have to allow the insertion of good genes in the place of bad genes. Although we know how to randomly insert genes into mice, we are far from being able to direct genes to appropriate sites on chromosomes and to insure that they work properly. The fact is, we don't know how to replace genes with the absolute accuracy required for germ-line engineering.

Molecular biology is, of course, still a young science, founded upon the discovery of the structure of DNA only 44 years ago. Its most sophisticated applications to direct the cure of human disease are only now being developed and may come within the next few years. There are, however, serious impediments to using the new technology for making inheritable changes. This does not mean we should forget the ethically difficult question of whether we should change human heredity. On the contrary, it is a deep question involving human values, and its discussion can illuminate our view of our own identity. Also, the impossible has a way of becoming possible, often through unpredictable routes. We should prepare as well as we can to integrate the techniques of the future into our lives. It is one of the most challenging areas of inquiry we can undertake.

RISK, REGULATION, AND BIOTECHNOLOGY

Malcolm Gladwell

INTRODUCTION

In the 1970s and 1980s, biotechnology and genetic engineering became the center of a major public policy debate. Biotechnology was controversial because it seemed to present unusual threats to the environment, and the prospect of entirely new life forms raised important moral and cultural issues. Resistance to the new technology was generally well-funded, well-organized, and highly vocal. Jeremy Rifkin and his Foundation for Economic Trends was probably the most effective of those people and organizations opposed to biotechnology in the United States. In Europe, the Socialist and the Green parties took the lead in raising public consciousness against biotechnology and marshaling support for the tight regulation or even prohibition of some research and development programs.

This article examines the regulation of biotechnology in the United States, stressing the importance of risk assessment. Malcolm Gladwell, a writer for the *Washington Post,* argues that the debate over biotechnology has become so politicized that people on both sides have missed the point that governmental regulation must above all be aimed at minimizing risk. Only in that way will regulation function in the best interests of the general public. As Gladwell sees it, it is incumbent on the federal government to reach a consensus on regulation now, while the threshold of risk remains low, so that rational policies and procedures will be in place to deal with problems that might present even greater hazards in the future.

Since this article appeared, the regulatory emphasis in the 1990s has shifted away from a focus on controlling the release of genetically engineered micro-organisms to seeking means of stimulating the growth of the industry. While this is consistent with the general trend in regulatory policy and shows a mature regard for the basic responsibilities of scientists, it may not be the best way of dealing with the risks inherent in the technology, which if anything may have increased since the late 1980s.

It is inconceivable, of course, that one photograph could alter the direction of an entire industry, especially when it depicts nothing more than a woman walking through a strawberry patch.

And yet in the world of biotechnology, which in its short ten-year history has not always moved on the most rational of courses, the picture taken on April 24, 1987, of Julianne Lindemann walking through the strawberry fields of northern California has come to take on a strange and special significance.

On that day a small West Coast biotech firm—Advanced Genetic Sciences—became the first company ever to receive government approval to take a manmade organism out of the laboratory and release it in the open air. It was a simple experiment. A common bacteria modified by the tools of genetic engineering was sprayed on strawberry plants to protect them against frost. But coming after five years of controversy and regulatory review, after lawsuits from angry environmentalists and hostile ordinances from local city councils, it represented a milestone in the history of the biotech industry: for the first time the government had given its imprimatur to the fruits of gene manipulation. After years of being cast as mad scientists, the AGS test meant that the biotechnology industry had finally gained acceptance.

But the picture ruined everything. By some whim of the California health authority, Lindemann was made to wear what appeared to be a space suit, as if the bacteria she was spraying were radioactive, or as if the field on which she stood was the surface of the moon. Why she was made to wear such a ridiculous getup is anyone's guess, since of course if the bacteria was ruled safe enough to be released into the environment then it was surely safe enough to be released by a scientist dressed like a normal human being. But even today, almost two years after the fact, there are those who will say that the effect of that picture, burned into the collective consciousness the following day on TV screens and newspapers around the world, was to contradict the entire exercise, to perpetuate the superstition that gene splicing was a strange and dangerous science to be carried out only under the most extreme precautions.

And as if the injustice of the image was not enough, they will also point to the gathered crowd of reporters and onlookers just a few feet behind Lindemann in the picture, munching on donuts, sipping coffee, and snapping away with cameras without any kind of protective gear at all.

In the twenty months since the Advanced Genetic Science's field test, a handful of other biotechnology companies have received the federal go-ahead to take their experiments out of doors. Some of the experiments have encountered the same degree of controversy as that first experiment. Some have been pulled off with a minimum of fuss. But all in some way have fallen under the shadow of that first test in a California strawberry patch.

It is not that the biotech industry feels its attempts to seek practical applications for the products of the laboratory have been overregulated. In fact there is general agreement that the broad expanse of unexplored territory opened up by biotechnology demands some sort of close scrutiny. But there has always been a sense that in some way the public perception of what biotechnology is, and what kind of regulations are required to control it, are out of sync with the actual risks presented by the technology itself.

Before any group of scientists can introduce some new creation into the world, they have to comply with a series of stringent and often confusing regulations involving two or even three separate government agencies. Some have had to defend their rights to conduct experiments in court against skeptical environmentalists, and at the very least to conduct extensive public relations campaigns to convince local communities that the genetically improved seeds or manmade micro-organisms conceived in a test tube will not run amok when released into the environment. Such efforts are deemed necessary in spite of overwhelming evidence that what is being created by the biotech industry is no more troubling or danger-ous than the work with improving crops and chemicals that has gone on for years before. Indeed, the evidence is just as overwhelming that the toll taken by such oversight in time and money may be curtailing the growth of the industry itself.

This is true not just of the few dozen firms that have used the techniques of genetic engi-neering to improve crop agriculture but also those who are looking to improve livestock, to develop stronger and more useful strains of domestic animals. They too have said that their efforts have become the subject not of too much scrutiny but of scrutiny that has missed the mark. It is as if the public that has greeted the fruits of this new science and the researchers and tiny companies that have spawned it were somehow speaking in a different language.

It is as if all the industry were made to dress in space suits, even as they perform the most mundane of tasks and even as onlookers nonchalantly sip their morning coffee and report on the brave new world of biotechnology for the evening news hour.

There are many reasons why this perceived incompatibility between the emerging field of biotechnology and the regulations that govern it should matter to Americans. The cliché that all of our lives may someday be touched by biotechnology may or may not be true, but it is cer-tainly the case that what is now a small industry will someday be a large one, and whatever impediments are placed on the growth of U.S. firms will inevitably end up as advantages for the Japanese or the Germans or the British or whomever our competitors may someday be.

More importantly, however, how the emerging field of biotech is treated by the public and the appropriate authority is a test case for how any new technology is greeted by society. With any new advance comes a necessary comparison of the risks presented by the new against the risks associated with the old, and the advantages of what is coming against what is already there. It is not clear that with biotechnology this has been done with any accuracy; at best it may be too soon to make that determination, as the regulatory wheels in Washington are still grinding; at worst we may have fashioned a system that both frustrates the growth of this promising technol-ogy and exposes the public to more dangers than would otherwise be the case.

Few stories better demonstrate the problems inherent in the present regulatory system than that of Gary Strobel, the Montana State University researcher who ran afoul of the public and regulatory authorities in the summer of 1987. In June of that year, Strobel inde-pendently injected a small group of elm trees on the MSU campus with a natural bacterium that had proved effective in protecting trees in the laboratory against Dutch Elm disease. Because the bacterium had been modified slightly by genetic means to make it more effective against the deadly Dutch Elm fungus, this was, for the purpose of federal authorities, a biotechnology experiment. And when the Environmental Protection Agency found out that Strobel had conducted his test without clearing it with the agency first and having its envi-ronmental impact reviewed by a panel of experts, he was sharply reprimanded and a year-long restriction on his research activities was imposed. Perhaps worse, he became the target for all those nervous about biotech's future. There were calls by some of his peers for the "book" to be thrown at him for recklessly endangering the public safety, and the clump of trees on which he performed his experiment was summarily cut down and burned.

There are several points worth making about Strobel's crime and punishment: to begin with, the rule he defied in not registering his test with the authorities is less a single standard than one part of a confusing patchwork of three separate sets of rules. Consider the questions Strobel had to answer before beginning his war on Dutch Elm disease. The Department of

Agriculture has rules about outdoor tests. Did they apply to Strobel? Not so, he found out. In the case of using bacteria to control a plant disease, USDA rules apply only to test sites of over ten acres. Strobel's was smaller than that. Then there are general principles laid down by the National Institutes of Health defining what is and what is not an experiment worthy of regulation. Did *they* apply to Strobel? Apparently not, for his bacterium contained no manmade DNA ligations. Finally, the EPA has jurisdiction over some types of outdoor experiments. Strobel assumed that the EPA followed the NIH's general guidelines for outdoor tests, but that is no longer true. As of the June 26, 1986, Federal Register, pages 23302–23393, the EPA has its own rules and Strobel's test fell within them. For not being familiar with that redefinition, Strobel was punished. As he would say later, "You almost have to be a lawyer before you can be a scientist."

Strobel was also punished even though almost no one believed that the bacterium he was injecting into his trees posed any general threat to the environment. As the EPA officials responsible for disciplining Strobel said, in a kind of grand bureaucratic doublethink, the decision to punish him was based upon his "failure to comply with agency regulations and policies, rather than because of any adverse effect this experiment may have." To translate, he was guilty of breaking rules designed to protect the environment even though he wasn't actually endangering the environment. He was arrested for resisting arrest.

It bears mentioning, although few bothered to at the time, that Strobel's experiment—at least in its preliminary stages—was a success. Strobel was able to cut down and burn his trees in the wake of the EPA investigation only because the bacterium with which he had inoculated them had kept them alive. Had the experiment been a failure, there would have been no clump of trees for investigators to discover, and no evidence of Strobel's apparent crime. In what may be the ultimate irony of the sad story of the destruction wrought by Dutch Elm disease in this country, Strobel's trees, too, were arrested for resisting arrest.

Several months later Strobel was brought before the Senate to testify about his act of disobedience and about the new possibility of reform. It is impossible to read his testimony without getting a sense of his indignation. Here in a country where there are thousands of toxic waste dumps and where millions of tons of chemicals are dumped on American cropland every year in the name of better agriculture, a man had his work destroyed for trying to find a cure for Dutch Elm disease without a permit.

"Some of the scientific and technological problems that our nation faces are extremely difficult to handle," Strobel told the Senate. "On top of this we have imposed a sea of regulatory actions by a myriad of federal agencies with conflicting definitions. The entire effect is one that is absolutely impossible for a scientific researcher (especially one in a small business or academic institution) to comprehend and to follow on a regular basis. . . . As one who has suffered the consequences of this complex system I feel that the time has come for sweeping changes in how we think about biotechnology and how we regulate it."

Biotech's regulatory problem is the product of the extraordinary expectations that have been swirling around the industry since the first human gene was synthesized and cloned more than a decade ago. From the beginning, the highest of claims were made for the new powers that were suddenly at the disposal of scientists. This was a tool, the public was told, that would transform the world. By the time small start-up companies began to form in the early 1980s to exploit the new technologies, to discover new drugs, or to create new strains of agricultural crops, biotechnology was a magic word among investors. Random groups of biologists, thrown together by entrepreneurs without any clear idea about what they would be producing or even when they could produce it, were able to raise millions from venture capitalists and millions more from the stock market entirely on the strength of the magical words genetic engineering.

At the same time the promises made on behalf of the new science attracted an active group of critics, regulators, environmentalists, and concerned citizens who saw in the claims made for biotechnology a series of unanswered questions. How safe is it to introduce genetically improved, manmade organisms into an environment that has evolved over millions of years? And if this new science will someday have an impact on all of society, then shouldn't all of society have a say in how it is developed?

These questions were raised perhaps most famously in Cambridge, Massachusetts, in the spring of 1976, when the city council took the scientists at Harvard University to task for conducting some of the pioneering experiments in genetic engineering without first informing the community. "This is a serious matter," said Cambridge mayor Alfred Velluci at the time. "If worse comes to worst, we could have a major disaster on our hands." Velluci, a populist type who once proposed solving the Cambridge parking problem by paving over Harvard Yard, made repeated references to Frankenstein during the debate, as a way of expressing his fears over the possible outcome of experiments then underway in the Harvard biology department to clone the human gene for insulin.

There is nothing wrong with the questions that Velluci and many since his time have raised in response to the biotechnology revolution. The problem is that the revolution itself isn't really a revolution at all, and that the claims that many of the new technology's critics have responded to have had more in common with the industry's press releases than with reality. This isn't to say that someday the ability to take natural substances, to copy them, or to manipulate their genetic makeup, or even to create new life forms entirely, won't profoundly alter American society and require stringent oversight to protect the public from undue environmental risk. But for the moment much of the furor over biotech is over a technological straw man.

In the area of drug research, for example, biotech's big breakthrough has been to use the body as a pharmacy, locating natural human proteins with therapeutic value, cloning them, and then re-introducing them to the body as drugs. The first human protein to be identified and cloned was insulin, which was then re-administered to diabetics. But insulin cloned from humans has turned out to be only marginally more effective—and slightly more expensive—than the purified pig's insulin that had been given to diabetics previously. The same is true for TPA, another of the early biotech products, a natural anti-blood clot protein that has been copied for use in unplugging blocked arteries in heart attack victims. Billed as biotech's first blockbuster drug, TPA is in fact only slightly better and much more expensive than traditional chemical remedies for heart attacks. Other promising cloned proteins are more cost effective than insulin or TPA, but few—at this point anyway—are the miracle drugs that genetic engineering was to bring to the benefit of Americans.

In the area of agriculture, biotechnology probably will bring dramatic changes—bigger and more productive farm animals, more effective and environmentally sound pesticides, improved crop strains with larger yields. But on closer examination, the so-called agricultural revolution is no more a revolution than biotech's entry into the pharmaceutical world. In most cases, for example, the organisms being created and cloned are actually only mild variations of macro-organisms that already exist in the environment. Strobel's Dutch Elm disease vaccine was a bacterium found on various leaves around the world and modified so that it could be injected into elm saplings. A number of biotech firms have begun experiments attempting to protect corn plants from their biggest pest—a caterpillar known as the European corn borer—using modified versions of a bacterium that is already used in another form as a pesticide. Even the much ballyhooed bacterium sprayed on the California strawberry field is of a family of bacteria that have been protecting plants from frost for millions of years.

To be sure, the variations created by genetic engineering on these familiar micro-organisms are entirely new. But many scientists stress that what is new isn't necessarily harmful, although it may raise a series of legitimate and sometimes difficult questions. According to principles developed by Harvard's Bernard Davis, genetically engineered micro-organisms (GEMs), like domesticated farm species, are not particularly apt to outsurvive unmanipulated species already present in an environment. And because nature is already so diverse, GEMs will not likely add significant amounts of genetic variation to the environment.

Besides, isn't that what genetic engineers are attempting with plants and other living organisms—transferring the genes of one to another, modifying the structure of life forms to suit changing environmental conditions—the same thing that has always been done by other means by scientists and farmers and indeed nature itself?

"The risks associated with the introduction of R-DNA engineered organisms are the same in kind as those associated with the introduction into the environment of unmodified organisms and organisms modified by other genetic techniques," a National Academy of Sciences panel stated in a white paper a year and a half ago.

Or, as one letter to a Cambridge newspaper on the Harvard debate put it: "We are amazed that anyone should express concern about the creation of a laboratory at Harvard to experiment with new life forms. A look around Harvard Square at nearly any time of day or night reveals life forms sufficiently grotesque to convince us it is already too late for such protest."

The way the regulations governing biotech tests currently stand, companies and researchers must apply to the EPA first for permission to conduct a small scale, one- or two-acre experiment. And then, if that test is judged to have been ecologically acceptable—not threatening the existing ecosystem or spreading beyond the target site—the EPA grants a permit for a full-scale experiment. Along the way, if their bacterium is classified by the U.S. Department of Agriculture as a "genetically engineered plant pest," they would have to get approval from that agency, as well as inform the National Institutes of Health of their activity.

To date, the biotech community has faced most of its difficulty in passing the first step of this review process. While chemical companies have for years been able to test their pesticide prototypes without government approval, two of the early proposals for tests of genetically engineered bacteria were rejected by the EPA, despite what the industry said was overwhelming evidence of the tests' safety. One biotech firm in Maryland, Crop Genetics International, was so nervous about how its applications for testing a bio-engineered corn pesticide would be treated by the authorities that it spent close to $8 million conducting safety tests and signed former EPA Chief William Ruckelshaus, *eminence grise* Elliot Richardson, and Bush adviser Robert Teeter to a special "Committee on Social Responsibility" to convince federal regulators of their commitment to playing by the rules.

To be fair, the situation can only improve. Crop Genetics and Advanced Genetics Sciences and the other biotech firms, in requesting permission to test, so far have been pioneers, presenting the EPA with an entirely new set of questions and problems. They have had to do more than their successors will. As well, it was not until last summer that the National Academy of Sciences and the Congressional Office of Technology Assessment weighed in with reports downplaying some of the concerns that had inhibited the EPA. The OTA was particularly blunt: "None of the small-scale field tests proposed or probable within the next several years are likely to result in an environmental problem that would be widespread or difficult to control. . . . Small-scale field tests are likely to be the only way potential risks from commercial-scale uses of genetically engineered organisms can be evaluated."

Even the EPA itself has now suggested that at some time in the near future, the go-ahead for field tests should be given entirely by community-based bio-safety committees, instead of being reviewed centrally by the EPA office in Washington.

Still, it is not clear that the problems that have surrounded biotech regulations are entirely over. Even as the EPA was suggesting that some oversight responsibility be delegated to local safety committees last summer, they were also drafting a new set of strict regulations covering a different category of tests involving the use of genetically engineered micro-organisms under the Toxic Substances Review Act.

What the EPA proposed was that federal oversight be extended to categories of commercial and industrial uses of micro-organisms that had not previously been covered by regulations. In some cases the proposals suggested that scientists conducting tests be required to answer no less than thirty-five questions to the satisfaction of the EPA before being permitted to go ahead with research. The rules are still under discussion and in fact prompted a fierce summer-long battle between the EPA and opponents of the rules throughout the federal bureaucracy, who claimed that the EPA was attempting to extend regulations to cover work that did not even remotely pose any safety or environmental threats.

What this says about the state of biotech regulation, however, is already painfully clear. "EPA's regulatory approach is at odds with the philosophy adopted by the FDA, USDA, National Science Foundation, and National Institutes of Health, as well as the government's position at the OECD [Organization of Economic Coordination and Development]," one of the industry's trade associations said in a statement last summer. Not even the government itself can decide what kind of risk is posed to the environment by genetic engineering.

There are other issues that continue to plague the biotech industry. For example, the OTA and some federal authorities have given their blessing to small-scale experiments. But how will regulators react when a biotech firm wants to jump from a relatively innocuous one-acre test to an experiment covering several hundred acres? And is throwing responsibility for approving tests to community-based safety committees really an advance? Some industry officials worry that this would simply make regulation more capricious, with parts of the country less convinced of the merits of biotechnology and making life worse for the industry than it was under the previous system. What would happen, after all, if Mayor Velluci and his visions of Frankenstein were on a local bio-safety committee?

The solution for biotechnology obviously must lie with more careful collection of data and gradual lifting of the regulatory umbrella as the risks become better known. There must also be a careful assessment of how the risks involved with biotechnology compare with the risks inherent in the methods and technology it replaces, how genetically engineered pesticides match up against chemicals that contaminate groundwater and lay waste to lab rats.

But in this, the biotech industry has not always been successful. In a press release last spring, for example, Crop Genetics International, the Maryland company with a new idea for protecting corn from caterpillar infestation, pointed out that one of the advantages of a genetically engineered corn pesticide was that the chemical currently used to protect corn from caterpillars has the unintended side effect of killing 2.5 million birds annually, among them the endangered bald eagle.

There was nothing untruthful about the CGI press release. At worst it was impolitic, pointing out an uncomfortable truth about the environmental toll that chemically based agriculture takes on the environment. But when word of the release came back to CGI's heavyweight panel on social responsibility, Ruckelshaus and three others on the committee quit, along with the company's lawyer. There were rumors subsequently that the company that makes the pesticide had put pressure on Crop Genetics, and that some members of the committee had important ties to the chemical industry they wished to protect. But the gist of the whole affair was always crystal clear. Like so many others who have weighed in on the biotech debate over the past few years, Ruckelshaus and company's sense of social responsibility extended to making biotech safe for the world. It did not extend to making the world safe for birds.

There are other areas, beyond the question of releasing genetically engineered organisms, where the regulation of biotechnology has appeared to turn more on emotional and political issues than on an accurate perception of risk. When the U.S. Patent Office in early 1988 first granted a patent for a genetically altered animal, the decision raised a storm of protest and calls for a moratorium on animal patents from some religious leaders, legislators, and biotechnology's traditional critics in the environmental community. But the rational connection between the group's disquiet over animal research and their calls for a patent moratorium was never clear. A patent, after all, is simply one of a number of legal tools an inventor can use to protect the fruits of his labor. Without patents, the industry made clear, the commercialization of animal research would simply go forward by other means: technological advances once made public would be kept as trade secrets, or buyers would be bound by legal contracts to respect intellectual property that the patent law would not. In short, while the arguments made by biotech's critics about the unanswered moral questions raised by pressing forward with genetic research with animals may well be sound, the expression of that concern was not. The would-be regulator had missed the mark. The industry, though clad in a ridiculous space suit, was lumbering on.

The debate about biotechnology, as essayist Lewis Thomas wrote in the *New England Journal of Medicine* some years ago, "has become an emotional issue, with too many irretrievably lost tempers on both sides. It has lost the sound of a discussion of technological safety, and now begins to sound like something else, almost like a religious controversy. . . ."

There is nothing especially unique about this kind of public policy debate in American life, of course. It is news to no one that the allocation of public resources often has less to do with maximizing the health and welfare of Americans than with responding to regulatory whims and imagined threats to health and safety. Still, with biotechnology, there seems to be a special imperative to decipher just where the true risk lies, and what it is the public deserves to be protected from. At the moment the stakes are simply strawberries that survive the nip of frost and a reprieve for the country's elm trees. But there may come a time when biotechnology moves beyond these early experiments to more profound manipulation of plant and animal life. What will happen then?

THE AMERICAN ENVIRONMENT

John Steele Gordon

INTRODUCTION

Since late Paleolithic times, when a great burst of creativity led to an expanded order of tools and weapons, humans have progressively gained mastery over their environment. Many anthropologists and paleontologists, for example, attribute the extinction of large-animal species to both climatological changes and to the introduction of such efficient new weapons as the bow and arrow. As it resulted, this was only the first time that technology adversely affected the environment. The mechanization of agriculture wiped out the forests of Europe and eastern North America by the late 1800s. But it was not until the tremendous growth of industry in the nineteenth and early twentieth centuries that technology seemed to threaten whole ecosystems, with dangerous consequences for human health and well-being.

This article by John Steele Gordon shows how perceptions of the environment have changed over time. In the nineteenth century, most Americans regarded nature and the environment as hostile entities to be exploited and controlled, and directed their technology to those ends. But a series of events, beginning with the Dust Bowl of the 1930s and culminating in the realization in the 1960s that modern pesticides and herbicides were causing lasting environmental damage, led to a change in the climate of opinion. By 1970, the common perception was that the natural world was fragile, and that it had to be protected and nourished.

Correspondingly, policies, programs, and technologies have been developed and implemented to mitigate the degradation of the environment. Smokestack "scrubbers" have eliminated much of the particulate emissions from heavy industry, municipal sewage treatment plants have cleaned up many of the nation's waterways, and new pesticides have been introduced that are more discriminatory and less persistent. But, in the minds of many, more still needs to be done. Emissions of carbon dioxide and the release of chlorofluorocarbons (CFCs) into the air have been linked to global warming and depletion of the ozone layer in the upper atmosphere. For the most part, the technology and the expertise are available to deal with these problems, but it will be costly. The question then becomes, as Gordon indicates, philosophical and economic: How clean is clean enough? Who will pay and how will they pay for additional, incremental improvements to the environment? In an advanced technological society like that of the United States, continued environmental progress will involve uncomfortable choices about individual technologies and may result in infringements on traditionally held freedoms.

Gordon's article, while focusing on the United States, stresses how the environment and technology demand thinking on a global scale. The destruction of the Amazonian rain forest affects Americans and Europeans just as much as it affects the people of Brazil. The decision-making process, therefore, involves the accumulation and interpretation of data from all over the planet, which is a time-consuming and expensive proposition. Furthermore, environmental considerations must be balanced against growth and development, especially in the Third World, where peoples are striving to improve their standards of living. These are worldwide concerns that demand the foresight and cooperation of all nations.

The Cuyahoga River died for our sins. In 1796 the Cuyahoga, which promised easy transportation into the wilderness of the Ohio country from Lake Erie, prompted the city of Cleveland into existence. Over the next 170 years a primitive frontier town grew into a mighty industrial city, one that stretched for miles along the banks of its seminal river.

By the mid-twentieth century, however, the river no longer served as a major artery of transportation, having been superseded by railroads and highways. Now, instead of carrying the products of civilization into the vast interior, it carried the effluent of a far more technically advanced civilization out into the lake. The once crystalline waters of the river had become turbid and rank with its new cargo of chemicals and sewage. Its once abundant wildlife had long since fled, leaving only a few carps and suckers to eke out a living in the foul sullage on its bottom, testifying thereby to the very tenacity of life itself.

Finally, late in the morning of June 22, 1969, the Cuyahoga could no longer bear the burden humankind had placed upon it. In a sort of fluvial *cri de coeur,* the river burst into flames.

The fire was no will-o'-the-wisp flickering over a transient oil stick. Rather, it roared five stories into the sky, reduced wooden railroad trestles to ruins, and demonstrated to the people of Cleveland and the nation as no scientific study or news report ever could that the burden being placed on the environment was reaching limits that could be crossed only at the peril of the future.

Less than a year later, on April 22, 1970, Earth Day was held, one of the most remarkable happenings in the history of democracy. Fully 10 percent of the population of the country, twenty million people, demonstrated their support for redeeming the American environment. They attended events in every state and nearly every city and county. American politics and public policy would never be the same again.

Today, nearly a quarter-century after the fire, sunlight once more sparkles off the surface of the Cuyahoga. Boaters cruise its waters for pleasure, and diners eat at riverside restaurants. Mayflies—so characteristic of a Great Lakes spring—once more dance in the air above it in their millions while their larvae provide food for at least twenty-seven species of fish that have returned to its waters.

The Cuyahoga is not pristine, and barring an alteration in human priorities and circumstances beyond anything now imagined, it will not become so. But it has changed greatly for the better and continues to improve. It is once more a living river.

The Cuyahoga and its history is a microcosm of the American environment. For the history of that environment is the story of the interaction between a constantly changing, ever-more-powerful technology and an only slowly shifting paradigm of humankind's proper relationship with the natural world.

"DOMINION . . . OVER EVERY LIVING THING"

Human beings evolved in the Old World, a fact that more than once would have sudden and drastic consequences for the New.

The beginning of the Upper Paleolithic period was marked by a dramatic technological development as humans acquired tools and weapons that were far more sophisticated than any known before and became the most formidable hunters the world has ever known. In the Old World both our prey and our competitors, evolving alongside, quickly learned to treat the emerging biological superpower with the greatest respect, and most were able to adapt successfully. But the New World lay in innocence while human hunters perfected their newfound skills in the Old.

When the land bridge that was a temporary consequence of the last ice age allowed humans to migrate into it, the results were swift and devastating: much of the North American Pleistocene fauna went extinct. Horses, camels, mastodons, mammoths, true elephants, several species of deer, bison, and antelope, ground sloths, glyptodonts, and giant beavers vanished, as did their associated predators, such as saber-toothed cats, giant lions, and cheetahs.

It cannot be known for sure to what extent the arrival of human hunters affected this great extinction, but there is little doubt that it was an important, perhaps fundamental, factor. But the evolutionary equilibrium that had been shattered by the arrival of the super-hunters eventually returned, for the human population of the New World, limited by numerous other factors besides food supply, remained low. And the surviving among the species they had encountered quickly adapted to the new conditions.

Thus the next human culture that appeared in the New World, the Europeans, found it to possess a biological abundance and diversity of, to them, astounding proportions. But these newcomers failed almost entirely to appreciate this aspect of the New World, for hunting in their culture had been reduced to, at most, a secondary source of food.

They were heirs to the agricultural revolution that began in the Old World at the end of the last ice age. It, too, was marked by a profound leap in technology. In turn the more settled conditions of agricultural communities allowed the development of still more elaborate technologies as well as social and political organizations of unprecedented complexity. The result was what we call civilization.

But the early civilizations were acutely aware that they were small islands surrounded by vast seas of wilderness from which savage beasts, and savage men, might come at any time and wipe them out. Thus their inhabitants came to look on the wilderness as an alien place, separate and apart. Not surprisingly under these circumstances, the religions that developed in the Near East in the wake of the agricultural revolution reflected this worldview, sanctioned it, and codified it. Because it became, quite literally, Holy Writ, it persisted unquestioned for centuries.

The Book of Genesis, in fact, could hardly be more direct on the subject. "God said unto [man], Be fruitful, and multiply, and replenish [i.e., fill] up the earth, and subdue it: and have dominion over the fish of the sea, and over the fowl of the air, and over every living thing that moveth upon the earth."

Over the next more than two thousand years, humans operating with this worldview in mind transformed the continent of Europe, and by the time they began to expand overseas, wilderness had disappeared from all but the margins of that continent.

Thus the world they encountered in North America was unlike anything they had ever seen. The greatest temperate forest in the world, teeming with life, stretched almost unbroken from the Atlantic seaboard to well west of the Mississippi. The grasslands that filled the Great Plains in the rain shadow of the Rocky Mountains also abounded with animal life as millions of bison, pronghorn antelope, elk, white-tailed and mule deer roamed it, as did their associated predators, the wolf, the mountain lion, the bear, and the jaguar.

Farther west still, the forests of the Northwest and the deserts of the Southwest reached to the Pacific.

A "HOWLING DESART"

When the new settlers arrived, they did not see the beauty or abundance of the wilderness that greeted them. Far from it; they regarded it as barren and threatening because the ancient paradigm that dated to the dawn of civilization still molded their thinking. Thus they regarded their first task in the New World to be a re-creation of what they had known in the Old, an environment shaped by the hand of man, for man's benefit.

But while they sought, as nearly as possible, to re-create the Europe they had left behind, converting the "remote, rocky, barren, bushy, wild-woody wilderness" into a "second England for fertilness," there was one way in which the New World was utterly unlike the Old: it possessed an abundance of land so great that it seemed to the early settlers, and to their descendants for many generations, to verge upon the infinite. "The great happiness of my country," wrote the Swiss-born Albert Gallatin, Jefferson's Secretary of the Treasury, "arises from the great plenty of land."

Because the supply seemed without end, the value placed on each unit was small. It is only common sense to husband the scarce and let the plentiful take care of itself. Caring for the land, an inescapable necessity in Europe, was simply not cost-effective here. After all, the settlers could always move on to new, rich land farther west. For three hundred years they did exactly that, with ever-increasing speed.

Americans also developed other habits in the early days that stemmed directly from the wealth of land and scarcity of the population. Today, when American archeologists investigate a site, they know that the place to look for the garbage dump is on the far side of the fence or stone wall that was nearest to the dwelling. In Europe that was likely to belong to a neighbor; in America it was often wilderness and thus beyond the human universe. This out-of-sight-out-of-mind attitude would have no small consequences when technology increased the waste stream by orders of magnitude.

The early settlers, while they greatly altered the landscape of the Eastern seaboard, clearing whole stretches of the primeval forest and converting the land to fields, pastures, and meadows, did not greatly diminish the biological diversity. They opened up the best land for farming but left untouched the steep or rocky areas as well as, to a great extent, the wetlands and mountains. Indeed in some ways the early settlers increased the diversity by expanding habitat for such grassland species as bluebirds, groundhogs, and meadowlarks. The ecosystem as a whole remained intact.

Only in the South, where plantation agriculture became the rule in areas to which it was suited, did monocultural husbandry greatly diminish the fertility and texture of the soil. Virginia, the largest and, thanks to its tobacco exports, most powerful of the colonies, found its yields declining sharply toward the end of the eighteenth century as the best land was exploited and exhausted. Erosion became an increasing problem. As early as the 1780s Patrick Henry thought that "the greatest patriot is he who fills the most gullies."

"A THOUSAND YEARS"

Meanwhile, as a new civilization was being built out of the wilderness of North America, new attitudes toward wilderness itself were emerging in Europe. The ancient paradigm that had gripped Western thinking since Genesis was beginning, partially, to shift at last.

In the seventeenth century, wilderness had been universally regarded as at best a waste, if not an evil. In the eighteenth, however, it began to be seen for the first time as a thing of beauty. Mountains came to be viewed as majestic, not just as an impediment to travel or a barrier against invasion.

In Britain the aristocracy began to lay out gardens, such as those by Capability Brown, that were highly stylized versions of nature itself, rather than the direct refutation of it that seventeenth-century gardens, like those at Versailles, had been.

Biology became a systematic science (although the word itself would enter the language only in the early nineteenth century). Linnaeus studied the relationships of plants and animals. Georges Cuvier, William Smith, and others began to examine fossils and to sense, for the first time, a history of the earth that was at variance with the account given in Genesis.

The new attitude toward wilderness soon came to this country and contributed to the growing American sense of uniqueness. James Fenimore Cooper's novels and Thoreau's essays displayed a love of wilderness that would have been inconceivable a century earlier.

Of course, in Europe wilderness was largely an abstraction. In America it was just down the road. At the end of the Revolution, it nowhere lay more than a few days on horseback from the Atlantic shore, and Thomas Jefferson, no mean observer, thought it would be "a thousand years" before settlement reached the Pacific.

Jefferson was wrong. He did not realize—no one could have—that a third technological revolution was just getting under way, one that would give humankind the power to transform the world far beyond anything provided by the first two. It had taken millennia to reshape the face of Europe to human ends. North America would be transformed in less than a century. But there would be a vast price to pay for this miracle.

The steam engine and its technological successors allowed energy in almost unlimited quantity to be brought to bear on any task. So forests could be cut, fields cleared, dams built, mines worked with unprecedented speed. As a result, in less than a single human lifetime an area of eastern North America larger than all Europe was deforested. Virtually uninhabited by Europeans as late as 1820, the state of Michigan by 1897 had shipped 160 billion board feet of white pine lumber, leaving less than 6 billion still standing.

But the new engines needed fuel. At first waste wood supplied much of it, and later coal and then oil. The byproducts of this combustion were dumped into the atmosphere as they had always been, but now their quantity was increasing geometrically. In 1850 Americans were utilizing more than eight million horsepower, animal and mechanical. By 1900 nearly sixty-four million, almost all mechanical, was being used by what economists call prime movers.

The factory system and mechanization brought many commodities within the financial reach of millions, while new transportation systems created national markets and made economies of scale both possible and necessary. This, in turn, caused the demand for raw materials to soar. The great mineral wealth that was being discovered under the American landscape was exploited with ever-increasing speed. Again the waste products were dumped at the lowest possible cost, which meant, in effect, on the far side of the nearest stone wall.

Increasing wealth and the new technologies allowed cities to bring in fresh, clean water for their rapidly increasing populations. This water was used to flush away the dirt and sewage of human existence, but only into the nearest body of water. The quality of life in the human environment was immeasurably improved by this, as the squalor that had characterized the urban landscape since Roman times disappeared. But the quality of the nation's waterways sharply deteriorated.

The new technology allowed us to turn more and more of the landscape to human use. The old-fashioned moldboard plow, in use since medieval times, could not deal easily with the rich, heavy soils and deep sod of the American Midwest. The steel plow invented by John Deere in 1837 quickly opened up what would become the breadbasket of the world. Wetlands could now be drained economically and made productive. Millions of acres vanished, and their vast and wholly unappreciated biological productivity vanished too.

So rapid an alteration of the landscape could only have a severe impact on the ecosystem as a whole. The loss of so much forest caused runoff to increase sharply, eroding the land and burdening the waters with silt, destroying more wetlands. Many animals' habitats disappeared. And because the ancient biblical notion that humans had dominion over the earth still held, others vanished entirely.

The beautiful Carolina parakeet, North America's only native parrot, proved a major agricultural pest. Because it lived in large, cohesive flocks, it made an easy target for farmers with the shotguns that the Industrial Revolution made cheap. It was extinct in the wild by the turn of the century; the last known specimen died in the Cincinnati Zoo in 1914.

Another avian casualty was the passenger pigeon, one of the great natural wonders of America, as amazing as Niagara Falls or the Grand Canyon. The passenger pigeon almost certainly existed in larger numbers than any other bird in the world. Moreover, it was concentrated in flocks of unbelievable immensity. Audubon reported one flock that took a total of three days to pass overhead and estimated that, at times, the birds flew by at the rate of three hundred million an hour.

The passenger pigeon nested in heavily forested areas in colonies that were often several miles wide and up to forty miles long, containing billions of birds. Trees within the colony each had hundreds of nests, and limbs often broke under the weight. The squabs, too heavy to fly when abandoned by their parents at the end of the nesting season, were easy prey.

With railroads able to ship the fresh-killed birds to the great Eastern cities quickly, hunters slaughtered them in the millions to meet the demand.

Unfortunately it turned out that passenger pigeons needed the company of huge numbers of their fellows to stimulate breeding behavior. Once the size of the flocks fell below a certain very large minimum, the birds stopped reproducing, and the population crashed. Just as with the Carolina parakeet, the last passenger pigeon died in the Cincinnati Zoo in 1914.

The herds of the Great Plains also fell to hunters. It is estimated that upward of thirty million bison roamed the grasslands of North America in the middle of the nineteenth century. By the dawn of the twentieth, less than a thousand remained alive.

"FOREVER WILD"

As early as the 1850s it was clear to the more thoughtful that something precious and irreplaceable was rapidly disappearing. The wilderness that had helped define the country seemed ever more remote. It was now recognized that the natural world could provide refreshment whose need was becoming more and more keenly felt.

Urban parks, such as New York City's incomparable Central and Prospect parks, were intended to provide the population with a taste of nature that many could now obtain no other way. But these parks were, like the aristocratic gardens created in eighteenth-century Britain, wholly man-made and no more truly natural than a sculpture is a rock outcropping.

Movements began to take hold to preserve portions of the fast-vanishing wilderness itself. As early as the 1830s the painter George Catlin put forward the idea of a wild prairie reservation, a suggestion that, alas, was not implemented before nearly all of the country's prairie ecosystem was destroyed. But the movement took root, and in 1864 the first act of preservation was undertaken when ownership of the Yosemite Valley and a stand of sequoias was transferred from the public lands of the United States to the state of California.

In 1872 the first national park in the world was created when reports of the splendors of Yellowstone were delivered to Congress. James Bryce, British ambassador to the United States, called the national parks the best idea America ever had. Certainly they have been widely copied around the world. Today American national parks protect 47,783,680 acres, an area considerably larger than the state of Missouri.

States, too, began to set aside land to protect what was left of the wilderness. New York turned five million acres—15 percent of the state's land area—into the Adirondack Park and Forest Preserve, to remain "forever wild."

In the 1870s Carl Schurz, Secretary of the Interior, began moving for the preservation of federally owned forests. Born in Europe, where forests had long since become scarce and thus precious, and where forest-management techniques were far more advanced than those in this country, Schurz and many others helped create a new concern for America's fast-dwindling woodlands. By the end of Theodore Roosevelt's Presidency, almost sixty million acres were in the forest reserve system.

Today hundreds of millions of acres in this country enjoy various levels of protection from development, and more are added every year. But while the parks and reserves created by this movement are national treasures that have greatly enriched the quality of life, their creation was predicated on the part of the ancient paradigm that still survived. That part held that the natural world and the human one were two separate and distinct places. And it was still thought that each had little effect on the other.

"THE HARMONIES OF NATURE"

It was George Perkins Marsh, lawyer, businessman, newspaper editor, member of Congress, diplomat, Vermont fish commissioner, and lover and keen observer of nature, who first recognized the folly of this unexamined assumption. Growing up in Vermont, he had seen how the clear-cutting of the forests and poor farming practices had degraded the state's environment.

In 1864 he published *Man and Nature,* which he expanded ten years later and published as *The Earth as Modified by Human Action.* Individual instances of human effect on the natural world had been noted earlier, but Marsh, like Darwin with evolution, gathered innumerable examples together and argued the general case. He decisively demonstrated that the impress of humankind on the whole world was deep, abiding, and, because it was largely unnoticed, overwhelmingly adverse. "Man is everywhere a disturbing agent," he wrote. "Wherever he plants his foot, the harmonies of nature are turned to discords."

Recognizing that technology, energy use, population, food production, resource exploitation, and human waste all were increasing on curves that were hyperbolic when plotted against time, he feared for the future. "It is certain," he wrote, "that a desolation, like that which overwhelmed many once beautiful and fertile regions of Europe, awaits an important part of the territory of the United States . . . unless prompt measures are taken."

Darwin's book *On the Origin of Species* provoked a fire storm of controversy in the intellectual world of his time when it was published in 1859. It changed humankind's perception of the world profoundly and immediately. But *Man and Nature* changed nothing. Published only five years later, it met with profound indifference, and its author sank into the undeserved oblivion of those who are out of sync with their times. As late as 1966, when the science of ecology he was instrumental in founding was already well developed, so commodious a reference work as the *Encyclopaedia Britannica* made no mention of him whatever.

Perhaps the difference was that Darwin's ideas had only philosophical, religious, and scientific implications. Marsh's ideas, on the other hand, had profound economic consequences. An America rapidly becoming the world's foremost industrial power did not want to hear them, even though as early as 1881 the mayor of Cleveland could describe the Cuyahoga River as "an open sewer through the center of the city."

"A DIFFERENT WORLD"

In fact, the seeds of the country's first great man-made ecological disaster were being planted even as Marsh wrote.

In the 1860s railroads pushed across the Great Plains and opened them up to settlement by connecting them to Eastern markets. On the high plains toward the Rockies, as hunters slaughtered bison and pronghorns by the millions, ranchers replaced them with cattle, which overgrazed the land. Then farmers began moving in.

World War I greatly increased the demand for wheat, while the tractor made plowing the tough, deep sod of the high plains a more practical proposition. The number of farms in the area east of the Rocky Mountains burgeoned in the 1920s, taking over more and more of the ranchland.

The mean annual rainfall in this area varied between ten and twenty inches, not enough for crop farming except in the best of years. But the early decades of the century happened to see many such years. Then, in the late twenties, the rains slacked off, and drought swept the plains.

This had happened hundreds of times in the past, and the plants and animals that had evolved there were adapted to it. Wheat and cattle were not. Worse, over the last few years, the sod, the deep net of grass roots that had bound the soil together, had been broken over millions of acres by the farmers with their plows. The topsoil, without which no plant can grow nor animal live, now lay exposed to the ceaseless, drying winds.

In 1933 no rain fell for months in western Kansas, and little elsewhere. The crops withered, the livestock died of thirst or starvation, and the dust, bound by neither sod nor moisture, began to blow. On November 11 a howling, rainless storm sprang up. "By midmorning," a reporter wrote of a farm in South Dakota, "a gale was blowing cold and black. By noon it was blacker than night, because one can see through the night and this was an opaque black. It was a wall of dirt one's eyes could not penetrate, but it could penetrate the eyes and ears and nose. It could penetrate to the lungs until one coughed up black. . . .

"When the wind died and the sun shone forth again, it was on a different world. There were no fields, only sand drifting into mounds and eddies that swirled in what was now but an autumn breeze. There was no longer a section-line road fifty feet from the front door. It was obliterated. In the farmyard, fences, machinery, and trees were gone, buried. The roofs of sheds stuck out through drifts deeper than a man is tall."

The dust of this storm, uncountable millions of tons of topsoil, darkened the skies of Chicago the following day and those of Albany, New York, the day after that. Terrible as it was, the storm proved but the first of many that ravaged the high plains in the next several years, as the drought tightened its grip and the unforgiving winds blew and blew. In the middle years of the 1930s, they laid waste thousands of square miles of what had been, just a few years earlier, a vibrant ecosystem. It was now the Dust Bowl. Upward of two hundred thousand people were forced to abandon their farms and trek westward in desperate search of the necessities of life itself.

The rains finally came again, and in the 1940s the discovery of the Oglala aquifer, a vast reservoir of water that underlies much of the Midwest, rescued the farmers who remained. Tapped by ever-deeper wells, the aquifer is now seriously depleted. And economics is slowly rescuing the land as the price of water increases every year.

It was always marginal for farming, and so it remains. Even with many, though mostly ill-conceived, federal programs, the farmers on the high plains are finding it ever harder to compete in world markets. Every year more and more farms are abandoned, and the land reverts to what in a perfect world it would never have ceased to be—shortgrass prairie.

"A PHRASE CONCEIVED IN ARROGANCE"

The technological leap that had begun in Jefferson's day only accelerated in the twentieth century. The burdens that had been placed on the environment in the nineteenth century by such things as fuel use and sewage disposal increased sharply as the population expanded and new technologies spread across the land.

The limits of the ability of the environment to cope with the load were being reached more and more often. In October 1947 a thermal inversion settled over Donora, Pennsylvania. The town is set in a natural basin and was home to much heavy industry. The layer of cold air trapped the effluent of that industry and of the cars and furnaces of the population. By the time the inversion ended, four days later, twenty people were dead and six thousand ill enough to require treatment.

To an astonishing extent—at least as viewed from today's perspective—the people of the time accepted such happenings as the price of the Industrial Revolution that had brought them so much wealth and material comfort. A *New Yorker* cartoon of the day showed a woman sitting at a table set for lunch in the garden of a New York brownstone. "Hurry, darling," she calls to her unseen husband, "your soup is getting dirty."

New burdens were also added. The chemical industry grew quickly in this century, fueled by an explosion in knowledge. The disposition of chemicals was, as always, over the nearest stone wall: into a landfill or convenient body of water.

Agriculture became more businesslike as farms grew in size, became much more mechanized, and increasingly specialized in one or two crops. Of course, even Patrick Henry had known, two centuries earlier, that monocultural farming depletes the soil and is vulnerable to insects and other pests. But now the chemical industry could overcome this, thanks to synthetic fertilizers and pesticides.

Such chemicals as DDT were greeted as miracles of modern science when they first became available, and their use spread rapidly. In 1947 the United States produced 124,259,000 pounds of chemical pesticides. Only thirteen years later, in 1960, production was up to 637,666,000 pounds of often far more potent pesticides.

Diseases such as malaria and agricultural pests such as the boll weevil were declared on the verge of eradication. And the "control of nature," the final realization of the dominion enjoined by Genesis, was said to be at hand. DDT and other pesticides sprayed from airplanes blanketed vast areas, to kill gypsy moths, budworms, and mosquitoes.

But there were troubling signs for the few who looked. The pesticides were nondiscriminatory; they killed all the insects they touched. Honeybees, essential for the pollination of many crops and innumerable natural plants, were often wiped out by spraying programs aimed at other insects. Beekeepers began to fight back with lawsuits. "It is a very distressful thing," one beekeeper wrote, "to walk into a yard in May and not hear a bee buzz."

More than two hundred new pesticides were introduced in the years following World War II. The reason was that the older ones became increasingly ineffective. Many species of insects go through numerous generations a year and can evolve very rapidly, especially when a severe pressure such as a new pesticide is applied. In a monument to the vigor with which life clings to existence, they did exactly that.

And birdwatchers noticed a troubling decline in the numbers of some species, especially the large raptors that lived at the top of the food chains. Charles Broley, a retired banker, banded bald eagles in Florida beginning in 1939 as a hobby. He usually banded about a hundred and fifty young birds a year on the stretch of coast he patrolled. Beginning in 1947, more and more nests were empty or held eggs that had failed to hatch. In 1957 he found only eight eaglets, the following year only one.

But these troubling events were scattered, knowledge of them dispersed over a huge country and many scientific disciplines. They were no match for the chemical companies. But these, it turned out, were no match for a frail middle-aged woman named Rachel Carson.

Rachel Carson was trained as a marine biologist, but she was a born writer. In 1952 her book *The Sea Around Us* was published with a very modest first printing. To everyone's astonishment—most of all hers—it became a titanic bestseller that made its author famous across America. Ten years later she published *Silent Spring*. It changed the world.

Again a huge bestseller, *Silent Spring* detailed in lucid, often poetic, and always accessible prose how pesticides were playing havoc with the air, land, and water of the country and how their uncontrolled use was doing far more harm than good. Further, it introduced millions of Americans to the concept that the natural world was an intimately interconnected web. This web, Carson made clear, included humans quite as much as every other living thing that shared planet Earth. What killed insects would, if not handled carefully, one day kill us too. George Perkins Marsh had said much the same thing a hundred years earlier. This time the people read and believed.

The ancient paradigm from the dawn of civilization, when man was frail and nature omnipotent, was dead at last. Dead with it was what had been in theory a dream and in fact a nightmare—the control of nature. It had been, Rachel Carson wrote on the last page of *Silent Spring,* "a phrase conceived in arrogance."

"THE SKY IS FALLING"

Within a few years the public demand for action in behalf of the environment became irresistible, and it caught a complacent government by surprise. John C. Whitaker, Nixon's cabinet secretary, later recalled that "we were totally unprepared for the tidal wave of public opinion in favor of cleaning up the environment."

Earth Day cleared up any lingering doubts about the public's opinion on the matter. Federal government agencies such as the Environmental Protection Agency were created, and goals and timetables for air and water quality were established. We Americans set out on a crusade to rescue the land from ourselves. In many ways we shared the fervor with which the medieval world had set out to rescue the Holy Land from the infidel.

Today, nearly a quarter-century after the crusade to the new Jerusalem of a clean environment began, there is vast progress to report. In 1959, 24.9 million tons of particulate matter—soot—were emitted into the air in the United States. By 1985, 7.2 million were, and less every year. In 1970, 28.4 million tons of sulfur oxides, a prime contributor to smog, were released by power plants and automobiles. In 1990, 21.2 million tons were, a drop of nearly 25 percent. Carbon monoxide emission has fallen by 40 percent since 1970, and lead has been eliminated as an additive to gasoline.

Cars being manufactured in the 1990s emit only a fifth as much pollution as those made before 1975. Thus 80 percent of all automobile pollution today is generated by just

10 percent of the cars on the road. In the next few years, as these clunkers end up on the scrap heap, automobile pollution will decrease sharply.

Already the number of days per year when the air quality is below standards in most of the country's cities has fallen significantly, by 38 percent in the 1980s alone. Even Los Angeles, the smog capital of the country thanks to its geography and automobile-oriented infrastructure, has enjoyed a 25 percent decline in smog-alert days.

In 1960 only about 50 million Americans were served by municipal sewage plants that provided secondary or tertiary treatment. Today more than half the population is. As a result, many urban waterways are now cleaner than they have been since the early 1800s. New York used to dump the sewage of eight million people into the Hudson, Harlem, and East rivers. Today, in a development that would have stunned turn-of-the-century New Yorkers, there is an annual swimming race around Manhattan Island.

Rural rivers too have greatly benefited. Most of the Connecticut River's four-hundred-mile length was declared "suitable only for transportation of sewage and industrial wastes" in the 1960s. Today 125 new or upgraded water treatment plants, costing $900 million, have transformed it. Fishing and swimming are now allowed almost everywhere, and wildlife such as ospreys, bald eagles, blue crabs, and salmon has returned in numbers.

The sludge that is the end product of sewage treatment was until very recently dumped in the ocean or into landfills. Now it is increasingly being sought by farmers as a cheap fertilizer and soil conditioner. New York City produces 385 tons a day, all of it once dumped beyond the continental shelf. One hundred tons of that is being used by farmers in Colorado and Arizona. Initially skeptical, fifty of those farmers recently sent New York's mayor a letter asking for more. He's likely to oblige. Boston sludge now fertilizes Florida citrus groves. And because sewage sludge not only fertilizes but improves soil quality, it is displacing chemical fertilizers.

As old factories reach the end of their productive lives and are replaced by new ones built under stringent controls, the non-sewage pollution of the waterways is also steadily declining. The violation rate (the percentage of tests where the amount of pollutants was found to be above standards) for lead and cadmium fell to less than one percent. Dissolved oxygen is an important measure of a water body's biological viability. The percentage of times it was found to be below standard fell 60 percent in the 1980s.

Many bodies of water, such as Lake Erie, declared dead in the 1970s, have bounded back with the improved situation and with the help of life's ferocious determination to go on living. The amounts of pesticides being used every year fell by more than a quarter in the 1980s, and those in use today are far less persistent and far less toxic than most of those in widespread use in the 1960s. The level of DDT present in human fatty tissue, a fair measure of its presence in the environment, was 7.95 parts per million in 1970. By 1983 it had fallen to 1.67 parts per million. Today, ten years later, no one even bothers to gather the statistic.

The land, too, has improved. In the eastern part of the United States, the area of forest land has been increasing for more than a century, as clear-cut areas have been allowed to regenerate. It will be another hundred years, at least, before they reach the climax stage, but they are on their way. And today 28 percent of all farmland is no longer plowed at all, and the percentage is growing quickly. Conservation tillage is used instead; the method sharply reduces erosion and improves soil quality while slashing costs, producing crops for as much as 30 percent less.

Programs to reduce the use of chemical fertilizers are being tried in more and more areas as farmers learn new techniques. In Iowa in 1989 and 1990 a joint EPA-state program helped farmers cut their use of nitrogen fertilizer by four hundred million pounds without sacrificing crop yields. Because agricultural fertilizers and pesticides now account for more than 65 percent of all water pollution (factories account for only 7 percent), this trend has no small implication for the future.

Wildlife is on the mend in many ways. To be sure, the number of species on the endangered list has grown sharply in the last two decades, but that is much more an artifact of increased knowledge than of a still-deteriorating situation.

Many species have rebounded sharply, thanks in some cases to protection and in others to the explosion of biological and ecological knowledge that has so marked the last twenty-five years. To give just two examples, alligators, once hunted mercilessly for their skins, are no longer on the list at all. And peregrine falcons, almost extirpated in the Eastern United States by DDT, have been with infinite care and effort put on the road to recovery. Today there is a pair nesting on the Verrazano Bridge at the entrance to New York's Upper Bay, and there is even a pair nesting on the top of the Met Life (formerly Pan Am) building in midtown, exploiting the distinctly unendangered local pigeon population.

Nor has public interest in rescuing the environment slackened. *The New York Times Index* for 1960 needed less than 19 inches to list all the references to air pollution that year, and only 15 for water pollution. In 1991 the two subjects required 87 and 107 inches respectively. Local organizations monitoring local situations have multiplied across the country. Many hire professionals, such as the Hudson River Fisherman's Association, whose "riverkeeper" patrols the Eastern seaboard's most beautiful waterway.

And public opinion has become a powerful force. In the fall of 1992 the governor of Alaska proposed culling the number of wolves in the state in order to increase the number of moose and caribou for human hunters. It was not long before he wished he hadn't. The state, heavily dependent on tourist dollars, was soon backpedaling furiously before the onslaught of intensely negative public reaction.

So is the American environment once more pristine? Of course not. Many pollutants have proved unexpectedly stubborn and persistent. Many businesses have resisted changing their ways. In most cities the storm and waste sewers are still one and the same, and sewage overflows in bad weather. It will take many years and billions of dollars to correct that. An unknowable number of species are still threatened by human activity.

But the nation's water, air, land, and wildlife all are better, in many respects, than they have been in a century, and they continue to improve. To put it another way, if the task of cleaning up the American environment were a journey from Boston to Los Angeles, we would be well past the Appalachians and might even have the Mississippi in sight.

Then why is the impression so widespread that we are, at best, entering Worcester, if not actually marching backward somewhere in Maine? There are many reasons, and as so often happens, human nature lies at the root of all of them.

A first reason is that environmental bureaucrats, like all bureaucrats, want to maximize the personnel and budgets of their departments. So from their point of view, it simply makes good sense to highlight new problems and to minimize news about the old ones that have been successfully addressed. Similarly, environmental organizations live and die by fundraising. The-sky-is-falling stories are simply far more effective in getting someone to reach for a checkbook than are things-are-looking-up stories. And environmental bureaucrats and lobbyists alike know that they must struggle hard to maintain their constituencies and budgets to fight the serious problems that do persist. They fear, not without reason, that if they don't play up the troubles that endure, they may lose the ability to address them at all—and we might lose much of what we've won.

A second reason is that the media have often failed to evaluate environmental stories with scientific competence and sometimes even honesty. As in fundraising, bad news sells better than good news.

As a result, tentative data have often been presented as irrefutable fact, and short-term or local trends have been extrapolated into global catastrophes. In the 1970s there were many stories about the coming ice age. Ten years later global warming was destined to extinguish civilization.

A third reason that things often seem to be getting worse here at home is extremists. Extremists are always present in great reform movements, and the goal of environmental extremists is not a clean environment but a perfect one. They are few in number, compared with the legions now dedicated to cleaning the American environment, but like many extremists, they are often gifted propagandists and they are willing to use ignoble means to further noble ends.

Consider the support given by some environmental organizations to the Delaney Clause. This law, passed in 1958, requires that even the slightest residue of pesticides that have been shown to cause cancer in laboratory animals may not be present in processed foods. The Delaney Clause made some sense in the 1950s, when our ability to detect chemicals was limited to about one part in a million and our knowledge of carcinogens was rudimentary at best. Today it is nothing short of ludicrous, for we can now detect chemicals in amounts of one part in a quintillion. To get some idea of what that means, here is the recipe for making a martini in the ratio of 1:1,000,000,000,000,000,000: Fill up the Great Lakes—all five of them—with gin. Add one tablespoon of vermouth, stir well, and serve.

As a result, to give just one example, propargite, a nonpersistent pesticide that controls mites on raisins, can't be used because it has been shown to cause cancer when fed to rats in massive doses. But a human being would have to eat eleven tons of raisins a day to ingest the amount of propargite needed to induce cancer in laboratory rats. Had it been available in the 1950s, propargite's use would have been perfectly legal because the infinitesimal residue would have been completely undetectable.

Every first-year medical student knows it is the dosage that makes the poison. Yet many environmental organizations are adamantly against any revision of the Delaney Clause for reasons that amount to nothing less than scientific know-nothingism. They are wasting time, money, and, most important, credibility on the chimera of perfection.

But time, money, and most of all credibility are precious commodities. For even if we are at the Mississippi on the journey to clean up the American environment, we still have two-thirds of the journey to go. And it will be the most difficult part.

For as we proceed, the problems will become more and more intractable, and thus more and more expensive to deal with. For instance, it was easy to get a lot of lead out of the atmosphere. We simply stopped adding it to gasoline as an antiknock agent, virtually the sole source of atmospheric lead. But getting the fertilizers and pesticides out of agricultural runoff—now far and away the greatest source of water pollution in the country—

will be another matter altogether, especially if we are to keep the price of food from rising sharply.

Part of the problem is the iron law of diminishing returns. Getting, say, 90 percent of a pollutant out of the environment may be easy and relatively cheap. But the next 9 percent might cost as much as the first 90, and so might the next .9 percent, and so on. At some point we have to say, "That's clean enough." Where that point will be, in case after case, is going to have to be decided politically, and democratic politics requires give and take on all sides to work.

Another part of the problem is that, increasingly, environmental regulations have been impinging on private property rights. In the early days, the environmental movement was largely about cleaning up the commons—the air and water that belong to us all. The rule of thumb was easy: he who pollutes—whether the factory owner or the commuter in his automobile—should bear the cost of cleaning up now and of preventing that pollution in the future. Today, however, new regulations are more likely to affect the ways in which someone can use his or her own property and thus gravely affect its economic value.

There is a genuine clash of basic rights here. One is the individual right to hold, enjoy, and profit from private property. The other is the general right to pass on to our children a healthy and self-sustaining environment.

To give just one specific example of how these rights can clash, a man in South Carolina bought beachfront property in the 1980s for $600,000. The property was worth that much because it consisted of two buildable lots. He intended to build two houses, one for himself and one to sell. But the state then changed the regulations, to protect the delicate shoreline ecosystem, and his property became unbuildable. Its value plummeted from $600,000 to perhaps $30,000.

Not surprisingly, the owner sued for the economic loss he had suffered. But the state ruled that it was merely regulating in the public interest and that no compensation was due as it was not a "taking": the property still belonged to the owner. The property owner argued that the regulations, however valuable a public purpose they served, had indeed effected a taking, because the state had sucked the economic value out of his property, leaving him the dried husk of legal title.

This case is still in the courts, and cases like it are multiplying. A general acknowledgment of the validity of both sides' rights and motives is necessary if difficult matters such as these are to be resolved successfully.

Still a third problem is that, increasingly, environmental issues are global issues, beyond the reach of individual sovereign states. Worse, scientists have been studying the earth as a single, interlocking ecosystem for only the last few decades. Global weather and ocean temperature data nowhere stretch back more than a hundred and fifty years and usually much less. The amount of data we possess, therefore, is often insufficient to allow for the drawing of significant conclusions. Has the recent increase in atmospheric carbon dioxide caused an increase in average temperatures, or has a normal cyclical increase in temperature caused an increase in carbon dioxide? We just don't know the answer to that question. But billions, perhaps trillions of dollars in spending may depend on the answer.

Another issue is growth versus the environment. Many feel that economic growth and increased pollution are two sides of the same coin, that it is impossible to have the one without the other. Others feel that economic growth is the very key to cleaning up the environment because it alone can provide the wealth to do so.

Obviously, in some absolute sense, the more production of goods and services, the more waste products that must be dealt with. But if the wealth produced greatly exceeds the pollution produced, the pollution can be dealt with while standards of living continue to rise. Certainly among the world's densely populated countries, the correlation between wealth and environmental quality is striking. People cannot worry about the problem of tomorrow's environment if the problem of tonight's supper looms large. It is landless peasants, more than timber barons, who are cutting down the Amazon rain forest.

So far there has been no flagging of the pace or weakening of the spirit on the crusade to a clean American environment. The commitment of the American people is firm. Doubtless it will remain firm, too, if, in the midst of the ferocious political debates sure to come, we all keep in mind the fact that honorable people can disagree about means without disagreeing about ends; that there is more than one road to the New Jerusalem; and, especially, that cleaning up the American environment is far too important to be left to bureaucrats, activists, journalists, and fanatics. This is our crusade.

AGRICULTURE FOR DEVELOPING NATIONS

Francesca Bray

INTRODUCTION

It is easy in the early twenty-first century to view all that has come before us as natural and inevitable. It is somehow comforting for students of the history of technology to look at change as evolutionary, with one invention building on another in a cumulative, progressive, and linear advance toward a better world. Yet, as Francesca Bray suggests in this selection, the Western model for agricultural development may have been based on a unique set of historical circumstances that have little or nothing to do with the developing or Third World. Even worse, efforts to impose the Western model on other countries may have had negative social and economic consequences.

It is clear from this article that the so-called green revolution, which saw the introduction of high-yield varieties of wheat, corn, and rice, was largely based on Western concepts of growth and development, and did little to take into account longer-term ideas of conservation and sustainability. The green revolution succeeded in one sense; it allowed the growing of enough staple grains to feed the world's population. But the technology polarized societies, drove farmers off the land, caused extensive environmental damage, and left many agricultural societies dependent on external supplies of fossil fuels and chemical fertilizers and pesticides. It was a classic instance of what some historians have seen as domineering Western paternalism and the failure of technocrats to understand the delicate economic and cultural synergisms of Third World agricultural societies.

Bray argues that it is time to think about alternatives. She proposes using a version of the East Asian wet-rice agriculture for the developing world. This form of agriculture is labor-intensive, at least early in the cultivation process, but later on involves little maintenance and requires virtually no capital inputs such as machinery or chemicals. Because of its scale, wet-rice agriculture promotes rural prosperity and independence and can form the basis for the development of a balanced agricultural-industrial economy. During the rule of Mao Zedong, China emphasized grain production to the virtual exclusion of all other agricultural products. The result was a phenomenal increase in productivity, but it came at the cost of severe environmental damage. Since the 1970s, China has gone back to traditional agricultural practices and introduced more crop diversification, with no loss in productivity and major gains in farm prices and income. The Japanese experience with small-scale agriculture has been less successful, but reforms are underway that should correct the problems that have led to high costs and excessive use of machinery and fertilizers.

Whether or not Bray's ideas will provide solutions to the problems of the economy and the environment in the Third World remains to be seen, but it is clear from events so far that Western agricultural methods and technologies have not been able to break the cycle of poverty and hunger that continues to haunt the world's developing nations.

People in the rich industrial countries have fixed ideas about the development of agriculture. Children at school learn about the technical progress from digging stick to hoe and from the cattle-drawn wooden ard to the tractor-driven, steel-shared plow. Economists and sociologists describe the shift from small family farms to large, efficient commercial enterprises. Human labor and skills yield to increasingly complicated machines. Although at times we feel pangs of nostalgia for the old ways, we know that the Western model traces the inevitable path of human progress.

Or does it? Mounting frustration over attempts to plan agricultural development around the world has made it clear that the way farming developed in Europe and North America may not, after all, be the best model in the poor countries of Africa, Asia, and Latin America—nor, indeed, for the survival of the biosphere. The Earth Summit held in 1992 in Rio de Janeiro marked the official endorsement of a new, critical approach to the world's problems with resources. Its key words are not "growth" and "development" but "conservation" and "sustainability." The basic philosophy of classical agricultural and economic development—more is better, for everybody—is now seriously in question.

Yet the world still faces urgent problems of poverty, hunger, and disease. Rural populations are especially deprived and vulnerable. The great question is whether agricultural policies based on conservation and sustainability can solve these acute problems. Or is conventional growth-driven development, for all its drawbacks, the only way to improve rural living standards? I shall argue here that the Western model may not be the ideal for every developing region.

As critics of classical development policies have pointed out, the world now produces more than enough food for everyone, but development has often worsened the inequities of distribution. In fact, this trend is hardly surprising if one examines the criteria that define development in agriculture. The "modernization" of agriculture, as generally understood, entails the application of science, technology, and capital to increase the output of just a few crops that have world markets—among them wheat and rice for human consumption, corn and soybeans for animal feed, and cotton for industry.

This approach gives rise to issues of equity and conservation. In terms of equity, the system favors rich farmers and puts poor ones at a disadvantage. In addition, specialization and economies of scale reduce economic diversity and employment opportunities in rural areas. The system entails three problems in conservation. Monoculture reduces biodiversity. The intensive use of fossil fuels and chemical inputs creates pollution; often the inputs of energy equal or even exceed the output of crops. Large-scale mechanized operations hasten soil erosion and other environmental degradation.

For these reasons, the trend of Western agricultural development toward industrial farming has come under increasing challenge from conservationists and also from social groups that feel threatened by it—among them Indians in the Mexican state of Chiapas and owners of small farms in France. Are there alternatives to the Western model, or do we need to invent new models? Environmentalists have identified several apparently sustainable local farming traditions—all of them forms of polyculture. All farming systems were originally polycultures providing a range of basic requirements for subsistence. In some Mediterranean areas today, one can find farmers planting wheat and barley around their olive trees. Much of the North American wheat belt used to support mixed grain and dairy farming. A form of polyculture that has recently attracted attention from agronomists because of its different sustainability is the system whereby corn, beans, and squash are planted in the same hole. They complement rather than compete with one another because their root systems draw nutrition and moisture from different levels of the soil. In fact, the roots of the bean actually fix nitrates and so furnish natural fertilizer for the corn. This highly intensive form of land use was first developed well over 2,000 years ago. It sustained great civilizations such as the Maya and continues to support dense pockets of population all over Central America.

Are there other types of agricultural systems that might support sustainable but intensive development on a scale large enough to address the dire problems of rural poverty faced by many developing nations? The answer requires first a definition of "sustainable." To my mind, a sustainable agricultural system cannot be judged simply by the ecological soundness of its farming methods. It must also provide a living for all its population, farmers and non-farmers alike. The majority of the world's poor live in the countryside; rural populations are still growing, and urban services and industries now absorb less labor than they once did. A sustainable agricultural system must therefore be able to create employment as well as to produce food. It should be flexible and diversified, able to yield not only subsistence but also marketable surpluses, and it should sustain an internal rural exchange of goods and services instead of depending heavily on the external world for both inputs and markets.

I want to propose that it is easier to plan development toward sustainable rural economies if we take as our model not the farming systems of the West, which inherently tend toward systems of monoculture and economies of scale, but systems of polyculture that use land intensively and offer a basis for economic diversification. Some food staples lend themselves more easily than do others to intensive polyculture. In this article, I use wet-rice farming in East Asia as my case, because its historical record is sufficiently rich to demonstrate a coherent pattern of technical and economic evolution. I do not suggest, however, that the world's problems will be solved if every region switches to wet rice. Almost any combination of food staples that uses land intensively will do.

The view of "proper" agricultural progress that the West has inflicted on the rest of the world has its historical roots in the development of farming in northwestern Europe and the grain belts of the New World—the regions that supplied food for the urban centers of the industrial revolution. But this dynamic, in which labor is a scarce resource and output is increased by substituting technical innovations for manpower and animals, is not inevitable; it is predicated on the conditions of production specific to those regions.

Northern Europe, where this dry-grain farming system evolved, has a short growing season. The staple cereals—wheat, barley and rye—bear seed heads, or panicles, with relatively few grains, at best a few dozen compared with 100 or more grains on a panicle of rice or millet. Each plant usually has no more than three or four stems, or tillers. In principle, one seed could produce some 200 offspring, but the biblical parable reminds us that many seeds die where they fall. Farmers in medieval Europe had to keep as much as a third of their crop for the next year's seed; another large portion went to feeding draft animals over the winter. Because the only fertilizer available was manure, land had to be left fallow often and could be planted with cereal only once every two or three years. In short, this farming system used land *extensively* and could not support high population densities. The typical 11th-century English holding, as recorded in the Domesday Book, was 30 acres (12 hectares).

Draft animals played a crucial role in this farming system. Yields were so low that it was impossible to till enough land for subsistence by manpower alone. Some plow teams consisted only of a pair or two of oxen, but in the heavy clay soils typical of northern Europe, where a plowshare had to dig deeply to turn the soil over, as many as a dozen oxen might form a team. Where draft animals and heavy implements figure prominently in agricultural production, it is clear that large farms which can afford more animals and equipment and can organize their use more efficiently, will have a significant advantage over smaller holdings. The larger the farm in medieval Europe, the more likely it was to produce surplus.

Urban markets for food grew in the 12th and 13th centuries, and the old feudal systems, under which serfs worked both their own strip of land and the lord's domain, began to break down. Manorial lords started to consolidate and enclose land holdings and farm them with wage labor. The laborers were often peasants who had lost traditional rights to land and its ownership became privatized. If landowners let the land to tenants, it was not to subsistence smallholders but to better-off farmers—small capitalists like the English yeomen, who could bear the risks of investment in animals and equipment. Capitalist relations in agriculture had formed in many parts of northwestern Europe before the 15th century. Markets in land and labor were well developed. The social relations necessary for the foundation of a modern mechanized agriculture were thus in place but the necessary technical expertise was lacking.

Development of this agricultural system was driven by the superior performance of large centrally managed units of production. The 18th century recorded improvements that included new crop varieties and breeds of animals, better plows and drainage systems, and crop rotation that combined cereals with fodder crops such as clover and turnips. All the experts agreed that only large farms were suitable for these "high farming" methods. Economies of scale dictated who could afford such improvements.

Before mechanization, many high farming innovations required increased labor as well as capital. In northwestern Europe, farmers had to compete with the new and expanding industries for workers; in the sparsely populated New World, labor was simply very scarce. Inventors had been tinkering with farm machinery as early as the 16th century, but without much success. By the early 19th century the need for such machines was felt acutely.

That was the time when engineers could at last draw on materials and expertise from the industrial sphere—steel, steam power and chemicals—to develop labor substitutes for agriculture. The first successful mechanical threshers came on the British market in the 1830s (provoking riots by agricultural laborers as they saw their precarious livelihoods threatened). Horsedrawn reapers, harvesters, and mechanical drills followed, and eventually in the 20th century the tractor replaced the horse. Chemical fertilizer eliminated the necessity for crop rotations and facilitated monoculture. Herbicides and pesticides further reduced the need for labor. The amount of agricultural land per agricultural worker in the U.S. today is 137 hectares, and a medium-size farm of the type usually run by a single family ranges between 20 and 100 hectares.

This is the historical experience from which our image of "normal" agricultural progress derives. Just as Western patterns of industrialism spread from nation to nation, defining our notions of a modern economy, so, too, after World War II the characteristics of the Western agricultural revolution defined the worldwide agenda of agricultural modernization. Such progress seemed normal and inevitable to the postwar agricultural economists and scientists, mostly from or trained in the U.S., who worked out a package of technical and economic aid to modernize agriculture in the poorer nations.

The new technology they developed gave such impressive initial results that it quickly came to be called the green revolution. The technology centers on the use of high-yielding varieties of wheat, corn, and rice. These varieties are hybrids that farmers cannot breed themselves and that need chemical fertilizers and herbicides to thrive. In experimental stations the hybrids produced such high yields that they were soon called miracle seeds. As Indian economist Vandana Shiva points out, however, comparisons between old and new varieties measure only the output of that one crop, not of the whole mixed cropping system that it often displaces, so the overall gains may be much less than claimed.

Because of the emphasis on monoculture, the agricultural agencies that supply technical information, seed and credit to farmers usually advocate large-scale cultivation and the consolidation of holdings to make mechanization feasible. Under these conditions, salable surpluses and profit margins (but not necessarily yields) are generally proportional to the size of the farm, and small farms lose their viability.

The primary aim of the green revolution policies of the 1960s and 1970s was the eradication of world hunger: the modernization of underproductive farming systems would increase the world output of staple grains. In this respect, the green revolution has been a great success. The world's production of the main staple grains (wheat, corn, and rice) would today be more than adequate to feed the world's population if it were not for problems of maldistribution.

But as farmers have been encouraged to concentrate on monoculture, they have become more vulnerable to crop pests and price fluctuations. The variety of local diets has been drastically reduced, as have employment opportunities. The new technology uses enormous amounts of chemicals and fossil fuels. In energy terms, it is less efficient than many traditional farming systems. Monoculture, mechanical plowing, the extension of crops into woodlands and pastures, and the use of chemical products all contribute to environmental degradation.

The second aim of green revolution policies was to generate rural prosperity through the production of marketable surpluses. It seemed clear that the application of science and capital would yield more efficient and productive farming practices. Theories in vogue at the time recognized that the capital requirements of this kind of modernization would initially favor wealthier farmers but assumed that soon the benefits would trickle down to the entire population.

In fact, many regions have experienced a severe economic polarization. Rich farmers add to their holdings while poor ones are edged out of farming into a dependent wage-labor force. The people who can afford to farm rely increasingly on the urban economy for goods, services and markets. Opportunities for work in the countryside diminish, but urban industry cannot generate enough jobs, and the unemployed congregate in city slums.

The parallels between the green revolution and the 18th-century modernization of Western farming are clear. If advocates of the green revolution neglected to consider the negative social and ecological consequences of their plans, it was largely because this style of development, with its reliance on capital and machinery, seems to represent the inevitable path to modernization.

It was in 1976, during a year spent studying farmers' reactions to the green revolution in the beautiful but poor Malaysian state of Kelantan, that I began to think about alternative models of agricultural development. Before I went to Kelantan, I had spent several years researching the history of rice cultivation in China. As I read more about agricultural development, I realized that many Japanese experts had reached conclusions similar to mine based on their historical experience. They, too, saw a logic in the historical intensification of Asian rice cultivation that was quite different from what had happened in the West. They also felt that the introduction of green revolution technology often represented a disastrous break with the past, and they suggested that there would be many advantages to adopting the "Japanese model."

Looking at the conditions of production and the consequences of development, one finds that the Japanese (or, better, East Asian) model, which centers on the production of wet rice, differs radically from the dry-wheat model of northern Europe. In China, Japan, Vietnam, and Korea, the use of land was intensified over the centuries because of the increasing availability of skilled labor. There were few economies of scale, smallholdings predominated, and intensive cropping patterns sustained a mixed farming system and a highly diversified rural economy that could provide a living for large populations.

Water is a crucial factor in shaping the development of rice cultivation. Rice is a monsoon crop; it can be grown in dry fields, but water is its natural habitat. The earliest find of domesticated rice so far is in a Neolithic Chinese village near Shanghai, situated at the edge of a shallow marsh and dated to approximately 5000 B.C. Other early sites dotted around southeastern continental Asia are also close to marshes or other natural water supplies.

A good rice field or paddy is one in which the water supply can be accurately regulated and drained. As a result, paddies are usually quite small by Western standards: a field 20 yards square would be considered large in China. Young rice seedlings need damp soil but rot in standing water; once they are about a foot tall, they like to have several inches of standing water through the period of flowering and ripening, after which the field should be drained for several days before harvesting.

Rainwater can easily be impounded in a field surrounded by bunds (small dikes), but it may evaporate before the rice is fully grown. Rice farmers in some regions therefore adopted rain-fed tank irrigation systems very early. Other forms of irrigation include the channeling of small streams into hillside terraces and the construction of diversion channels from larger rivers—in which case the water usually has to be pumped up into the fields. All these forms were common in China and Japan by medieval times and allowed rice farming to spread from small river valleys up mountainsides and down into the deltaic floodplains. Constructing bunds, irrigation networks, tanks or terraced fields requires large initial investments of labor, but thereafter maintenance is relatively cheap and easy. So it is not surprising that rice farmers have often preferred intensifying production in their existing fields to extending the cultivated area.

Water enhances the sustainability of rice systems. Unlike dry fields, rice paddies gain rather than lose fertility over the years. Whatever the original structure and fertility of the soil, over several years of continuous wet-rice cultivation the top few inches of soil turn to a fine, gray, low-acidity mud with a layer of hardpan below that retains the water. Nitrogen-fixing organisms that occur naturally in the water serve as a manure. Traditional rice varieties usually respond well to organic fertilizers; lime and soybean waste were widely used in both China and Japan by the 17th century, giving annual yields of up to six tons per hectare in some double-cropping areas.

Rice plants have several seed-bearing stems, and each seed head contains on average about 100 grains. The technique of transplanting rice seedlings augments these traits. A small patch of fertile land is meticulously tilled, manured, and sowed with carefully selected pregerminated seed. Meanwhile the main field is soaked, plowed, and harrowed to create a fine silky mud. After a month or so, the seedlings are pulled up, the sickly ones are discarded, and the tops of the leaves of the healthy ones are chopped off. Then the seedlings are replanted in shallow water in the main field.

This procedure is labor intensive, but it permits the careful selection of healthy plants and the efficient use of small amounts of manure. Moreover, the plant responds to the transplanting process by growing more tillers. By the time the seedlings are transplanted, they need only a few weeks in the main field. Hence, the land can be used for other crops in the off-season.

Wet-rice cultivation has enormous potential for expanding the uses of land. Tanks, channels, and bunds may occupy as much as a fifth of the land, but no space need be wasted. Fish nibble the weeds in the tanks or eat snails in the paddy, and ducks feed on the fish. Narrow bunds serve for growing vegetables, and broad bunds may be planted with mulberries to feed silkworms, whose droppings are used as manure. After the rice is harvested, the field can be drained to grow barley, vegetables, sugarcane, or tobacco.

The alternation of winter rice with summer wheat became common in the lower Yangtze region of China 1,000 years ago. A judicious choice of fast-maturing varieties and the abundance of water afforded 17th-century farmers in the Canton region two or even three crops per year plus a few side crops of vegetables; yearly yields totaled as much as seven tons per hectare. Because fields were small, farm implements were small, light, and cheap. A single water buffalo served the needs of a typical farm; if production was really intensive, the farmer might give up plowing altogether in favor of hoeing.

In general, rice farming did not require much capital outlay compared with dry-wheat farming, and there were few economies of scale to be practiced. Although a landlord in south China might own as much land as his English counterpart, his home farm would be of modest size, and the rest would be let out in small parcels to many tenants, chosen not for their capital assets but for their skills and experience. The system did not polarize rural society and drive poor people out. The relative advantage of smallholdings guaranteed access to land for large numbers of peasants, even if it was through the exploitative relation of tenancy.

The labor requirements of wet-rice farming are high but intermittent. Peasants in medieval China and Japan could therefore use rice farming as the basis for the commercial production of vegetables, sugar, silk, or tea or for the household manufacture of textiles, liquor, bean curd, or handicrafts. Rice served as the foundation of a rural economy that both required and absorbed the labor of a dense population.

Economic historians have often equated this system with "agricultural involution," by which individuals work harder and harder for ever decreasing returns. The assertion might be true if calculations were based only on rice yields, as if one were dealing with a monoculture. But when all the other goods produced in such an economy are taken into account, the system appears in a much more favorable light. Although its capacities for expansion are not infinite, they are considerable. During several centuries of population growth, China's rice regions established the foundation for a rural economy in which many of the people made salable goods at home. Only after 1800 did rural living standards begin sharply declining—a trend that was exacerbated by the effects of multiple wars.

A similar process of rural development took place in Japan, creating the basis for the building of the modern state. This achievement is one reason Japanese agronomists see their system as an exportable model. Yet in Japan as in the West, industrialization was achieved through ruthless patterns of exploitation. Between 1600 and 1800 the rural economy expanded in conjunction with the growth of trade and cities. Techniques for growing rice were improved, and land became so productive that the Meiji government of 1868 to 1912 was able to fund the construction of a modern industrial state mostly through raising agricultural taxes. But this level of extraction left tenant farmers in a state of near destitution that the state did not feel obliged to address until the introduction of universal suffrage in 1945.

The new regime set out to guarantee rice self-sufficiency and to eliminate rural poverty. Land reforms were enacted to do away with tenancy and set stringent limits on the purchase of land. This policy institutionalized the tiny but independent family rice farm, supplying a framework for the successful long-term balancing and integration of rural and urban development.

Yet Japanese agriculture today is in a state of crisis. Except for the aberrant poor harvest of 1993 caused by bad weather, rice is overproduced and wastefully produced, in large part because of heavy subsidies and price support paid by the government since the 1950s. The strategy of increasing rural incomes by raising rice prices has backfired. Until the 1960s Japanese farmers used moderate inputs and simple machinery. Since the 1960s, mechanization has taken over in rice production with small-scale tractors, transplanters, and harvesters. Almost all farmers own a full range of expensive machinery, and the average use of fertilizer per hectare is 1,110 kilograms (compared with 160 in the U.S. and 48 in Thailand). As long ago as 1977, the Japanese economist Taketoshi Udagawa calculated that energy inputs amounted to three times the food energy of the rice. It costs 15 times as much to produce a kilogram of rice in Japan as in Thailand and 11 times as much as in the U.S.

No one in Japan today would call this policy economically sustainable. Nor is it any longer conservationally sound. Although the irrigated fields and channels still protect Japan's narrow river valleys from floods, the channels and soil are saturated with chemicals. No fish or frogs swim in the paddies now.

Japan's current crisis makes it clear that the East Asian model of agriculture, too, can go awry. Yet it would be tragic if the Japanese gave in tamely to the advice they are hearing to adopt the Western style rather than seeking creative endogenous solutions that might be ecologically and socially more rewarding.

Such solutions may be already at work. Through recent economic reforms in Japan, Taiwan, and China, the patterns of land use and economic diversification based on rice cultivation have brought about a modernization characterized by an unusual degree of balance between rural and urban development. The rising ratio of farm-household income to the household income of industrial workers in Japan shows the trend: 69 percent in 1960, 92 in 1970, 115 in 1980 and 113 in 1988.

What are the implications for sustainable rural development elsewhere? This is a problem faced not only by nations with large and impoverished rural populations, such as Mexico and India, but also by wealthy nations, such as France, that want to avoid further rural depopulation. Monoculture is not an irreversible trend, but in today's global economy, rural diversification does require structured support and fair prices for agricultural products. In Japan, where consumers will pay high prices for fruits and vegetables, large numbers of rice farmers have been persuaded to switch part of their land to orchards and truck farms. In China, the state abandoned the Maoist policy of "putting grain first" in the late 1970s. It allowed farmers to combine a basic level of grain farming with all kinds of other crops and livestock. At the same time, farm prices were increased to a realistic level. Agricultural production shot up overnight. Farmers produced not just food but also the raw materials for the development of rural industry. Moreover, they became wealthy enough to consume a wide range of industrial goods. China's current spectacular growth rates can be understood only against this background of rural revitalization.

The examples of premodern China and Japan show that intensive polyculture, precisely because it does not depend on expensive inputs, can yield a livelihood for poorer farmers, offer widespread access to land, and generate other employment opportunities. Ideally, polyculture should not only support rural diversification but also lessen dependence on industrial inputs. Mayan peasants can grow corn without buying chemicals because beans naturally manufacture nitrates. But a farmer does not have to operate at the scale of peasant subsistence to do without chemicals. In California, organic vegetable growers and wine producers are developing interplanting techniques (another form of polyculture) to substitute for chemical pesticides. They grow more kinds of plants, hire more workers, and buy fewer chemicals—and they are doing a big business.

The examples I have cited should be a stimulus to look closely at other non-Western agricultural systems. If we are to find long-term solutions to the truly modern problem of feeding the world without destroying it, we have much to learn from such systems.

A NEW ENERGY PATH FOR THE THIRD WORLD

Nicholas Lenssen

INTRODUCTION

Agriculture is one of many problems challenging Third World nations in the early twenty-first century. Equally pressing are energy resources and power technology. Many of the same issues apply to both agriculture and energy: the failure of the Western model of development to mesh with Third World requirements; the need to encourage sustainable development; and the question of how to meet increasing energy demands and raise standards of living without doing irreparable harm to the environment. At first glance, these may not seem to be problems that are of much importance to us in the First World, but we have a considerable stake in the peace and prosperity of developing nations, if only because rising incomes in the countries of the Third World can make them major consumers of advanced Western goods and services.

In this article, Nicholas Lenssen explains that the developing nations have relied heavily on fossil fuels to meet their burgeoning energy needs, resulting in crippling debts and severe environmental and health problems. Even more worrisome, many of these countries suffer from acute energy shortages, and an estimated 2.1 billion people have no access to electricity at all. The peoples of developing nations are caught in a dilemma. They need more energy just to maintain, let alone expand, their economies. Yet to do so using conventional Western technologies can lead only to further impoverishment, depletion of resources, and continued decline in infrastructure and standards of living.

Lenssen presents a two-pronged solution to the energy problems of the Third World. First, there must be stress on efficiency and conservation. Across the board, Third World countries use 40 percent more energy than developed nations to produce the same quantity of goods and services. A relatively small investment in efficiency now could yield considerable long-term benefits. Second, the Third World, especially, must break out of its dependency on coal and oil and actively pursue such alternatives as natural gas, solar, wind, and geothermal power, and biomass sources of energy. Readers need to ask themselves, though, how the Third World can effect these changes. Can they be done without first having fundamental political reforms? And, is it realistic to expect a new United Nations agency to spearhead efforts at improving Third World power technology? As with so many other aspects of twentieth-century technology, these are hard questions for which there are no simple answers.

———

In their efforts to improve the lives of the 4 billion people who live in Africa, Asia, and Latin America, development agencies have clung to a questionable assumption: that a growing energy supply is the necessary foundation for expanding industries, providing jobs, and raising standards of living in the Third World. On the face of it, that assumption seems logical enough, since high energy use is a conspicuous trait of the most developed nations. In practice, the notion of equating energy consumption with economic health has begun to unravel.

Developing countries have more than quadrupled their energy use since 1960, doubling their per capita use. Yet the strategies that have been so successful in achieving this growth have left these nations staggering from oil price shocks, struggling with foreign debt, and suffering from serious environmental and health problems—while still facing severe energy shortages.

Despite more rapid energy development in the South than in the North, the income gap between the hemispheres has been growing, not shrinking. In 1960, the richest fifth of the world's countries produced 30 times more income per person than the poorest fifth, according to the United Nations Development Programme. By 1989, the disparity had widened to 60 to 1. Over the past decade, per capita incomes have declined in some 50 countries. In Latin America, where some of the world's largest energy projects have been built, three-quarters of the population saw its income fall in the 1980s.

This occurred partly because developing economies were saddled with back-breaking debts to foreign banks and governments—debts totaling $1.43 trillion in early 1993. And as debt deepened poverty by siphoning off state funds, rising energy use deepened the debt. In Brazil and Costa Rica, for example, one of every four borrowed dollars went to pay for giant electric power projects.

At the same time, environmental and health costs associated with energy use and production are taking a mounting toll. In coal-dependent China, acid rain falls on at least 14 percent of the country, damaging forests, crops, and water ecosystems, and cities have 14 times the level of suspended particles found in the United States.

Elsewhere, urban air is choked with pollution from motor vehicles. Mexico City, where ozone levels violated international standards 303 days in 1990, is joined by Bangkok, Nairobi, Santiago, and São Paulo in the growing list of cities whose people suffer lung damage despite per capita levels of energy consumption far below those of Northern cities.

Conventional energy development has also increased the threat of global warming. Although industrial countries are responsible for 79 percent of the fossil-fuel-derived carbon dioxide emitted since 1950, and still accounted for 69 percent of the total in 1990, future growth in fossil-fuel use is predicted to be greater in the South than in the North. If recent trends continue, emissions in the developing world will grow from 1.8 billion tons of carbon in 1990 to 5.5 billion tons in 2025, according to the UN's Intergovernmental Panel on Climate Change (IPCC). China alone is expected to emit more carbon dioxide by 2025 than the current combined total of the United States, Japan, and Canada. Such increases would boost global emissions by half at a time when, according to the IPCC, they should be cut by at least 60 percent if the atmospheric concentration is to be stabilized and climate change minimized.

For all the ills brought on by expanded energy use, many developing countries are still contending with shortages of electricity. India's shortfall averages 9 percent, rises to 22 percent during peak periods, and is worsening. China's shortfall results in regular shutdowns of industry; it idled one-fourth of the country's industrial capacity in 1987. According to World Bank estimates, electricity shortages are costing Latin America's industry as much as $15 billion per year in lost output. And then there are the 2.1 billion people worldwide who live in areas with no electricity at all.

With such a gulf between supply and demand, funding agencies and Third World government planners can be expected to continue their efforts to expand energy supplies for years to come. After all, people in the developing world still use just one-ninth as much commercial energy on average as those in industrial countries. Yet if developing countries are to achieve the hoped-for gains in living standards, they need to meet their energy demand in a way that allows them to close the economic gap between North and South and maintain the health of their people, forests, cropland, and waterways.

Developing countries can achieve sustainable energy development by following a two-part strategy. First, they will need to emphasize the use of more energy-efficient technologies in everything from industrial processes to consumer products. Over the next 35 years, $350 billion invested in efficiency improvements could eliminate the need for $1.75 trillion worth of power plants, oil refineries, and other energy infrastructure by reducing growth in energy demand, according to a study at the Lawrence Berkeley Laboratory (LBL). This would free up money for vastly larger investments in food production, health, education, and other neglected needs. Second, the Third World will need to develop its own alternatives to costly oil and polluting coal. Many developing countries have extensive untapped reserves of natural gas, which could supplant oil and coal in buildings, transport, industry, and power generation. And all have enormous potential to rely on solar, wind, biomass, or geothermal energy. Through a combination of efficiency and alternative energy sources, developing countries can "leapfrog" to the advanced technologies being commercialized in industrial countries today, avoiding billions of dollars of misdirected investments in infrastructure that is economically and environmentally obsolete.

USING ENERGY WISELY

Since the 1973 Arab oil embargo, industrial countries have made large gains in using energy economically. Energy use by the 24 member nations of the Organization for Economic Cooperation and Development (OECD) rose only one-fifth as much as economic growth between 1973 and 1989. However, these gains have largely bypassed developing countries, where energy use expanded 20 percent faster than economic growth during the same period.

Developing-country economies now require 40 percent more energy than industrial ones to produce the same value of goods and services. This is mainly because they are using outdated technologies that squander energy. The gross inefficiency of these technologies—whether wood stoves, cement plants, light bulbs, or trucks—offer innumerable opportunities to limit energy consumption and expenditures while expanding the services they provide. For example, the congressional Office of Technology Assessment estimates that nearly half of overall electricity use in the South can be cut cost-effectively.

Half of Third World commercial energy consumption goes to industry, yet for each ton of steel or cement produced, the typical factory in the global South uses far more energy than its Northern counterpart. Steel plants in developing countries consume roughly one-quarter more energy than the average plant in the United States, and about three-quarters more than the most efficient plant. Fertilizer plants in India use about twice as much oil to produce a ton of ammonia as a typical British plant. Pulp and paper facilities consume as much as three times more energy for the same amount of output. Such records are often the result of poor maintenance and operation procedures and can be readily improved—given sufficient information and incentive to do so. A study by Indonesian researchers, for example, found that that country's industries could cut energy use 11 percent without any capital investment, simply by changing operating procedures. Similarly, a Ghanaian survey found potential savings of at least 30 percent in medium- to large-scale industries.

Some of the biggest opportunities to save energy and money can be found in the electric power industry. Third World power plants typically burn one-fifth to two-fifths more fuel for each kilowatt-hour generated than those in the North, and they experience far more unplanned shutdowns for repairs, as they are often operated by undertrained staff and poorly maintained, according to the World Bank. Because the developing world is still in the early stages of building its industrial infrastructure, it has opportunities to base future development not just on more efficient processes but also on more efficient products. Building a $7.5 million factory for making compact fluorescent light bulbs, for example, would eliminate the need to construct $5.6 billion worth of coal-fired power plants, if the bulbs (which need 75 percent less power than incandescent ones) were used domestically, calculates Ashok Gadgil of LBL.

In agriculture, too, there is an urgent need for movement toward greater energy efficiency: farming is likely to become more energy-intensive as population growth drives up the demand for food. Besides requiring large amounts of chemicals, agriculture in developing countries is often a major consumer of electricity. India's 8 million irrigation pumps, which use nearly one-quarter of the country's electricity, employ inefficient motors and poorly designed belts, and are plagued by leaky foot valves and high friction losses. Using more efficient pumps could cut electricity consumption by roughly half, at a cost of only 0.1 cent per kilowatt-hour saved, according to Jayant Sathaye of LBL.

Although industry and agriculture still consume most of the commercial energy in developing countries, the urban residential and commercial sectors are growing much faster. In China, for example, only 3 percent of Beijing's households had refrigerators in 1982; six years later, 81 percent did. Unfortunately, a typical Chinese refrigerator uses 365 kilowatt-hours of electricity per year, whereas a South Korean model of the same size uses 240 kilowatt-hours and a Danish one needs less than 100 kilowatt-hours. Industrial planners and manufacturers in developing countries are rarely concerned with the energy efficiency of their products—only with producing and selling more of them by keeping the initial cost as low as possible.

The same can be said of architects and civil engineers. Much of the developing world relies on air conditioning in commercial buildings. Improved building designs—including insulation, better windows, and natural ventilation—could cut cooling needs and costs, but such designs are not widely used. In Bangkok, for example, large offices typically use windows made of a single sheet of glass. By substituting advanced double-paned windows with a special low-emissivity coating (which filters out infrared rays but passes visible light), builders would reduce not only the subsequent electricity costs but the initial costs of construction, since they would then be able to install smaller, less expensive air conditioners.

Efficiency improvements can even be made in the use of biomass—wood, charcoal, or agricultural residues—for cooking, allowing women to spend less time or money acquiring fuel. Although energy-efficient stoves promoted by development agencies in the 1970s were costly and unreliable, an improved charcoal stove—ceramic jiko—has become a major success in Kenya and other African countries. In India, a government program had distributed some 6 million advanced cookstoves by early 1989.

A third venue of rapidly growing energy consumption is transportation. In China, transportation doubled its percentage of national oil consumption between 1980 and 1988. In most developing countries, this accounts for over one-half of total oil consumption and one-third of commercial energy use. Congestion in Bangkok has dropped the average vehicle speed from 7 miles per hour in 1980 to about 3 today. Although major improvements are needed in traffic management, mass transportation, and land-use planning, just promoting wider use of bicycles and other nonmotorized vehicles would stem automotive ills while increasing the mobility of the poor.

In combination, the efficiency potential now within reach for industry, agriculture, construction, and transportation could provide an enormous boost to the economies of developing countries. By investing $10 billion a year, these countries could cut future growth of their energy demand in half, lighten the burden of pollution on their environments and health, and stanch the flow of export earnings into fuel purchases. Gross savings would average $53 billion a year for 35 years, according to the LBL study.

Although such large-scale savings remain paper prophecies, some countries have achieved notable successes. In 1980, China launched an ambitious program to improve energy efficiency in major industries. By directing roughly 10 percent of its energy investment to efficiency over five years, the nation cut its annual growth in energy use from 7 percent to 4 percent, without slowing growth in industrial production. Efficiency improvements accounted for more than 70 percent of the energy savings, with shifts toward less energy-intensive industries yielding the remainder. And efficiency gains were found to be one-third less expensive than comparable investments in coal supplies. One result was that China's energy consumption expanded at less than half the rate of economic growth from 1980 through 1988.

Brazil's National Electricity Conservation Program has catalyzed impressive savings of energy and money. Over four years, it spent $20 million on more than 150 efficiency projects and programs, for which local government and private industry provided matching funds. Most of the money went to education and promotion programs to increase awareness of the savings efficiency could generate. The program also encouraged the National Development Bank to offer low-interest loans to businesses willing to invest in efficiency. These efforts yielded electricity savings worth between $600 million and $1.3 billion in reduced need for power plants and transmission lines, estimates Howard Geller, executive director of the American Council for an Energy-Efficient Economy, who has intensively studied the Brazilian energy sector.

Brazil and China need not be anomalies: similar potential exists throughout the developing world. Halving the rate at which Third World energy demand grows over the next 30 years would hold the overall increase to a doubling of consumption rather than a tripling. That difference could have profound consequences for environmental and human health worldwide—and for the ability of the developing world to meet the basic needs of its growing population.

DEVELOPING ALTERNATIVES

If Third World countries squeeze all the waste they can out of the way they use energy, they will greatly reduce the need for larger supplies. But in the long run, it will still be necessary to develop new energy sources. Unfortunately, government planners and international institutions still assume that developing countries have to follow the energy path the North blazed a century ago—a strategy that relies primarily on expanding supplies of coal and oil. These two fossil fuels already provide 51 percent of all energy used in developing countries, and more than 75 percent of commercial energy.

While a few developing nations have improved their export-import balance sheets through oil sales, most face a continual drain on their economies as a result of their dependency on oil. Scarce foreign exchange earned through exports of agricultural products or minerals is spent to import oil for domestic consumption, draining resources away from development. Three-fourths of developing countries are oil importers. And of the 38 poorest countries, 29 import more than 70 percent of their commercial energy—nearly all of it in the form of oil.

Although energy planners have promoted alternatives to fossil fuels, these pose problems of their own. Hydroelectric power provides a third of developing countries' electricity, and less than 10 percent of its technical potential has been tapped. Yet efforts to exploit the rest have run into roadblocks, and orders for large dams have declined in recent years as the real costs—both in capital and in displacement of people—of building them have become more apparent. Nuclear power, too, has fallen short of its promise to supply cheap electricity in developing countries, just as it has elsewhere. The Third World accounts for only 6 percent of the world's nuclear generating capacity, with many programs—including those of Argentina, Brazil, and India—over budget, behind schedule, and plagued by technical problems. Because of its high cost and complex technology, nuclear power is not a viable option for the vast majority of developing countries.

But other, more manageable energy sources are available and waiting to be put to wider use. Natural gas is an obvious example. When oil companies operating in developing countries find natural gas in an exploratory well, they usually cap the well and write the venture off as a tax loss. Such gas reservoirs are simply too small to develop for export markets. Yet locally, the gas in these so-called noncommercial wells could be used for cooking and producing electricity, and could replace coal and oil in factories and motor vehicles. A natural gas well just one-hundredth the size needed for commercial export would be cost-effective for local use, according to Ben W. Ebenhack, a petroleum engineer at the University of Rochester who heads a project to tap previously drilled wells in Africa for local use. The key is building the infrastructure needed to bring natural gas to the large markets awaiting it.

Petroleum geologists have already found substantial reserves of natural gas in some 50 developing countries, and many other countries hold great promise. Most of these stocks are in oil-producing countries such as Algeria, Indonesia, Mexico, Nigeria, and Venezuela, many of which have burned off gas as a waste byproduct of petroleum production without capturing any useful energy.

Nevertheless, the revival of natural gas that has taken place in North America and Europe in recent years has also occurred to some extent in the South. Government and private engineers have drawn up plans for vast networks of gas pipelines that would connect developing countries. In Latin America, Argentina could soon be piping gas over the Andes to smog-choked Santiago, Chile. Another network, which received its initial go-ahead in 1992, will feed Bolivian gas to southern Brazil and northern Argentina. And in southeast Asia, Thailand hopes to build a gas grid with neighboring Malaysia and Myanmar (formerly Burma).

Even China is reconsidering natural gas as part of its effort to slow growth in oil and coal use. The government formed a gas research institute in 1986 and decided in early 1992 to build a pipeline from a large offshore gas field discovered earlier during an unsuccessful search for oil. Gas commonly accompanies coal as well as oil. It is therefore likely that China, with its enormous coal reserves, is well endowed with natural gas, too.

Developing countries also have abundant supplies of renewable energy resources, such as sunlight, wind, biomass, and heat from deep within the earth, which are becoming more economical. The past decade has seen dramatic technological improvement in tapping these renewables—the costs of solar and wind energy systems, for example, have been slashed by 66 to 90 percent. Electricity sources such as solar thermal power and photovoltaics could be the least expensive route for developing countries, predicts World Bank economist Dennis Anderson. The availability of land is not a problem: for solar energy to double the Third World's energy consumption, only 0.2 percent of the acreage in these countries would be needed.

Many renewables are already less expensive than fossil fuels or nuclear power, once social and environmental costs—such as air pollution, resource depletion, and government subsidies—are included. But even if social and environmental costs are not included, it still makes sense for energy planners to take immediate advantage of renewable energy's potential. Investments in uses that are viable today can stimulate development of the technological and business infrastructure and the domestic expertise, both private and public, needed to apply renewables on a large scale in the future.

Using the sun to heat water is already a cost-effective way to save electricity. Total capital costs for solar hot water are, on average, nearly 25 percent lower than those for electric hot water when the cost of building power plants is included, according to data collected by the Office of Technology Assessment. Solar heating industries have already sprung up in many developing countries. Residents of Botswana's capital, Gaborone, have purchased more than 3,000 solar water heaters, displacing nearly 15 percent of residential electricity demand. Some 30,000 of these heaters have been installed in Colombia, and 17,000 in Kenya. In Jordan, 12 percent of the urban water heating systems are solar.

Villagers in some rural areas use photovoltaic cells to power lights, radios, and even televisions, needs that are usually met with kerosene lamps and disposable or rechargeable batteries. With the help of nongovernmental organizations and private businesses, more than 100,000 photovoltaic lighting units have been installed in developing countries such as

Colombia, the Dominican Republic, Mexico, and Sri Lanka. In Africa, photovoltaic lighting has undergone a virtual boom since the mid-1980s: Kenya has 10 private companies selling photovoltaics, with as much as 1,000 kilowatts installed.

For grid-connected power supplies, geothermal power plants and new wind generators based on variable-speed turbines and advanced blades can produce electricity at a cost comparable to that from coal-fired power plants. India leads the developing world in wind energy, with 38 megawatts of capacity installed by the beginning of 1992. Aided by Danish companies, the country plans to install 1,000 megawatts of domestically manufactured wind turbines by the end of the decade. According to Worldwatch Institute estimates, wind could provide more than 10 percent of developing countries' electricity.

Geothermal energy already plays a major role in some countries; in 1990 it produced 21 percent of the electricity in the Philippines, 18 percent in El Salvador, and 11 percent in Kenya. Yet this resource is abundant—and still largely untapped—in Bolivia, Costa Rica, Ethiopia, India, and Thailand. Another two dozen countries, including Brazil and Pakistan, appear to have equally good, though less explored, potential.

Another advanced technology suitable for developing countries is fuel cells. With even higher efficiency and lower pollution than combined-cycle gas turbines, these battery-like devices convert natural gas, biomass, or hydrogen to electric power and heat. Industrial countries, including Japan and the United States, are commercializing fuel-cell technologies that could be useful in developing countries, especially since fuel cells are modular and require less maintenance than standard electric power plants. India has funded a fuel-cell demonstration project, though investment throughout the developing world has so far been low.

Biomass supplies 35 percent of developing countries' energy but could contribute more if existing agricultural and industrial wastes were better utilized and if more energy crops were produced. Efficient electric power can be generated by gas turbines fired with agricultural residues or with forestry wastes that would otherwise be burned at paper and pulp factories. If sugar mills burned all their residues in advanced gas turbines, they would produce more than a third as much electricity as is now consumed in developing countries, according to Robert H. Williams and Eric D. Larson of Princeton University.

Hundreds of millions of acres of degraded lands could be returned to productivity by planting fast-growing trees and other crops suitable for energy use, according to the United Nations Solar Energy Group for Environment and Development. Any such attempt to boost biofuels production, however, would require major investments by governments and private companies. Past efforts to entice villagers to plant more trees have failed more often than not, particularly if the undertaking is packaged as an energy project instead of as a timber- or food-producing venture.

One key may be to integrate biomass energy production with a comprehensive agricultural development strategy that produces marketable items. Agroforestry techniques, for example, offer a way to boost both food yields and wood harvests. Research in Kenya and Nigeria has shown that mixing corn and leucaena trees can produce 39 to 83 percent more corn than does growing corn itself, while yielding at least 2 tons of wood per acre. Of course, this approach can do little to help the poorest of the poor, who are landless; indeed, it is difficult to disentangle rural energy problems of land ownership and economic equity. But agroforestry could be a boon to landed farmers.

Together with efficiency improvements on the demand side, an energy system run on renewable energy resources and natural gas has the potential to meet all the new energy needs of developing countries, according to Amulya Reddy and his colleagues at the Indian Institute of Science in Bangalore. Reddy's group crafted a plan that could meet the state of Karnataka's electricity needs in the 1990s for only $6 billion of investment, rather than the $17.4 billion a government committee had proposed to spend on large hydroelectric, coal-fired, and nuclear power plants.

Among the new supplies in Reddy's plan are natural gas, solar hot water, and more efficient use of sugar mill wastes and other biomass. Unlike the state's plan, which foresees continuing power shortages despite the enormous investment, Reddy's proposal would electrify all homes in the state and employ more people. At the same time, it would boost carbon-dioxide emissions by only one-fiftieth the amount the government plan envisions.

SUSTAINABLE STRATEGIES

Even if piecemeal attempts to improve efficiency and exploit alternative sources are successful, comprehensive changes will be needed to ensure that a country's energy development is sound. The kinds of policies that can help make this happen include expunging destructive subsidies from energy prices, so that users will have incentives to conserve; shifting emphasis in energy planning from building new power plants and supplies to providing more efficient energy services; and shifting supply-end investment from coal and oil to more benign sources.

Implementing these policies will require major institutional changes, from international development agencies, governments, electric utilities, individual industries, and nongovernmental organizations advocating sustainable development. And it is critical that support from the North include not only the billions of dollars annually provided in foreign assistance but also the power of example. That has already occurred to some degree in the development of more energy-efficient industrial processes and consumer products, but the example will become far more persuasive when it includes more substantial shifts to renewable, nonpolluting energy sources and less energy-intensive lifestyles.

Abundant opportunities for promoting end-use efficiency can be found in industrial equipment, home appliances, buildings, and transportation. Some measures are relatively simple: adopting product efficiency standards, putting efficiency labels on products, and publicizing the benefits of efficient products to consumers.

Other measures are more complex but no less effective. Utilities, for example, can adopt a policy known as integrated resource planning. Originally pioneered by U.S. utilities and regulators, and now spreading to Canada, Japan, and Western Europe, this policy requires power companies considering new generating capacity to compare the cost of expansion with the cost of improvements in customer energy efficiency. If efficiency measures prove less expensive, utilities invest money in those, instead of in new generating capacity. They also have the option of investing in alternative technologies, such as solar water heaters, that cost-effectively reduce power consumption. Integrated resource planning was recently adopted in Thailand, where utilities expect as a result to save at least $180 million by 1997.

To encourage such policies, lending agencies need to shift their priorities. The World Bank has started to show more interest in energy efficiency and new energy sources—it recently formed an alternative energy unit in its Asian section, for example, and in 1991 gave India a $450 million loan to expand its use of natural gas. But like most other multilateral development banks, it still tends to equate energy with expanding centralized electric power. When lending agencies do attempt to promote efficiency, they usually rely on politically difficult price hikes. Instead, the banks could encourage the use of integrated resource planning—as the Asian Development Bank which operates much like the World Bank, has recently started to do—while investing directly in energy efficiency.

A step in the right direction is the Global Environment Facility (GEF), an international fund set up in 1990 and administered by the World Bank, the United Nations Development Programme, and the United Nations Environment Programme. The GEF finances efficiency and renewables projects by making grants designed to slow global warming. It has supported some promising initiatives, including a $7 million project for household photovoltaics in Zimbabwe and a $3.3 million project for energy from sugarcane residues in Mauritius. And it is considering several other worthy ideas: installing efficient lighting in Mexico, capturing methane from coal mines in China, financing improvements in electricity end-use in Thailand, developing biomass-fueled gas turbines in Brazil, and promoting a variety of renewables in India.

But GEF has two limitations. First, its total funds—$1.3 billion for three years, of which only 40 to 50 percent can be energy-related—are not enough to reform energy development worldwide. The multilateral development banks lend 30 times as much per year on traditional energy projects. Second, the inclusion of efficiency and renewables projects in its portfolio sustains the false notion that they are not economical on their own, but simply a means to reduce carbon-dioxide emissions. The institution's real impact will be felt once the development banks' entire energy loan portfolios follow the pattern of today's GEF grants.

The GEF's shortcomings expose a glaring weakness of the United Nations: there is no central U.N. energy office other than the International Atomic Energy Agency. A new, broader agency could take the leading role in promoting efficient energy systems. Such an institution could be decentralized, incorporating research stations in key regions around the world that could design and demonstrate renewable and efficient technologies, gather and disseminate information, and train technicians and professionals in developing countries. The centers would be particularly useful to smaller developing countries that do not have the resources of nations such as Brazil or India.

At the national level, government programs can be funded by energy taxes or carbon taxes, which are based on the carbon content of the fuel. In early 1992, the Thai parliament levied a tax on petroleum products and natural gas, equivalent to just over 1 cent per liter of petroleum product, that will provide $50 million to $60 million a year for investments in efficiency and renewables. Ghana already funds its independent energy board with a small tax on fossil fuels, and Tunisia originally funded its efficiency program through a modest tax on oil. More general application of carbon taxes would encourage research and investment in efficiency and renewables. The Italian government, for example, has recommended that part of the revenue from a proposed European Community carbon tax go to sustainable energy investments in the South.

Such proposals underscore the gradual realization in the North that energy and environmental stability are closely linked. But developing countries need a new energy path for reasons quite apart from threats to the earth's climate. Cutting the cost of energy services, as well as the environmental and health costs of air pollution, would allow developing countries to invest in more pressing areas. In Brazil, for example, about 30 percent of children are malnourished and 78 percent do not complete primary school. With the technologies of efficiency and renewables, and with the policies for their dissemination that have already proved effective, Brazil could shift $2 billion to $3 billion a year out of the power sector and roughly double its funding for nutrition, preventive health care, and water and sanitation programs. Throughout the South, investments in transportation and communication systems, health and education infrastructure, water supplies, and shelter could be stepped up.

Indeed, an energy strategy based on clean and efficient sources is a cornerstone of sustainable development and is essential if the countries of the South are to improve their living standards. As countries move to this new strategy, their energy economics will shift from obstructing development to enabling it.